A county-by-county guide to
REPAIRERS AND RESTORERS OF
ART AND ANTIQUES

The
B O N H A M S
Directory 1994

COMPILED BY
TIM FORREST AND JOHN KIRKWOOD

WITH AN INTRODUCTION BY
THE DUCHESS OF DEVONSHIRE

KYLE CATHIE LIMITED

IMPORTANT NOTICE TO READERS

Entries in *The Bonhams Directory* are intended only as a means of identifying and locating specialist goods and services, and inclusion does not imply recommendation by Bonhams. Prospective customers must satisfy themselves as to the appropriateness, quality and cost of the goods or services offered.

Customers should also ask about the security of the premises and establish whether the restorer provides insurance cover or if it is necessary for the customer to arrange appropriate cover under existing policies, including transit to and from the workshop. If your property is not covered the risk is yours.

Neither Bonhams nor the Publishers will enter into correspondence concerning entries in *The Directory* but recommendations and/or complaints (which should be sent to Tim Forrest, c/o Bonhams, Montpelier Street, London SW7 1HH) will be followed up and taken into account in any future editions.

First published in Great Britain in 1993 by
Kyle Cathie Limited
7/8 Hatherley Street, London SW1P 2QT

Introduction © 1993 The Duchess of Devonshire
'Seeking Professional Advice' copyright © 1992 by Annabelle Ruston
This compilation copyright © Bonhams 1993

Tim Forrest and John Kirkwood are hereby identified as compilers of this work in accordance with Section 77 of the Copyright, Designs and Patents Act 1988.

ISBN 1 85626 094 1

A CIP catalogue record for this book is available from the British Library.

Filmset by Selwood Systems, Midsomer Norton
Printed by Butler & Tanner, Frome and London

CONTENTS

HOW THE DIRECTORY WORKS

Each section of the book contains alphabetical lists of restorers and services in the following order:

England – by county (London is treated as a county and the postal districts follow each other alphabetically; West Midlands comes under M, East and West Sussex under S and North, South and West Yorkshire under Y)
Northern Ireland – by county
Southern Ireland – by county
Scotland – by region
Wales – by county

Double rules divide the entries for each county or region.

The *Collectors' Items* section is divided alphabetically by subject (Cameras, Dolls and Dolls' Houses, etc), with lists within each subject arranged as above. *Musical Instruments* follow *Collectors' Items*.

Arms and Armour are followed by *Sporting Equipment*, again divided alphabetically into subjects.

Specialist Booksellers are followed by *Specialist Photographers*.

If a restorer provides services that fall into more than one section, these are cross-referenced at the end of each entry.

Many thanks to the staff of Bonhams for their encouragement and support, especially: Helen Grantham, Odile Jackson, Heather Mann and Nicola Winter.

INTRODUCTION BY THE DUCHESS OF DEVONSHIRE

If you happen to live in what is now called a historic house and if that house has its quota of furniture, paintings, books, carpets, bronzes, sculptures, tapestries, bindings, frames, textiles, clocks, silver, china, drawings, glass, prints, stuffed birds, antiquities, wood carvings, curiosities and even toys, it will also have suffered centuries of children, dogs, cats, mice, moth, carpet beetle, woodworm, death watch beetle, the old enemy sunlight and even moonlight, said by some to be most damaging of all.

Over the years these inescapable everyday hazards conspire to torment this housekeeper as she sees the objects in her care deteriorating before her eyes.

Our houses, whether big or small, were built, decorated and furnished at the behest of their owners to be lived in. Most of the owners have families so hide and seek, sardines, kick the can, catapults, roller-skating, billiard fives, darts and other time-honoured occupations of children have deleterious effects on the possessions of their parents. Childless owners still have to contend with dust, airborne pollution, fluctuation of temperature and humidity which are sent to try all householders and their beloved objects.

If the rooms get too hot your instinct is to open the window: in flies the carpet beetle which chews up the rugs. Birds fly in too and perch on the best picture with dire results. If the rooms are too cold, turn up the heating and the furniture cracks in the strangest places.

That isn't the end of the story. What about the bacon beetle? If denied the food after which he is named this little epicure likes nothing better than a globule of fat from the belly of your best stuffed fish.

Even those things which appear to be indestructable can go wrong. There is a bronze disease and a pewter disease; and lead statues in the garden suffer from the weather. The diseased stones in the mineral cases at Chatsworth so intrigued my sister Nancy Mitford that she described their malady in one of her books. But she could not prescribe a cure.

Collectors and inheritors of antiques have a protective feeling towards their inanimate objects and suffer with them when things go wrong. Whether you are responsible for a huge house full of interesting things or whether you have one treasured possession, the time will come when it needs attention and the problem is who to go to for advice and help.

We have come a long way since Evelyn, Duchess of Devonshire (my grandmother-in-law) astonished some people from the V&A by telling them she used a little hammer to bang the furniture and give the woodworm concussion.

A new generation of restorers and conservators has grown up and their services are available all over the country. Now the rural dweller need not take his car to London with the ailing object in the boot – he can find the help he needs near at hand.

There has never been such a keen interest in antiques of all kinds as there is now. No longer do their owners take them for granted as part of the indoor scenery and think it almost vulgar to talk about them. They are noticed and discussed by all who come to the house where they belong. This impresses on the owner – if he was unaware of it before – his responsibility and, indeed, his duty to take care of his possessions. He must decide the vexed argument as to whether the thing is to be just cleaned and conserved or fully restored. In either case he can find the person to consult in these pages.

There is no more satisfying feeling than seeing the old friends, once in a sad state, come to life again for your pleasure and for the pleasure of generations to come.

I heartily recommend this directory as the only publication offering such a comprehensive source of references and contacts.

SEEKING PROFESSIONAL ADVICE

A brown stain appears on your Victorian watercolour or the writing surface on your antique desk needs re-leathering – who do you ask for advice? Should you restore the work to resemble its original state, or conserve it from further deterioration leaving its appearance imperfect? Your local antique shop may offer conservation services, but how can you be sure that they will do a professional job? Works of art can be irreparably damaged by incompetent conservators and the use of inappropriate materials and techniques. Both the financial value and the physical appearance of the work can be severely diminished. However, there exist several professional associations who would be happy to discuss your requirements and to give you unbiased advice as to your choice of conservator. (See the Glossary at the back of this book for addresses and telephone numbers.)

The Conservation Unit (part of the Museums and Galleries Commission) holds a computerised list of 550 conservation workshops. For a fee of five pounds they will send you a detailed report on the appropriate conservators. The list includes experts in such diverse areas as taxidermy, mother-of-pearl, rocking horses and musical boxes. Recommended workshops must have been established for seven years and references and other documentation are requested. The Unit also holds details of over 300 societies and organisations relevant to conservation in the UK. The organisations listed include special-interest groups such as the Society of Gilders, the Federation of Master Organ Builders and the Guild of Toy Makers. Many of these bodies would be happy to discuss the care of your work of art with you.

The United Kingdom Institute for Conservation (UKIC) has 2,000 conservator members worldwide, specialising in furniture, porcelain, glass, textiles, paintings, metals, books and objects. They publish a wide range of informative material and hold conferences. If you send them an SAE stating your geographical location and area of interest they will send you a list of appropriate conservators.

The British Antique Furniture Restorers Association (BAFRA) has eighty-four members who have all been closely vetted by the Association.

Members must have been working as restorers for a minimum of six years; their work is inspected by Committee members and references are followed up. So if you select a BAFRA-recommended restorer you can be sure of the highest standards of workmanship.

The Fine Art Trade Guild is the trade association representing those involved in the picture business. It was established in 1910 to regulate the trade and improve standards of practice. Guild staff are happy to help you to find a framer with expertise in conservation framing methods. Guild-recommended framers work to a strict code of practice and are answerable to the Framers' & Retailers' Committee. You can contact the Guild with queries ranging from the framing of tapestries and fabric art to frame restoration and re-gilding. They can also put you in touch with stockists of fine art products, such as picture-hanging systems and acid-free packing materials. If you are looking for a dealer who specialises in a particular artist or type of art, the Guild can also help you.

There are two bodies representing picture restorers. The Institute of Paper Conservation (IPC) is concerned with works on paper such as watercolours, prints and maps, and the Association of British Picture Restorers (ABPR) is concerned with oil paintings. The IPC holds a register of over 100 conservators and will recommend one local to you. The ABPR has sixty full members who have all been closely vetted by the Committee. Vetting procedures are so strict that over half of the applicants fail to be admitted, so you can rest assured that your painting will receive the best possible treatment from an ABPR member.

The Scottish Society for Conservation and Restoration (SSCR) publishes informative leaflets and promotes interest in conservation. However, it does not refer people to specific conservators. You should contact the Scottish Conservation Bureau, part of Historic Scotland, if you need a conservator for your work of art. They publish a list of 180 conservators working in fourteen different fields, and will advise you and help you to find a conservator. The Irish Professional Conservators and Restorers Association (IPCRA) also publishes a directory of its members.

If someone recommends a conservator to you, you can always ring up the appropriate association and enquire whether that person or workshop is known to them. There are several other points you should check with a conservator before entrusting him/her with your work of art. Ask for details of previous clients and work undertaken, and follow up these references. If the conservator has repeatedly worked for a specialist organisation such as the National Trust or your local museum, this should be taken as a good sign. Many conservators keep a summary of their work experience and training on file for potential clients, otherwise you should ask if they attended an established course or served an apprenticeship in a reputable workshop. It is also important to check that the workshop is secure and that your work of art will be properly insured. Be sure to discuss the work to be carried out in detail, so that you know exactly what is being done to your work of art and why. Explain how you want the object to look and discuss whether or not this is possible or advisable.

You must also remember that conservation is an on-going process. Your conservator should advise you as to the safest conditions in which to keep your work of art and how best to maintain it. For example, works of art displayed in rooms with high central heating may require a humidifying device to keep the atmosphere moist. Your conservator should also explain any signs to look for which mean that further deterioration is beginning.

The main point to remember is that it is better to do nothing than to rush in and do the wrong thing without due care and attention. Do not hesitate to contact any of the above organisations for advice and information, as they would be only too glad to help you.

ANNABELLE RUSTON
Framing and Gallery Manager
Fine Art Trade Guild

OIL PAINTINGS, WATERCOLOURS, PRINTS AND PHOTOGRAPHS

DO

Always carry pictures with the surface facing you
Transport pictures upright in a car or van
Stack pictures face to face in twos to avoid frame and canvas damage
Ensure that holly does not fall down behind a picture
Remember that sunlight is the enemy of any work on paper

DON'T

Hang paintings over a radiator
Hang watercolours in a bathroom or other damp place
Hang pictures in any room subject to extremes of temperature
Try to clean your own pictures
Dust glass over pastels too vigorously: static electricity can cause the pastel to transfer
Allow glass to be in contact with any picture surface

ADAM GALLERY

13 John Street, Bath, **Avon BA1 2JL**
TEL   0225 480406
OPEN   9.30–5.30 Mon–Sat.

Specialise in consolidation, restoration and cleaning of oil paintings and cleaning, defoxing and conservation of watercolours and drawings.

PROVIDE Home Inspections. Free Estimates. Collection/Delivery Service by arrangement.
SPEAK TO Paul or Philip Dye.
SEE Picture Frames.

DAVID A. CROSS GALLERY

7 Boyce's Avenue, Clifton, Bristol, **Avon BS8 4AA**
TEL   0272 732614
OPEN   9.30–6 Mon–Fri; 9.30–5.30 Sat.

Specialise in restoring oil paintings, watercolours and prints of all periods.

PROVIDE Home Inspections. Free Estimates. Chargeable Collection/Delivery Service.
SPEAK TO Jo David.

THE FRAME STUDIO

2nd Floor, 14 Waterloo Street, Clifton, Bristol, **Avon BS8 4BT**
TEL   0272 238279
OPEN   10–6 Tues–Sat.

Specialise in restoring oil paintings and watercolours.

PROVIDE Home Inspections. Free Estimates. Chargeable Collection/Delivery Service.
SPEAK TO Graeme Dowling.
Member of the Guild of Master Craftsmen.

GEORGE GREGORY

Manvers Street, Bath, **Avon BA1 1JW**
TEL   0225–466055
FAX   0225 482122
OPEN   9–1, 2–5.30 Mon–Fri; 9.30–1 Sat By Appointment.

Specialise in cleaning and restoring old prints.

PROVIDE Home Inspections. Free Estimates.
SPEAK TO Mr H. H. Bayntun–Coward.

INTERNATIONAL FINE ART CONSERVATION STUDIOS

43–45 Park Street, Bristol, **Avon BS1 5NL**
TEL   0272 293480
FAX   0272 225511
OPEN   10–5.30 Mon–Fri.

Specialise in the conservation and restoration of oil paintings from both traditional and modern periods with sizes ranging from small easel paintings to very large wall murals. Recent examples include works by Van Dyck, Hondecoeter, Luca Giordano, Monet, Whistler and Sargent.

PROVIDE Free Estimates.
SPEAK TO A. J. Bush, S. R. Sands or R. J. Pelter.
Full Members of ABPR.

ANTHONY REED

94–96 Walcot Street, Bath, **Avon BA1 5BG**
TEL   0225 461969 or 0272 333595
OPEN   9–6 Mon–Sat.

Specialise in cleaning and restoring oils, watercolours and prints.

PROVIDE Home Inspections. Chargeable Estimates. Chargeable Local Collection/Delivery Service.
SPEAK TO Anthony Reed.
Member of the IIC.
SEE Furniture, Picture Frames.

SIMON WELLBY AND NICHOLAS WRIGHT

Epstein Building, Mivart Street, Easton, Bristol, **Avon BS5 6JF**
TEL   0272 354478
OPEN   9–6 Mon–Fri.

Specialise in restoring oil paintings, lining, transfer and panel work.

PROVIDE Home Inspections.
Free/Chargeable Estimates.
Free/Chargeable Collection/Delivery Service.
SPEAK TO Simon Wellby or Nicholas Wright.
Mr Wellby is a Full Member of ABPR.

K. A. WHEELER

4 Bayswater Avenue, Westbury Park, Bristol, **Avon BS6 7NS**
TEL   0272 423003
OPEN   By Appointment Only.

Specialise in conserving and restoring fine prints, watercolours and drawings. Reports and photo documentation supplied if required.

PROVIDE Free Estimates.
SPEAK TO Keith Wheeler.
Member of the Institute of Paper Conservation and the UKIC. This studio is included on the register maintained by the Conservation Unit of the Museums and Galleries Commission.
Established 1970.

JACEK CZECZOT BSc, MA.

The Studio, Conservation of Paintings, 13 Crispin Field, Pitstone, **Bedfordshire LU7 9BG**
TEL   0296 668392 FAX
OPEN   10–7 Mon–Fri.

Specialise in restoring easel and mural paintings, no watercolours or paperwork.

PROVIDE Home Inspections.
Free/Chargeable Estimates. Chargeable Collection/Delivery Service. Chargeable Written Reports.
SPEAK TO Czeczot.
Member of IIC and UKIC. This workshop is included on the register of conservators maintained by the Conservation Unit of the Museums and Galleries Commission.

SUSAN CLOWES LAMBERT

E Becker Ltd, Unit 4, Cherrycourt Way, Stanbridge Road, Leighton Buzzard, **Bedfordshire LU7 8UH**
TEL   0525 853033
FAX   0525 853032
OPEN   9–5 Mon–Fri.

Specialise in conserving and restoring works of art on paper, paintings, prints, drawings.

PROVIDE Home Inspections. Free Estimates. Chargeable Collection/Delivery Service.
SPEAK TO Susan Clowes Lambert or David Lambert.
Member of IPC and UKIC.
SEE Picture Frames.

DAVID MITCHELL

45 St. Michael's Road, Bedford, **Bedfordshire MK40 2LZ**
TEL   0234 359976
OPEN   9–6 Mon–Fri or By Appointment.

Specialise in cleaning oil paintings, holes filled and repaired, touching up.

PROVIDE Home Inspections.
Free/Chargeable Estimates. Chargeable Collection/Delivery Service.
SPEAK TO David Mitchell.
Member of UKIC and BAFRA.
SEE Furniture, Clocks

ALWAY FINE ART CONSERVATION

Riverside Corner, Windsor Road, Datchet, **Berkshire SL3 9BT**
TEL   0753 541163
FAX   0753 541163
OPEN   By Appointment.

Specialise in conservation and restoration of works of art on paper.

PROVIDE Home Inspections. Free Estimates. Free Collection/Delivery Service.
SPEAK TO John Alway.
Member of IPC.

THE COLLECTORS' GALLERY

8 Bridge Street, Caversham Bridge, Reading, **Berkshire RG4 8AA**
TEL   0734 483663
OPEN   10–5 Mon–Fri; 10–4 Sat.

Specialise in conserving and restoring 18th and 19th century oils and watercolours.

PROVIDE Home Inspections. Free Estimates. Collection/Delivery Service by arrangement.
SPEAK TO Helen Snook.

HERON PICTURES

High Street, Whitchurch–on–Thames, Reading, **Berkshire RG8 7EX**
TEL   0734 843286
OPEN   10–7 Tues–Sat.

Specialise in cleaning and restoring oil paintings.

PROVIDE Home Inspections. Free Estimates. Free Local Collection/Delivery Service.
SPEAK TO George Duckett.
SEE Picture Frames.

LEADON FINE ARTS

134 Silverdale Road, Earley, Reading, **Berkshire RG6 2LX**
TEL   0734 264999
OPEN   By Appointment.

Specialise in cleaning works of art on paper and restoring oils.

PROVIDE Home Inspections. Free Estimates. Collection/Delivery Service.
SPEAK TO D. J. Dodds.
SEE Picture Frames.

ARTHUR CLARK T/A CLARK GALLERIES

Daneswood, Church Lane, Deanshanger, Milton Keynes, **Buckinghamshire MK19 6HG**
TEL   0908 563369
OPEN   9–5.30 or By Appointment.

Specialise in restoring oil paintings and also relining.

PROVIDE Home Inspections. Chargeable Estimates. Chargeable Collection/Delivery Service.
SPEAK TO Arthur Clark.
Established 1963. Full Member of ABPR. This workshop is included on the register of conservators maintained by the Conservation Unit of the Museums and Galleries Commission.

INTERNATIONAL PICTURE RESTORATION

Lavinia Beard, Coppins Cottage, Iver, **Buckinghamshire SL0 0AT**
TEL   0753 654617
OPEN   By Appointment.

Specialise in conservation and restoration of oil paintings on canvas and panel.

PROVIDE Free Estimates.
SPEAK TO Lavinia Beard.
Member of Antique and Fine Art Disasters Unit, Associate Member of ABPR. This studio is included on the register of conservators maintained by the Conservation Unit of the Museums and Galleries Commission.

BRIAN E. NEWSON

9 Slade Road, Stokenchurch, **Buckinghamshire HP14 3QQ**
TEL   0494 482123
OPEN   9–6 Mon–Fri.

Specialise in all aspects of oil painting conservation.

PROVIDE Home Inspections. Free Local Estimates. Free Collection/Delivery Service.
SPEAK TO Brian Newson.
Member of UKIC and Full Member of ABPR. This workshop is included on the register of conservators maintained by the Conservation Unit of the Museums and Galleries Commission.

H. S. WELLBY LTD
The Malt House, Church End, Haddenham, **Buckinghamshire HP17 8AB**
TEL 0844 290036
OPEN 9–5 Mon–Sat.

Specialise in the lining, cleaning and restoration of oil paintings.

PROVIDE Home Inspections. Free Estimates. Free Collection/Delivery Service.
SPEAK TO Christopher Wellby.
Full Member of ABPR.

ELIZABETH WINTGENS GALLERY
96 High Street, Marlow, **Buckinghamshire SL7 1AQ**
TEL 0628 482759
FAX 0628 898186
OPEN 9.30–5.30 Mon–Sat.

Specialise in complete picture care and conservation service for watercolours, prints and easel paintings.

PROVIDE Home Inspections. Free Estimates. Free Local Collection Delivery Service.
SPEAK TO Michael Wintgens.
Member of IIC and Fine Art Trade Guild.
SEE Picture Frames

CAMBRIDGE FINE ART LTD
Priesthouse, 33 Church Street, Little Shelford, Cambridge, **Cambridgeshire CB2 5HG**
TEL 0223 842866 or 843537
OPEN 10–6 Mon–Sat.

Specialise in restoring oil paintings and watercolours (1780–1950).

PROVIDE Free/Chargeable Estimates. Chargeable Collection/Delivery Service.
SPEAK TO Ralph Lury.

ALAN CANDY
Old Manor House, 4 Cambridge Street, Godmanchester, Huntingdon, **Cambridgeshire PE18 8AT**
TEL 0480 453198
OPEN By Appointment.

Specialise in restoring oils, watercolours and prints.

PROVIDE Free Estimates.
SPEAK TO Alan Candy.

WENDY A. CRAIG
Cambridge Conservation Studio, Balsham Road, Linton, Cambridge, **Cambridgeshire CB2 6LE**
TEL 0223 881295
FAX 0223 894056
OPEN 9–6 Mon–Sat.

Specialise in conserving and restoring works of art on paper. Collection surveys and advice on storage and environment.

PROVIDE Home Inspections. Free Estimates. Free/Chargeable Collection/Delivery Service.
SPEAK TO Wendy Ann Craig.
This workshop is included on the register of conservators maintained by the Conservation Unit of the Museums and Galleries Commission.
SEE Picture Frames.

JULIE CRICK
Studio 5, Hope Street Yard, Cambridge, **Cambridgeshire CB1 3NA**
TEL 0223 410586
OPEN By Appointment.

Specialise in restoring oil paintings.

PROVIDE Home Inspections. Free

Estimates. Free/Chargeable Collection/Delivery Service.
SPEAK TO Julie Crick.
Member of UKIC, Associate Member of ABPR, Diploma in Conservation. This workshop is included on the register of conservators maintained by the Conservation Unit of the Museums and Galleries Commission.
SEE Picture Frames.

KATHRYN OAT JOHNSON

Thatched Cottage, Walden Road, Littlebury, **Cambridgeshire CB11 4TA**
TEL   0799 521777 FAX
OPEN   By Appointment.

Specialise in restoring oil paintings on canvas.

PROVIDE Home Inspections. Chargeable Estimates. Free/Chargeable Collection/Delivery Service.
SPEAK TO Kathryn Oat Johnson.
Member of UKIC and Associate Member of ABPR.

BO KILLANDER

Pampisford Hall, Sawton, **Cambridgeshire CB2 4EZ**
TEL   0223 832149
OPEN   8–6 Mon–Fri.

Specialise in conservation and restoration of all forms of easel paintings, traditional and contemporary.

PROVIDE Home Inspections. Free Estimates. Collection Delivery Service.
SPEAK TO Bo Killander.
Member of NFK Swedish Section (IIC Nordic Group) and UKIC.

HARPER FINE PAINTINGS

Overdale, Woodford Road, Poynton, **Cheshire SK12 1ED**
TEL   0625 879105
OPEN   By Appointment.

Specialise in restoring 18th, 19th and early 20th century British and European oils and watercolours.

PROVIDE Home Inspections. Chargeable Estimates. Free Collection/Delivery Service.
SPEAK TO Peter Harper.

DEBBIE COLEMAN

Watchtower Studio, Church End, East Looe, **Cornwall PL13 1BX**
TEL   0503 263232 or 263344
OPEN   10.30–5 Mon–Sat or By Appointment.

Specialise in restoring oil paintings, watercolours, prints and drawings.

PROVIDE Home Inspections. Free Estimates. Collection/Delivery Service.
SPEAK TO Debbie Coleman. Associate Member of ABPR. This workshop is included on the register of conservators maintained by the Conservation Unit of the Museums and Galleries Commission.
SEE Picture Frames.

JOHN AND ELIZABETH CYNDDYLAN

Tre'staenog, Penbeagle Way, St. Ives, **Cornwall TR26 2EY**
TEL   0736 797715
OPEN   9–5 Mon–Fri; 9–1 Sat.

Specialise in restoring oil and tempera on panels and canvas.

PROVIDE Home Inspections. Free Local Estimates. Free Local Collection/Delivery Service.
SPEAK TO John or Elizabeth Cynddylan.
Member of UKIC and IIC.
SEE Porcelain.

TAMAR GALLERY (ANTIQUES & FINE ART)

5 Church Street, Launceston, **Cornwall PL15 8AW**
TEL   0566 82444
OPEN   By Appointment.

Specialise in restoring and cleaning watercolours of all periods.

PROVIDE Free Estimates.
SPEAK TO N. O. Preston.

NICOLA DUNCAN
Kings Newton House, Main Street, Kings Newton, Nr. Melbourns, **Derbyshire DE73 1BX**
TEL   0332 863399
OPEN   10–6 Mon–Fri.

Specialise in restoring works of art on paper, watercolours, prints, drawings.

PROVIDE Home Inspections. Free Estimates. Free Collection/ Delivery Service.
SPEAK TO Nicola Duncan.
Member of IPC.

NIGEL BLOWER CONSERVATION OF PAINTINGS
Address witheld by request, Dorchester, **Dorset DT2 0LX**
TEL   0935 83096
OPEN   9–6.30 Mon–Sat.

Specialise in restoring easel paintings on canvas and panel.

PROVIDE Home Inspections. Free Estimates. Free Collection/Delivery Service.
SPEAK TO Nigel Blower.
Associate Member of ABPR.

RITA BUTLER
Stour Gallery, 28 East Street, Blandford, **Dorset DT11 7DR**
TEL   0258 456293
OPEN   10–1, 2–4 Tues, Thur–Sat; 10–1 Wed.

Specialise in cleaning and restoring oil paintings, watercolours and prints.

PROVIDE Home Inspections. Free

Estimates. Chargeable Collection/Delivery Service.
SPEAK TO Rita Butler.

GALERIE LA FRANCE
647 Wimborne Road, Winton, Bournemouth, **Dorset BH9 2AR**
TEL   0202 522313
OPEN   8.30–1, 2–5.30 Mon–Fri; 9–1 Sat.

Specialise in cleaning and restoring oils, watercolours and prints.

PROVIDE Home Inspections. Free Estimates. Free/Chargeable Collection/Delivery Service.
SPEAK TO Pierre Lafrance.
SEE Picture Frames.

THE SWAN GALLERY
57 Cheap Street, Sherborne, **Dorset DT9 3AX**
TEL   0935 814465
FAX   0308 68195
OPEN   9.30–5 Mon–Sat; 9.30–1 Wed.

Specialise in cleaning works of art on paper.

PROVIDE Free Estimates.
SPEAK TO Simon Lamb.

WESSEX PICTURE RESTORERS
Northwood, Monkton Wylde, Bridport, **Dorset DT6 6DE**
TEL   03005 456
OPEN   By Appointment Only.

Specialise in restoring oil paintings, wax/resin relining with vacuum hot table.

PROVIDE Chargeable Home Inspections. Free Estimates. Chargeable Collection/Delivery Service.
SPEAK TO Elizabeth Hopley or Iain Geffers. Mr Geffers is a Full Member of ABPR. Mrs Hopley is an Associate

Member of ABPR. This workshop is included on the register of conservators maintained by the Conservation Unit of the Museums and Galleries Commission.

ALLYSON McDERMOTT (INTERNATIONAL CONSERVATION CONSULTANTS)

Lintz Green Conservation Centre, Lintz Green House, Lintz Green, Rowlands Gill, **Durham NE39 1NL**

TEL   0207 71547 or 0831 104145 or 0831 257584
FAX   0207 71547
OPEN   9–5.30 Mon–Fri.

Specialise in conservation of easel paintings, pastels, chalks, prints, drawings, photographs, watercolours and historic wallpapers.

PROVIDE Home Inspections. Free Estimates. Chargeable Collection/Delivery Service.
SPEAK TO Allyson McDermott or Gillian Lee.
They have a Southern Regional Office at 45 London Road, Cheltenham, **Gloucestershire**.
SEE Art Researchers, Carpets, Lighting, Picture Frames, Specialist Photographers.

S. BOND & SON

14/15 North Hill, Colchester, **Essex CO1 1DZ**

TEL   0206 572925
OPEN   9–5 Mon–Sat.

Specialise in restoring oil paintings.

PROVIDE Home Inspections. Free Estimates. Free Local Collection/Delivery Service.
SPEAK TO Robert Bond.
This family firm has been established 140 years and is run by the fifth generation.
SEE Furniture.

RICHARD ILES GALLERY

10 Northgate Street, Colchester, **Essex CO1 1HA**

TEL   0206 577877
OPEN   9.30–4.30 Mon–Sat.

Specialise in restoring 19th and early 20th century watercolours.

PROVIDE Free Estimates.
Speak to Richard Iles.
SEE Picture Frames.

MEYERS' GALLERY

66 High Street, Ingatestone, **Essex CM4 0BA**

TEL   0277 355335
OPEN   10–5 Mon–Sat; closed Wed.

Specialise in restoring oil paintings and watercolours.

PROVIDE Home Inspections. Free Estimates. Free Local Collection/Delivery Service.
SPEAK TO Mrs Meyers.
Member of LAPADA.

MILLSIDE ANTIQUE RESTORATION

Parndon Mill, Parndon Mill Lane, Harlow, **Essex CM20 2HP**

TEL   0279 428148
FAX   0279 415075
OPEN   10–5 Mon–Fri.

Specialise in cleaning and restoring watercolours, prints and oil paintings. Also do watercolour tinting of sepia and black and white prints.

PROVIDE Home Inspections. Free/Chargeable Estimates. Chargeable Collection/Delivery Service.
SPEAK TO David Sparks or Angela Wickliffe–Philp.
SEE Picture Frames, Porcelain, Silver.

PEARLITA FRAMES LTD

30 North Street, Romford, **Essex RM11 2LB**

TEL   0708 760342
OPEN   9–5.30 Mon–Sat.

Specialise in restoring oil paintings, watercolours and engravings.

PROVIDE Home Inspections. Free Estimates. Free Collection/Delivery Service.
SPEAK TO Trevor Woodward.
SEE Picture Frames.

ELIZABETH POWELL
5 Royal Square, Dedham, Colchester, **Essex CO7 6AA**
TEL   0206 322279
OPEN   9–5.30 Mon–Sat.

Specialise in conserving and restoring oil paintings, watercolours, pastels and prints.

PROVIDE Home Inspections. Free Estimates. Free Local Collection/Delivery Service.
SPEAK TO Elizabeth Powell.
Member of IIC.

CHRISTINE SNELL PICTURE CONSERVATION
Painter's Farm, Butlers Lane, Ashdon, Saffron Walden, **Essex CB10 2ND**
TEL   0799 523332
OPEN   10.30–5 Mon–Fri; closed Wed.

Specialise in restoring oil paintings.

PROVIDE Home Inspections. Free Estimates.
SPEAK TO Christine Snell.
Associate Member of ABPR and UKIC.

ASTLEY HOUSE FINE ART
Astley House, High Street, Moreton–in–Marsh, **Gloucestershire GL56 0LL**
TEL   0608 50601
FAX   0608 51777
OPEN   9–5.30 Mon–Sat; closed Wed.

Specialise in cleaning and restoring oil paintings, watercolours.

PROVIDE Free Estimates. Chargeable Collection/Delivery Service.
SPEAK TO David or Nanette Glaisyer.
SEE Picture Frames.

KEITH BAWDEN
Mews Workshop, Montpellier Retreat, Cheltenham, **Gloucestershire GL50 2XS**
TEL   0242 230320
OPEN   7–4.30 Mon–Fri.

Specialise in conserving and restoring all aspects of paintings.

PROVIDE Free Estimates. Home Inspections. Local Collection/Delivery Service.
SPEAK TO Keith Bawden.
SEE Clocks, Furniture, Silver, Porcelain.

CLEEVE PICTURE FRAMING
Coach House Workshops, Stoke Road, Bishops Cleeve, Cheltenham, **Gloucestershire GL52 4RP**
TEL   0242 672785
FAX   0242 676827
OPEN   9–1, 2–5.30 Mon–Fri; 9–1 Sat.

Specialise in restoring and conserving oil paintings, watercolours, papers and prints.

PROVIDE Home Inspections. Free Estimates. Free Collection/Delivery Service.
SPEAK TO James Gardner.
SEE Picture Frames.

G. M. S. RESTORATIONS
The Workshops (rear of Bell Passage Antiques), High Street, Wickwar, **Gloucestershire GL12 8NP**
TEL   0454 294251
FAX   0454 294251
OPEN   8–5 Mon–Fri.

Specialise in restoring oil paintings and watercolours.

PROVIDE Home Inspections. Refundable Estimates. Chargeable Collection/Delivery Service.
SPEAK TO Mr G. M. St George–Stacey.
Member of LAPADA, Upholsterers Guild, Guild of Master Craftsmen, Guild

of Woodcarvers, Guild of Antique Dealers and Restorers.
SEE Furniture.

PIPPA JEFFRIES
1 St James Terrace, Suffolk Parade, Cheltenham, **Gloucestershire GL50 2AA**
TEL   0242 239895
OPEN   9–6 Mon–Fri or By
          Appointment.

Specialise in relining and all aspects of restoration of oil paintings on canvas and panel.

PROVIDE Home Inspections. Free Estimates. Chargeable Collection/Delivery Service.
SPEAK TO Pippa Jeffries.
Associate Member of ABPR. This workshop is included on the register of conservators maintained by the Conservation Unit of the Museums and Galleries Commission.

A. J. PONSFORD ANTIQUES
51–53 Dollar Street, Cirencester, **Gloucestershire GL7 2AS**
TEL   0285 652355
OPEN   8.30–5.30 Mon–Fri.

Specialise in restoring oil paintings.

PROVIDE Home Inspections. Free Estimates. Free Collection/Delivery Service.
SPEAK TO A. J. Ponsford.
SEE Furniture, Picture Frames.

GRAINNE WHITTLEY CONSERVATION AND RESTORATION OF WORKS OF ART ON PAPER
2 Durban Villas, Bath Road, Nailswort, **Gloucestershire GL6 0HJ**
TEL   0453 833687
OPEN   9–6 Mon–Sat.

Specialise in restoring works of art on paper, including prints, drawings, watercolours.

PROVIDE Home Inspections. Free Estimates. Free Collection/Delivery Service.
SPEAK TO Grainne Whittley (Miss). Member of UKIC and IPC. BA (Hons) in Conservation from Camberwell College of Arts and Crafts.
SEE Picture Frames, Books

ANN BROOMFIELD
Blanton House, Bridge Street, Wickham, **Hampshire PO17 5JJ**
TEL   0329 833598
OPEN   9.30–5 By Appointment.

Specialise in restoring paintings.

PROVIDE Home Inspections. Free/Chargeable Estimates. Chargeable Collection/Delivery Service.
SPEAK TO Ann Broomfield. Member of UKIC and IIC. This workshop is included on the register of conservators maintained by the Conservation Unit of the Museums and Galleries Commission.

CORFIELD RESTORATIONS LTD
120 High Street, Lymington, **Hampshire SO41 9AQ**
TEL   0590 673532
OPEN   9.15–5.30 Mon–Sat.

Specialise in picture restoration.

PROVIDE Home Inspections. Free Estimates. Local Free Collection/Delivery Service.
SPEAK TO Alan Bloomfield or Michael Corfield.
Also at Setters Farm, Lymington. 0590 671977.
SEE Furniture, Picture Frames.

R. & L. LANCEFIELD
"Toad Hall", Burnetts Lane, Horton Heath, Eastleigh, **Hampshire SO5 7DJ**
TEL   0703 692032
OPEN   9–5.30 Mon–Fri or By
          Appointment.

Specialise in restoring prints.

PROVIDE Home Inspections. Free Estimates. Free/Chargeable Collection/Delivery Service.
SPEAK TO Rex Lancefield.
Member of IPC. This workshop is included on the register of conservators maintained by the Conservation Unit of the Museum and Galleries Commission.
SEE Books.

JOAN A. LEWRY
'Wychelms', 66 Gorran Avenue, Rowner, Gosport, **Hampshire PO13 ONF**
TEL   0329 286901
OPEN   By Appointment.

Specialise in cleaning, conserving and restoring pictures.

PROVIDE Home Inspections. Refundable Estimates. Free Local Collection/Delivery Service.
SPEAK TO Joan Lewry.

DRIAN SCOTT
Coach Hill House, Burley Street, Nr. Ringwood, **Hampshire BH24 4HN**
TEL   04253 3361
OPEN   By Appointment.

Specialise in restoring, mounting and framing Oriental paintings on paper or silk.

PROVIDE Free Estimates. Chargeable Collection/Delivery Service.
SPEAK TO Ian Scott.

A. SCOTT–MONCRIEFF
6 Newcombe Road, Southampton, **Hampshire SO1 2FL**
TEL   0703 635706
OPEN   9–5 Mon–Fri.

Specialise in restoring easel paintings.

PROVIDE Home Inspections.
Free/Chargeable Estimates. Chargeable Collection/Delivery Service.
SPEAK TO A. Scott–Moncrieff.

Associate Member of UKIC, Associate Member of ABPR.

J. T. BURNS
Fairview Cottage, Shucknall Hill, Hereford, **Hereford & Worcester HR1 3SW**
TEL   0432 850213
OPEN   10–5 Mon–Sat.

Specialise in restoring and conserving oil paintings only, including cleaning, varnishing, re–lining and damage repair.

PROVIDE Home Inspections. Free Estimates. Chargeable Collection/Delivery Service.
SPEAK TO Mr or Mrs Burns.
Member of UKIC, Associate Member of ABPR. This workshop is included on the register of conservators maintained by the Conservation Unit of the Museums and Galleries Commission.

EDWIN COLLINS
Coltsfoot Gallery, Hatfield, Leominster, **Hereford & Worcester HR6 0SF**
(Please use Herefordshire if writing).
TEL   056 882 277
OPEN   By Appointment.

Specialise in restoring and conserving all works of art on paper.

PROVIDE Home Inspections. Free Estimates.
SPEAK TO Edwin Collins.
Member of IPC.
SEE Picture Frames.

JAMES GRINDLEY
2 Fownhope Court, Fownhope, Hereford, **Hereford & Worcester HR1 4PB**
TEL   0432 860396
OPEN   By Appointment.

Specialise in restoring and conserving works of art on paper, particularly watercolours and prints.

PROVIDE Free Estimates.
SPEAK TO James Grindley.

HAY LOFT GALLERY
Berry Wormington, Broadway,
Hereford & Worcester WR12 7NH
TEL   0242 621202
OPEN   10–5.30 Mon–Fri or By
        Appointment.

Specialise in restoring paintings,
particularly 19th century.

PROVIDE Home Inspections. Free
Estimates.
SPEAK TO Jane or Sally Pitt.

T. M. HUGUENIN
20 Albany Terrace, Worcester,
Hereford & Worcester WR1 3DU
TEL   0905 28133
OPEN   Mon– Sat By Appointment.

Specialise in restoring works of art on
paper, prints, drawings, watercolours.

PROVIDE Home Inspections. Free
Estimates. Chargeable
Collection/Delivery Service.
SPEAK TO T. M. Huguenin.
Member of UKIC and IPC. This
workshop is included on the register of
conservators maintained by the
Conservation Unit of the Museums and
Galleries Commission.
SEE Picture Frames.

GEORGE JACK & CO.
Notre Val, Laverton, Broadway,
Hereford & Worcester WR12 7NA
TEL   038673 691
FAX   038673 691
OPEN   By Appointment.

Specialise in restoring oil paintings from
16th century to present day but
particularly the 19th century period.

PROVIDE Home Inspections. Negotiable
Estimates. Free Collection/Delivery
Service.
SPEAK TO Mr George Jack.
Mr Jack has forty–four years' experience.

Full Member of ABPR. Associate
Member IIC. This workshop is included
on the register of conservators
maintained by the Conservation Unit of
the Museums and Galleries Commission.

KATE NEWTON
Yew Tree Cottage, Logaston, Woonton,
Hereford, **Hereford and Worcester
HR3 6QH**
TEL   0544 327712
OPEN   9–5 Mon–Fri.

Specialise in restoring art on paper,
including prints, drawings,
watercolours.

PROVIDE Home Inspections. Free
Estimates. Chargeable
Collection/Delivery Service.
SPEAK TO Kate Newton.
Member of IPC.
SEE Books.

EUGENE B. OKARMA
Brobury House Gallery, Brobury,
Hereford & Worcester HR3 6BS
TEL   09817 229
OPEN   9–4 Mon–Sat.

Specialise in restoring old prints,
watercolours and oil paintings.

PROVIDE Local Home Inspections.
SPEAK TO Mr Okarma.
SEE Picture Frames.

LEONORA WEAVER
6 Aylestone Drive, Hereford,
Hereford & Worcester HR1 1HT
TEL   0432 267816
OPEN   By Appointment.

Specialise in restoring and hand–
colouring prints.

PROVIDE Free Estimates.
Collection/Delivery Service sometimes
available.
SPEAK TO Leonora Weaver.
SEE Books.

JOHN ESSEX

The Studio, Chapel Street,
Berkhamstead, **Hertfordshire**
HP4 3EA
TEL   0442 864821
OPEN   9.30–5 Mon–Fri By
        Appointment only.

Specialise in wax impregnating and glue
lining up to nine by fifteen feet. Their
speciality is panel work from rejoins and
blister laying to semi and total transfers
on to conservation panels.

PROVIDE Home Inspections. Free
Estimates. Chargeable
Collection/Delivery Service.
SPEAK TO John Essex.
Full Member of ABPR.

HERTFORDSHIRE CONSERVATION SERVICE

Seed Warehouse, Maidenhead Yard, The
Wash, Hertford, **Hertfordshire**
SG14 1PX
TEL   0992 588966 or 0992 504662
        ANS 0992 588966
FAX   0992 503184
OPEN   9–6 Mon–Fri By Appointment.

Specialise in restoring works of art on
paper, including prints, drawings,
wallpaper and photographs.

PROVIDE Home Inspections.
Free/Chargeable Estimates. Chargeable
Collection/Delivery Service.
SPEAK TO J. M. Macqueen.
This workshop is included on the register
of conservators maintained by the
Conservation Unit of the Museums and
Galleries Commission.
SEE Collectors (Dolls), Lighting,
Porcelain, Furniture, Picture Frames,
Carpets.

ST OUEN ANTIQUES LTD

Vintage Corner, Old Cambridge Road,
Puckeridge, **Hertfordshire SG11 1SA**
TEL   0920 821336
FAX   0920 822877
OPEN   10–5 Mon–Sat.

Specialise in restoring 19th century
paintings.

PROVIDE Home Inspections. Refundable
Estimates. Chargeable Collection/
Delivery Service.
SPEAK TO Tim or John Blake.
SEE Furniture.

CHARLOTTE HOOKER

Jasmine Cottage, Front Street, Laxton,
Nr. Goole, **North Humberside**
DN14 7TS
TEL   0430 430681
OPEN   8.30–5.30 Mon–Fri.

Specialise in a full restoration service for
oil paintings on any support in situ or in
workshop. Will give advice about care
and housing of oil paintings.

PROVIDE Home Inspections.
Free/Chargeable Estimates.
SPEAK TO Charlotte Hooker.
Member of UKIC.
SEE Picture Frames.

NICHOLAS ARDIZZONE

4 Golden Street, Deal, **Kent CT14 6JU**
TEL   0304 361139
OPEN   8.30–5.30 Mon–Sat.

Specialise in restoring objects on paper,
including prints, drawings and
photographs.

PROVIDE Home Inspections. Free
Estimates. Chargeable
Collection/Delivery Service.
SPEAK TO Nicholas Ardizzone.
Member of IPC. Camberwell Graduate
(HNO).
SEE Books.

FRAN BIRD PAPER CONSERVATOR

Hogtrough Cottage, Hogtrough Hill,
Brasted, Westerham, **Kent TN16 1NX**
TEL   0959 565163
FAX   0959 565163
OPEN   9–5 Mon–Fri or By
        Appointment.

Specialise in restoring prints.

PROVIDE Home Inspections. Free Estimates. Local Free Collection/Delivery Service. SPEAK TO Fran Bird. Member of IPC. SEE Books.

CASTLE FINE ART STUDIO
26 Castle Street, Dover, **Kent CT16 1PW**
TEL   0304 206360
OPEN   10–1, 2–5.30 Mon–Fri; 10–1 Sat.

Specialise in restoring works of art on paper, prints, drawings, watercolours.

PROVIDE Home Inspections. Free Estimates. Free Local Collection/Delivery Service. SPEAK TO Ms Deborah Colam. Member of IPC. This workshop is included on the register of conservators maintained by the Conservation Unit of the Museums and Galleries Commission. SEE Books, Picture Frames.

CLARE GALLERY
21 High Street, Royal Tunbridge Wells, **Kent TN1 1UT**
TEL   0892 538717
FAX   0323 729588
OPEN   9–5.30 Mon–Sat.

Specialise in restoring 19th and 20th century oil paintings and watercolours.

PROVIDE Home Inspections. Free Estimates. Chargeable Collection/Delivery Service. SPEAK TO M. Ettinger. SEE Picture Frames.

ROGER GREEN FINE ART
Hales Place Studio, High Halden, Nr. Ashford, **Kent TN26 3JQ**
TEL   0233 850716
FAX   0233 850219
OPEN   9–5 Mon–Sat.

Specialise in conservation and restoration of oil paintings and paper art.

PROVIDE Local Home Inspections. Free Estimates. SPEAK TO Roger Green or Ellen Green. SEE Picture Frames.

FRANCIS ILES FINE PAINTINGS
Rutland House, 103 High Street, Rochester. **Kent ME1 1LX**
TEL   0634 843081
FAX   0474 822403
OPEN   9–5.30 Mon–Sat.

Specialise in conserving and restoring oil paintings and works on paper.

PROVIDE Home Inspections. Free Estimates. Free Collection/Delivery Service. SPEAK TO Jeanette or Lucy Iles. SEE Picture Frames.

GILLIAN M. KINLOCH
Adams Well, Gover Hill, Maidstone, **Kent ME18 5JP**
TEL   0732 850845
OPEN   9–6 Mon–Sat or By Appointment.

Specialise in restoring oil paintings and providing advice on all aspects of restoration and conservation.

PROVIDE Home Inspections. Free Estimates. Chargeable Collection/Delivery Service. SPEAK TO Gillian Kinloch. Associate Member of ABPR and Member of IIC. This workshop is included on the register of conservators maintained by the Conservation Unit of the Museums and Galleries Commission.

LIBRARY CONSERVATORS
'Draycott', Green Lane, Temple Ewell, **Kent CT16 3AR**
TEL   0304 823060 or 206360
OPEN   10–5.30 Mon–Sat.

Specialise in restoring watercolours, drawings and oils.

PROVIDE Home Inspections. Free/Chargeable Estimates. Free/Chargeable Collection/Delivery Service.
SPEAK TO Louise Drover or Deborah Colam.
Member of IPC. This workshop is included on the register of conservators maintained by the Conservation Unit of the Museums and Galleries Commission.
SEE Picture Frames, Books.

G. & D. I. MARRIN & SONS

149 Sandgate Road, Folkestone, **Kent CT20 2DA**
TEL   0303 53016
FAX   0303 850956
OPEN   9.30–5.30 Mon–Sat.

Specialise in restoring prints.

PROVIDE Home Inspections. Chargeable Estimates. Chargeable Collection/Delivery Service.
SPEAK TO John or Patrick Marrin.
SEE Books.

W. J. MORRILL

437 Folkestone Road, Dover, **Kent CT17 9JX**
TEL   0304 201989
OPEN   8.30–5 Mon–Thur. 8.30–1 Fri.

Specialise in relining and restoring oil paintings of all periods.

PROVIDE Home Inspections. Free Collection/Delivery Service.
SPEAK TO Mr Barnes.
SEE Picture Frames.

BARBARA WILDMAN

9 Woodside Terrace, Nelson, **Lancashire BB9 7TB**
TEL   0282 699679
OPEN   By Appointment.

Specialise in restoring oil paintings of all periods, including re-lining.

PROVIDE Home Inspections. Free Estimates. Chargeable Collection/Delivery Service.
SPEAK TO Barbara Wildman.
SEE Picture Frames.

RICHARD ZAHLER

Lane House, Fowgill, Bentham, Lancaster, **Lancashire LA2 7AH**
TEL   05242 61998
OPEN   9–6 Mon–Fri or By Appointment.

Specialise in restoring easel paintings, icons, ceiling and some mural types, watercolours, prints, drawings, sketches, Oriental works of art. Will cosmetically clean whole collections in situ for customers who wish to rejuvenate their collections harmoniously. Also provide an emergency first aid service when unforeseen damage has occurred.
SPEAK TO Richard Zahler.
Member of UKIC and the Guild of Master Craftsmen. This workshop is included on the register maintained by the Conservation Unit of the Museums and Galleries Commission.
SEE Books, Picture Frames, Furniture.

JOHN GARNER

51–53 High Street East, Uppingham, **Leicestershire LE15 9PY**
TEL   0572 823607
FAX   0572 821654
OPEN   9–5.30 Mon–Sat; By Appointment Sun.

Specialise in restoring 18th and 19th century pictures.

PROVIDE Home Inspections. Free Collection/Delivery Service.
SPEAK TO John or Paul Garner.
SEE Furniture.

JULIET HAWKER
Ford House Studio, 7 Queen Street,
Uppingham, Rutland, **Leicestershire
LE15 9QR**
TEL   0572 821733
OPEN   10–4 Mon–Thur or By
        Appointment. It is advisable to
        phone for directions.

Specialise in restoring and cleaning
paintings in oil and acrylic on canvas,
panel or metal. Large works can be
treated on location.

PROVIDE Home Inspections. Free
Estimates. Free Local
Collection/Delivery Service.
SPEAK TO Juliet Hawker.
Associate Member of ABPR and UKIC.
This workshop is included on the register
of conservators maintained by the
Conservation Unit of the Museums and
Galleries Commission.

THE OLD HOUSE GALLERY
13–15 Market Place, Oakham,
Leicestershire LE15 6DT
TEL   0572 755538
OPEN   10–5 Mon–Fri; 10–4 Sat; closed
        Thur p.m.

Specialise in restoration of oils and
watercolours.

PROVIDE Home Inspections. Free Local
Collection/Delivery Service.
SPEAK TO Richard Clarke.
SEE Picture Frames.

SUE RAWLINGS
17 Nithsdale Crescent, Market
Harborough, **Leicestershire
LE16 9HA**
TEL   0858 464605
OPEN   9–5.30 Mon–Fri.

Specialise in restoring works of art on
paper.

PROVIDE Home Inspections. Free
Estimates. Free Local
Collection/Delivery Service.

SPEAK TO Sue Rawlings.
Member of IPC. This workshop is
included on the register of conservators
maintained by the Conservation Unit of
the Museums
and Galleries Commission.
SEE Books

BURGHLEY FINE ART CONSERVATION LTD
Burghley House, Stamford,
Lincolnshire PE9 3JY
TEL   0780 62155
OPEN   By Appointment.

Specialise in conserving and restoring
easel paintings, wall paintings (oil on
plaster).

PROVIDE Home Inspections. Free
Estimates. Chargeable
Collection/Delivery Service.
SPEAK TO Michael Cowell.
Any work undertaken is fully
documented.
SEE Furniture, Picture Frames.

SARAH COVE: CONSERVATION OF PAINTINGS
Nr. Stamford, **Lincolnshire PE10 0NF**
TEL   077 832239 or 081 801 9039(
        answerphone)
OPEN   9.30–6 Mon–Fri By
        Appointment Only.

Specialise in conservation and
restoration of easel paintings,
particularly English portraiture and 18th
and 19th century landscape. Also modern
mixed media works. Will carry out
collection surveys and give advice on
treatment, future planning,
transportation, framing etc.

PROVIDE Chargeable Home Inspections.
Refundable Estimates. Chargeable
Collection/Delivery Service.
SPEAK TO Sarah Cove or Alan Cummings.
Associate Member of IIC, UKIC and
ABPR. This workshop is included on the
register of conservators maintained by

the Conservation Unit of the Museums and Galleries Commission.

SARAH JENNINGS CONSERVATION OF FINE ART

The Manor, Timberland, Lincoln, **Lincolnshire LN4 3RZ**
TEL   0526378 388
OPEN   By Appointment.

Specialise in conserving and restoring paintings in oil, tempera, fresco, on copper, wood, plaster, board and canvas.

PROVIDE Home Inspections. Refundable Estimates. Chargeable Collection/ Delivery Service.
SPEAK TO Sarah Jennings.

HIRST CONSERVATION

Laughton, Sleaford, **Lincolnshire NG34 0HE**
TEL   05297 449/517
FAX   05297 518
OPEN   9–5 Mon–Fri.

Specialise in conservation of painted and applied decoration on plaster, stone, canvas, wood and metal substrates. Surveys and investigation, specifications and estimates. Analysis of plaster and paint layers.

PROVIDE Home Inspections. Free/Chargeable Estimates. Chargeable Collection/Delivery Service.
SPEAK TO Elizabeth Hirst.
Member of UKIC, IIC, Stone Federation. This workshop is included on the register of conservators maintained by the Conservation Unit of the Museums and Galleries Commission.
SEE Picture Frames, Porcelain.

PHILIP YOUNG (PAINTINGS CONSERVATION)

22 Colman's Court, Limehouse Cut Studios, 46 Morris Road, **London E14 6NT**
TEL   071 515 2826
OPEN   By Appointment.

Specialise in restoring all types of easel paintings, including oil, tempera, acrylic on all support types. Specialist in 20th century painting and contemporary artworks. Facilities available for large works.

PROVIDE Home Inspections. Free/Chargeable Estimates. Chargeable Collection/Delivery Service.
SPEAK TO Philip Young.
Member of UKIC and IIC. Associate Member of ABPR.

PAOLA CAMUSSO

46 Pennybank Chambers, 33–35 St. John's Square, **London EC1M 4DS**
TEL   071 250 3278
FAX   071 250 0297
OPEN   10–6 Mon–Fri.

Specialise in restoring oil paintings on canvas, panel and metal.

PROVIDE Home Inspections. Free Estimates. Free Collection/Delivery Service.
SPEAK TO Ms Paola Camusso.
Associate Member of ABPR. This workshop is included on the register of conservators maintained by the Conservation Unit of the Museums and Galleries Commission.
SEE Porcelain.

HOWARD & STONE CONSERVATORS

27 Pennybank Chambers, 33–35 St John's Square, **London EC1M 4DS**
TEL   071 490 0813
OPEN   9.30–6 Mon–Fri.

Specialise in conserving prints, drawings and watercolours.

PROVIDE Home Inspections. Free Estimates. Chargeable Collection/Delivery Service.
SPEAK TO Deryn Howard or Rosemary Stone.

MARIA KELLER CONSERVATION AND RESTORATION
Unit 46, Pennybank Chambers, St John's Square, **London EC1M 4DS**
TEL　　071 386 8723 or 071 250 3278
OPEN　　10–7 Mon–Fri or By Appointment.

Specialise in restoring paintings on canvas, panel and copper in oil and tempera from local repairs of canvas to full restoration.

PROVIDE Home Inspections. Free Estimates. Chargeable Collection/Delivery Service.
SPEAK TO Maria Keller.
Member of ABPR and UKIC. This workshop is included on the register of conservators maintained by the Conservation Unit of the Museums and Galleries Commission.
SEE Porcelain.

RILEY, DUNN & WILSON LTD
Pegasus House, 116–120 Golden Lane, **London EC1Y 0UD**
TEL　　071 251 2551
FAX　　071 490 2338
OPEN　　9–5 Mon–Fri.

Specialise in restoring prints and drawings.

PROVIDE Home Inspections. Free Estimates. Free Collection/Delivery Service.
SPEAK TO the Office Manager.
SEE **West Yorkshire, Central.**
SEE Books.

PRUDENCE SEWARD
30 Sekforde Street, **London EC1R 0HH**
TEL　　071 251 8152
OPEN　　By Appointment.

Specialise in conserving works of art on paper.

PROVIDE Home Inspections. Free Estimates. Chargeable Collection/Delivery Service.
SPEAK TO Prudence Seward.
Ms Seward is ARCA, Dip. Conservation, Camberwell and a Member of UKIC. This workshop is included on the register of conservators maintained by the Conservation Unit of the Museums and Galleries Commission.
SEE Picture Frames.

JENNIFER ARCHBOLD
54 Northchurch Road, **London N1 4EJ**
TEL　　071 254 1562
OPEN　　By Appointment.

Specialise in conservation of easel paintings, oil, acrylic, tempera, mixed media on canvas or panel.

PROVIDE Home Inspections. Free Local Estimates.
SPEAK TO Jennifer Archbold.
Member of IIC and UKIC. Associate Member of ABPR. This workshop is included on the register of conservators maintained by the Conservation Unit of the Museums and Galleries Commission.

GRAHAM BIGNELL PAPER CONSERVATION
Standpoint Studios, 45 Coronet Street, **London N1 6HD**
TEL　　071 729 3161
OPEN　　9–6 Mon–Fri; By Appointment Sat.

Specialise in restoring prints, drawings, watercolours and posters.

PROVIDE Home Inspections. Free/Chargeable Estimates. Chargeable Collection/Delivery Service.

SPEAK TO Graham Bignell.
Member of AIC, UKIC and IPC. This workshop is included on the register of conservators maintained by the Conservation Unit of the Museums and Galleries Commission.

PETER CHAPMAN ANTIQUES
Incorporating CHAPMAN RESTORATIONS
10 Theberton Street, **London N1 0QX**
TEL   071 226 5565
FAX   081 348 4846
OPEN   9.30–6 Mon–Sat.

Specialise in cleaning, relining and restoring oil paintings.

PROVIDE Home Inspections. Refundable Estimates. Chargeable Collection/Delivery Service.
SPEAK TO Peter Chapman or Tony Holohan.
SEE Furniture, Picture Frames, Porcelain, Silver.

WARWICK MacCALLUM
Unit N3, Metropolitan Workshops, Enfield Road, **London N1 5AZ**
TEL   071 254 0401
OPEN   By Appointment Only.

Specialise in all aspects of the conservation and restoration of easel paintings; oil, tempera or acrylic on canvas, wood or card. Also specialise in the restoration of very large paintings and all restoration is to museum standards. Reports and photo documentation supplied if required.

PROVIDE Home Inspections.
Free/Chargeable Estimates. Chargeable Collection/Delivery Service.
SPEAK TO Warwick MacCallum.
Member of UKIC. Full Member of ABPR.

JOHN JONES FRAMES LTD
4 Morris Place, off Stroud Green Road, **London N4 3JG**
TEL   071 281 5439
FAX   071 281 5956
OPEN   8–6 Mon–Fri; 9–2 Sat; 12–4 Sun.

Specialise in restoring prints, watercolours and paintings.

PROVIDE Free Estimates. Chargeable Collection/Delivery Service.
SPEAK TO John Jones or John Dawson or Nick Hawker.
SEE Picture Frames, Specialist Photographers.

LAILA HACKFORTH–JONES
15 Lansdowne Road, **London N10 2AX**
TEL   081 883 8809
OPEN   By appointment.

Specialise in restoring prints, drawings, watercolours and all fine art on paper.

PROVIDE Home Inspections. Free Estimates.
SPEAK TO Laila Hackforth–Jones.
Member of IPC.

THOMAS MILNE
55 Rosebery Road, **London N10 2LE**
TEL   081 883 4609
OPEN   Mon–Fri By Appointment.

Specialise in restoring works of art on paper.

PROVIDE Home Inspections. Chargeable Estimates. Chargeable Collection/ Delivery Service.
SPEAK TO Thomas Milne.
Member of UKIC and IPC.
Conservation Unit intern, Tate Gallery London.
SEE Books.

SUDBURY–JONES LTD
44–48 Birkbeck Road, **London**
N12 8DZ
TEL   081 446 3164
OPEN   9–6 Mon–Sat; 10–2 Sun.

Specialise in a comprehensive picture restoration service. Oil paintings re-lined, cleaned and varnished. Watercolours and prints de-acidified, cleaned and restored.

PROVIDE Home Inspections. Free Estimates. Collection/Delivery Service.
SPEAK TO Tom Jones or Chris Frost.
SEE Picture Frames.

THE PAINTING CONSERVATION STUDIO
Address witheld by request.
TEL   071 281 9997
OPEN   10–5 By Appointment.

Specialise in restoring easel paintings. Collection surveys.

PROVIDE Home Inspections. Free/Chargeable Estimates. Chargeable Collection/Delivery Service.
SPEAK TO Carol Willoughby, Isabel Horovitz, Andrea Gall, Helen White, Amanda Paulley.
This workshop is included on the register of conservators maintained by the Conservation Unit of the Museums and Galleries Commission.
SEE Picture Frames.

DEANSBROOK GALLERY
134 Myddleton Road, **London**
N22 4NQ
TEL   081 889 8389
OPEN   10–5 Tues–Sat.

Specialise in restoring oil paintings and prints.

PROVIDE Home Inspections. Free Estimates. Chargeable Collection/Delivery Service.
SPEAK TO Anthony Edmunds.
SEE Picture Frames.

CATHERINE RICKMAN ART CONSERVATION
11 Berkley Road, **London NW1 8XX**
TEL   071 586 0384
OPEN   9–6 Mon–Fri By Appointment.

Specialise in restoring works of art on paper, prints, drawings, watercolours, wallpapers.

PROVIDE Home Inspections. Free Verbal Estimates.
SPEAK TO Catherine Rickman.
Member of IPC, UKIC, IIC and AIC.
This workshop is included on the register of conservators maintained by the Conservation Unit of the Museums and Galleries Commission.
SEE Books.

COLLERAN and CIANTAR LTD
17 Frognal, **London NW3 6AR**
TEL   071 435 4652 or 0895 256410
FAX   071 435 4652 or 0895 256410
       Open 9–5 Mon–Fri or By Appointment.

Specialise in conserving and restoring watercolours, drawings, prints and other items on paper.

PROVIDE Chargeable Home Inspections. Free/Chargeable Estimates. Collection/Delivery Service by arrangement.
SPEAK TO Kate Colleran or Marcel Ciantar.

JUDITH MacCOLUM
143 King Henry's Road, **London**
NW3 3RD
TEL   071 722 6208
OPEN   By Appointment.

Specialise in restoring prints and drawings.

PROVIDE Chargeable Local Home Inspections. Free Estimates. Collection/Delivery Service.
SPEAK TO Mrs Judith MacColum.

Member of IPC. This workshop is included on the register of conservators maintained by the Conservation Unit of the Museums and Galleries Commission.

JOHN DENHAM GALLERY

50 Mill Lane, **London NW6 1NJ**
TEL   071 794 2635
OPEN   11–5 Sun, Tues–Fri.

Specialise in restoring oil paintings and works of art on paper.

PROVIDE Home Inspections. Free Estimates. Free Collection/Delivery Service.

SPEAK TO John Denham.
SEE Picture Frames.

JOHN JACOBS

240 Webheath, Netherwood Street, **London NW6 2JX**
TEL   071 328 6354
OPEN   10–6 Mon–Fri or By Appointment.

Specialise in restoring oil paintings on canvas, paper or board, specialising in structural work.

PROVIDE Home Inspections. Free Estimates. Chargeable Collection/Delivery Service.
SPEAK TO John Jacobs.
Full Member of ABPR.

JANE AND PAUL ZAGEL

31 Pandora Road, **London NW6 1TS**
TEL   071 794 1663
OPEN   9–6 Mon–Fri.

Specialise in restoring watercolours, prints and gouache drawings. Fine art photography undertaken as part of the restoration record.

PROVIDE Home Inspections. Refundable Estimates. Chargeable Collection/Delivery Service.
SPEAK TO Jane Zagel.
This workshop is included on the register of conservators maintained by the

Conservation Unit of the Museums and Galleries Commission.
SEE Books, Specialist Photographers.

FRANCES BUTLIN

73 Loudoun Road, **London NW8 0DQ**
TEL   071 328 1395
OPEN   10–5.30 Mon–Fri.

Specialise in restoring easel paintings on canvas, panel and cooper or metal.

PROVIDE Home Inspections. Free Estimates. Chargeable Collection/Delivery Service.
SPEAK TO Frances Butlin.
Member of IIC, UKIC and Associate Member of ABPR. This workshop is included on the register of conservators maintained by the Conservation Unit of the Museums and Galleries Commission.

DROWN AND COMPANY LTD

117 Boundary Road, **London NW8 0RG**
TEL   071 624 6100
OPEN   9–6 Mon–Fri or By Appointment.

Specialise in restoring and conserving oil paintings of all periods with emphasis on Impressionist and Modern fields.

PROVIDE Home Inspections. Normally Free Estimates. Free Collection/Delivery Service.
SPEAK TO David or Duncan Drown.
David Drown is a Fellow of the IIC and a Full Member of ABPR. Duncan Drown is a Member of UKIC.

WELLINGTON GALLERY

1 St John's Wood High Street, **London NW8 7NG**
TEL   071 586 2620
OPEN   10–5.30 Mon–Sat.

Specialise in restoring oil paintings.

PROVIDE Home Inspections. Free Estimates. Chargeable Collection/Delivery Service.

SPEAK TO Mrs Maureen Barclay or Mr K.
J. Barclay.
Member of LAPADA.
SEE Furniture, Porcelain, Silver.

ANTHEA PELHAM BURN
4 Whitehorse Mews, Westminster Bridge
Road, **London SE1 7QD**
TEL   071 261 1366
FAX   071 401 9049
OPEN   10–7 Mon–Fri or By
       Appointment.

Specialise in restoring and conserving
oil paintings on canvas or panel, 16th
century to Modern. Large works
undertaken. Work undertaken in situ
anywhere in UK.

PROVIDE Home Inspections. Refundable
Estimates. Chargeable Collection/
Delivery Service.
SPEAK TO Anthea Pelham Burn.
Associate Member of ABPR and Member
of UKIC. This workshop is included on
the register of conservators maintained
by the Conservation Unit of the
Museums and Galleries Commission.

SOPHIA FAIRCLOUGH
5 Whitehorse Mews, Westminster Bridge
Road, **London SE1 7QD**
TEL   071 261 0735
FAX   071 4019049
OPEN   9.30–6 Mon–Fri.

Specialise in restoring watercolours,
drawings, pastels, prints, parchment,
large works and Modern on paper.

PROVIDE Home Inspections. Free
Estimates. Local Collection/Delivery
Service.
SPEAK TO Sophia Fairclough.
Member of UKIC, IPC and IIC. This
workshop is included on the register of
conservators maintained by the
Conservation Unit of the Museums and
Galleries Commission.

TRADE PICTURE SERVICES LIMITED
Neckinger Mills, Abbet Street, **London
SE1 2AN**
TEL   071 237 4388
FAX   071 237 4388
OPEN   9–5.30 Mon–Fri.

Specialise in lining, conservation and
restoration of oil paintings. Also ceiling
and wall paintings.

PROVIDE Home Inspections.
Free/Refundable Estimates. Free
Collection/Delivery Service.
SPEAK TO Matthew Goldsmith.

VOITEK
Conservation of Works of Art, 9
Whitehorse Mews, Westminster Bridge
Road, **London SE1 7QD**
TEL   071 928 6094
FAX   071 928 6094
OPEN   10.30–5 Mon–Fri.

Specialise in conserving and restoring
Old Master drawings, prints,
watercolours and works of art on paper.

PROVIDE Home Inspections. Delivery
Service.
SPEAK TO Elizabeth Sobczynski.
SEE Porcelain.

ALEXANDRA WALKER
4 Whitehorse Mews, 37–39 Westminster
Bridge Road, **London SE1 7QD**
TEL   071 261 1419
OPEN   10–6 Mon–Fri.

Specialise in restoring easel paintings of
all periods.

PROVIDE Home Inspections.
Free/Chargeable Estimates.
SPEAK TO Alexandra Walker.

VALENTINE WALSH
3 Whitehorse Mews, **London SE1 7QD**
TEL   071 261 1691
FAX   071 401 9049
OPEN   By Appointment.

Specialise in restoring easel paintings from 1400 to 1950 particularly paintings on panel and can also accommodate very large paintings.

PROVIDE Home Inspections. Free/Chargeable Estimates. Free/Chargeable Collection/Delivery Service.
SPEAK TO Valentine Walsh.
Member of UKIC. This workshop is included on the register of conservators maintained by the Conservation Unit of the Museums and Galleries Commission.
SEE **Borders**

CLAIRE GASKELL
32 St John's Park, **London SE3 7JH**
TEL   081 858 2756
OPEN   10–5 Mon–Fri.

Specialise in restoring prints, drawings, watercolours, Japanese prints and Indian paintings on paper.

PROVIDE Home Inspections. Free Estimates. Free Collection/Delivery Service.
SPEAK TO Claire Gaskell.

GREENWICH CONSERVATION WORKSHOPS
Spread Eagle Antiques of Greenwich, 8–9 Nevada Street, **London SE10 9JL**
TEL   081 305 1666
OPEN   10–5.30 Mon–Sat.

Specialise in restoring oil paintings, watercolours and prints.

PROVIDE Home Inspections. Refundable Estimates. Free/Chargeable Collection/Delivery Service.
SPEAK TO Richard Moy.
SEE Furniture.

RELCY ANTIQUES
9 Nelson Road, **London SE10 9JB**
TEL   081 858 2812
FAX   081 293 9848
OPEN   10–6 Mon–Sat.

Specialise in restoring oil paintings and prints.

PROVIDE Home Inspections. Free/Chargeable Estimates. Collection/Delivery Service by arrangement.
SPEAK TO Robin Challis.
SEE Collectors (Scientific Instruments), Furniture, Silver.

DAVID WRIGHT CONSERVATION AND FINE ART
Wellington House, Burgos Grove, **London SE10 8LL**
TEL   081 692 4283
OPEN   9–6 By Appointment.

Specialise in restoring works of art on paper, including watercolours, drawings, engravings, lithographs, etchings, aquatints and woodcuts.

PROVIDE Home Inspections. Free Estimates. Collection Delivery Service.
SPEAK TO David Wright.
Member of IPC.

KIM ELIZABETH LEYSHON PICTURE RESTORER
2 Waleran Road, **London SE13 7PG**
TEL   081 318 1277
OPEN   By Appointment.

Specialise in restoring works of art on paper, Old Master and modern prints, drawings, watercolours, Indian miniatures.

PROVIDE Home Inspections. Free Estimates. Free Collection/Delivery Service.
SPEAK TO Kim Leyshon.
Member of IPC, IIC and UKIC. This workshop is included on the register of conservators maintained by the Conservation Unit of the Museums and Galleries Commission.
SEE Books.

ORDE SOLOMONS
50 Amersham Road, **London**
SE14 6QE
TEL   081 692 2016
OPEN   By Appointment.

Specialise in restoring historic wallpaper schemes and any decorative wall coverings, including paper, lincrusta, Tynecastle, Chinese, William Morris, papier mâché and artificial leather.
PROVIDE Home Inspections.
Free/Chargeable Estimates. Chargeable Collection/Delivery Service.
SPEAK TO Orde Solomons.
Member of Wallpaper History Society and wallpaper conservator to the National Trust and English Heritage. Longest established and most experienced conservator of European wallpaper in the UK.
This workshop is included on the register of conservators maintained by the Conservation Unit of the Museums and Galleries Commission.

MARIE LOUISE LOPEZ
25 Crewys Road, **London SE15 2BJ**
TEL   071 358 9641
OPEN   By Appointment Mon–Sat.

Specialise in restoring all works of art on paper, including prints, drawings and watercolours. Full documentation, photographs and condition reports supplied.
PROVIDE Home Inspections.
Free/Chargeable Estimates. Free Local Collection/Delivery Service.
SPEAK TO Marie Louise Lopez.
Member of UKIC, IPC and Wallpaper History Society. This workshop is included on the register of conservators maintained by the Conservation Unit of the Museums and Galleries Commission.
SEE Books.

PETER ROBERT MALLOCH
75C London Road, **London SE23 3TY**
TEL   081 699 8754
OPEN   By Appointment.

Specialise in restoring oil paintings and pastels.
PROVIDE Free Estimates.
SPEAK TO Peter Malloch.

CLARE REYNOLDS
20 Gubyon Avenue, **London SE24 ODX**
TEL   071 326 0458
OPEN   9–5 Mon–Fri.

Specialise in restoring works of art on paper.
PROVIDE Home Inspections. Free Estimates. Chargeable Collection/Delivery Service.
SPEAK TO Clare Reynolds.
SEE Books.

JANE McNAMARA CONSERVATOR
14 Chelsfield Gardens, **London SE26 4DJ**
TEL   081 699 7173
OPEN   9–5 Mon–Fri By Appointment.

Specialise in conservation of art on paper, prints, drawings, watercolours, paper–based photographs, fans and parchment.
PROVIDE Home Inspections. Free Estimates. Free London Collection/Delivery Service.
SPEAK TO Jane McNamara.
Member of IPC. This workshop is included on the register of conservators maintained by the Conservation Unit of the Museums and Galleries Commission.
SEE Collectors (Paper)

KING STREET GALLERIES
17 King Street, **London SW1Y 6QU**
TEL   071 930 9993 FAX
OPEN   9.30–5.30 Mon–Fri; 10–1 Sat.

Specialise in restoring oils and watercolours.
PROVIDE Home Inspections. Free

Estimates. Chargeable
Collection/Delivery Service.
SPEAK TO Hal O'Nians.

AMANDA MEHIGAN
11 Charlwood Place, **London SW1V
2LX**
TEL   071 834 3477 or 071 821 5453
OPEN   By Appointment Only.

Specialise in conservation and
restoration of art on paper, especially in
Old Master prints and drawings.

PROVIDE Free Estimates.
SPEAK TO Amanda Mehigan.
Member of IPC. This workshop is
included on the register of conservators
maintained by the Conservation Unit of
the Museums and Galleries Commission.

CLAUDIO MOSCATELLI
46 Cambridge Street, **London SW1V
4QH**
TEL   071 828 8457
OPEN   9–5 Mon–Fri or By
          Appointment.

Specialise in restoring oil paintings,
relining, retouching, varnishing.

PROVIDE Home Inspections. Free
Estimates. Chargeable
Collection/Delivery Service.
SPEAK TO Claudio Moscatelli.

SHEPHERDS
BOOKBINDERS LTD
76B Rochester Row, **London SW1P
1JU**
TEL   071 630 1184
FAX   071 931 0541
OPEN   9–5.30 Mon–Fri; 10.30–1 Sat.

Specialise in restoring works of art on
paper, including prints and watercolours.

PROVIDE Free Estimates.
SPEAK TO Jan Blake or Rob Shepherd.
SEE Books.

MARIA ANDIPA ICON
GALLERY
162 Walton Street, **London SW3 2JL**
TEL   071 589 2371
FAX   071 589 2371
OPEN   11–6 Mon–Fri; 11–2 Sat.

Specialise in restoring icons from all
Eastern European countries, Syria,
Egypt, Ethiopia. Also give lectures on
restoration.

PROVIDE Home Inspections.
Free/Chargeable Estimates. Chargeable
Collection/Delivery Service.
SPEAK TO Maria Andipa.

JOHN CAMPBELL
PICTURE FRAMES LTD
164 Walton Street, **London SW3 2JL**
TEL   071 584 9268
FAX   071 581 3499
OPEN   9.30–5.30 Mon–Fri; 10–5 Sat.

Specialise in restoring oil paintings and
watercolours.

PROVIDE Home Inspections. Free
Estimates. Free Collection/Delivery
Service.
SPEAK TO Roy Hogben.
Member of the Guild of Master
Craftsmen.
SEE Picture Frames

PATRICK CORBETT
1 Beaufort Street, **London SW3 5AQ**
TEL   071 352 7883
FAX   071 352 1033
OPEN   9.30–6 Mon–Fri.

Specialise in restoring oil paintings,
especially 17th century Dutch and
Flemish, 18th century English and in
particular the works of George Stubbs.

PROVIDE Home Inspections. Free
Estimates. Free Collection/Delivery
Service.
SPEAK TO Patrick Corbett.
Full Member of ABPR, Associate
Member IIC and UKIC. This workshop

is included on the register of conservators maintained by the Conservation Unit of the Museums and Galleries Commission.

GREEN AND STONE
259 Kings Road, **London SW3 5EL**
TEL   071 352 6521
FAX   071 351 1098
OPEN   9–5.30 Mon–Fri; 9.30–6 Sat.

Specialise in restoring oil paintings, watercolours and prints.

PROVIDE Local Home Inspections. Free Estimates. Free Local Collection/ Delivery Service.
SPEAK TO Mrs Hiscott or Miss Moore.
SEE Lighting, Picture Frames.

MALCOLM INNES GALLERY
172 Walton Street, **London SW3 2JL**
TEL   071 584 0575
OPEN   9.30–6 Mon–Fri; Sat 10–1.

Specialise in restoring oil paintings.

PROVIDE Free Estimates. Chargeable Collection/Delivery Service.
SPEAK TO Malcolm Innes or Emma Shelton–Agar.
SEE **Lothian.**
SEE Picture Frames.

STAVROS P. MIHALARIAS
2A Avenue Studios, Sydney Close, **London SW3 6HN**
TEL   071 589 6114
FAX   071 581 2962
OPEN   10–4 Mon–Fri.

Specialise in restoring icons.

PROVIDE Free Estimates.
SPEAK TO Miss Hilary Pinder. Full Member of ABPR.

ALAN H. K. BRADFORD
38 Tournay Road, **London SW6 7UF**
TEL   071 381 3783
FAX   071 381 3783
OPEN   9–6 Mon–Fri or By Appointment.

Specialise in restoring oil paintings.

PROVIDE Home Inspections. Free Estimates. Collection Delivery Service.
SPEAK TO Alan Bradford.
Member of UKIC and IIC. Associate Member of ABPR.

COOPER FINE ARTS LTD
768 Fulham Road, **London SW6 5SJ**
TEL   071 731 3421
OPEN   10–7 Mon–Fri; 10–4 Sat.

Specialise in restoring oil paintings and watercolours.

PROVIDE Free Estimates.
SPEAK TO Jonathan Hill–Reid.
SEE Picture Frames.

KING'S COURT GALLERIES
951–953 Fulham Road, **London SW6 5HY**
TEL   071 610 6939
FAX   071 731 4737
OPEN   10–5.30 Mon–Sat.

Specialise in paper conservation and restoration, including engravings, decorative and sporting prints.

PROVIDE Home Inspections. Free Estimates. Chargeable Collection/Delivery Service.
SPEAK TO Mrs J. Joel.
Member of the Fine Art Trade Guild.
SEE **Surrey.**
SEE Books.

JANE LEE
40 Chipstead Street, **London SW6 3SS**
TEL   071 731 6039
OPEN   9–5 Mon–Fri.

Specialise in relining, conserving and restoring oil and tempera on panel and canvas.

PROVIDE Home Inspections. Free/Chargeable Estimates. Chargeable Collection/Delivery Service.
SPEAK TO Jane Lee.

Member of UKIC. This workshop is included on the register of conservators maintained by the Conservation Unit of the Museums and Galleries Commission.

BRIGID RICHARDSON
91 Langthorne Street, **London SW6 6JS**
TEL   071 381 0198
OPEN   Mon–Sat By Appointment.

Specialise in conservation of works of art on paper, prints, drawings, watercolours, wallpaper.

PROVIDE Home Inspections.
Free/Chargeable Estimates. Chargeable Collection/Delivery Service.
SPEAK TO Brigid Richardson.
Member of IPC. This workshop is included on the register of conservators maintained by the Conservation Unit of the Museums and Galleries Commission.
SEE Books.

20th CENTURY GALLERY
821 Fulham Road, **London SW6 5HG**
TEL   071 731 5888
OPEN   10–6 Mon–Fri; 10–1 Sat.

Specialise in restoring oil paintings.

PROVIDE Free Estimates.
SPEAK TO Erika Brandl.
SEE Picture Frames.

CLARE FINN & CO. LTD
38 Cornwall Gardens, **London SW7 4AA**
TEL   071 937 1895
FAX   071 937 4198
OPEN   By Appointment.

Specialise in restoring oil, tempera and easel paintings and oil mural paintings.

PROVIDE Home Inspections. Refundable Estimates. Chargeable Collection/Delivery Service.
SPEAK TO Clare Finn or Deborah Bichner.
Member of IIC, UKIC and IPC. This workshop is included on the register of conservators maintained by the

Conservation Unit of the Museums and Galleries Commission.

SIMON FOLKES
Studio 6, 5 Thurloe Square, **London SW7 2TA**
TEL   071 589 1649
OPEN   By Appointment.

Specialise in restoring 15th–early 20th century oil paintings.

PROVIDE Home Inspections.
Free/Chargeable Estimates. Free Local Collection/Delivery Service. SPEAK TO Simon Folkes.
This workshop is included on the register of conservators maintained by the Conservation Unit of the Museums and Galleries Commission.

DORETTA MESHIEA
12A Ennismore Gardens, **London SW7 1AA**
TEL   071 581 8397
FAX   071 499 1272
OPEN   10–5 Mon–Fri.

Specialise in restoring works of art on paper and refurbishment of collections.

PROVIDE Home Inspections. Chargeable Estimates. Chargeable Collection/Delivery Service.
SPEAK TO Doretta Meshiea.
Member of IPC.
SEE Books.

DEREK AND ROGER HULME FINE ART RESTORERS
31 Palfrey Place, **London SW8 1PE**
TEL   071 735 1218
FAX   071 582 9975
OPEN   8–6 Mon–Fri.

Specialise in conserving and restoring European Old Master and modern oil paintings. They also do in–house lining of paintings, transferring and panel work.

PROVIDE Home Inspections. Chargeable

Estimates. Collection/Delivery Service by arrangement.
SPEAK TO Derek or Roger Hulme.
This is a third–generation firm.
They are both Full Members of ABPR.

LOWE AND BUTCHER
Unit 23, Abbey Business Centre, Ingate Place, **London SW8 3NS**
TEL   071 498 6981
OPEN   10–5 Mon–Fri.

Specialise in restoring Old Master, 19th Century and Impressionist oil paintings.
PROVIDE Home Inspections.
Free/Refundable Estimates. Free Collection/Delivery Service.
SPEAK TO D. C. Butcher.

SUSANNAH WATTS–RUSSELL
44 Lamont Road, **London SW10 0JA**
TEL   071 352 4508
OPEN   By Appointment.

Specialise in restoring oil paintings.
PROVIDE Home Inspections. Free Estimates. Free Collection/Delivery Service.
SPEAK TO Susannah Watts–Russell.

SOPHIE WYSOCKA
2 Knights Studios, Hortensia Road, **London SW10 0QX**
TEL   071 352 0547
OPEN   By Appointment.

Specialise in restoring large paintings for private collections, schools and churches.
PROVIDE Home Inspections. Free Estimates.
SPEAK TO Mrs S. Wysocka.
Member of UKIC and CAS. Associate Member of ABPR.

BATES AND BASKCOMB
191 St. John's Hill, **London SW11 1TH**
TEL   071 223 1629
OPEN   9.30–5.30 Mon–Fri or By Appointment.

Specialise in restoring works of art on paper, including prints, drawings, watercolours, gouaches, pastels, and photographs.
PROVIDE Local Home Inspections.
Free/Chargeable Collection/Delivery Service.
SPEAK TO Debbie Bates or Camilla Baskcomb.
SEE Books.

HELEN DE BORCHGRAVE
Fine Art Restorer, 103 Albert Bridge Road, **London SW11 4PF**
TEL   071 738 1951
OPEN   By Appointment.

Specialise in cleaning, relining and restoring oil paintings on canvas, panel or board. Large or awkward paintings can be cleaned and restored on site.
PROVIDE Home Inspections. Free Local Estimates. Collection/Delivery Service.
SPEAK TO Helen de Borchgrave.
Member of UKIC and IIC. Associate Member of ABPR. This workshop is included on the register of conservators maintained by the Conservation Unit of the Museums and Galleries Commission.
SEE Picture Frames.

JACQUELINE TABER
46 Church Road, **London SW13 9HH**
TEL   081 876 6294 or 0206 729 334
OPEN   10–5 Tues–Sat or By Appointment.

Specialise in conserving and restoring oil paintings.
PROVIDE Home Inspections. Free Estimates. Collection/Delivery Service by arrangement.
SPEAK TO Jacqueline Taber.
Associate Member of APBR. This workshop is included on the register of conservators maintained by the Conservation Unit of the Museums and Galleries Commission.

TREVOR CUMINE
133 Putney Bridge Road, **London**
SW15 2PA
TEL   081 870 1525
OPEN   By Appointment.

Specialise in picture lining.
SPEAK TO Trevor Cumine.
SEE Picture Frames.

SHEILA FAIRBRASS
27 Dalebury Road, **London**
SW17 7HQ
TEL   081 672 4606
OPEN   9–7 By Appointment Only.

Specialise in restoring works of art on
paper particularly, 20th century art.

PROVIDE Free/Chargeable Estimates.
SPEAK TO Sheila Fairbrass.
Fellow of IIC. This workshop is included
on the register of conservators
maintained by the Conservation Unit of
the Museums and Galleries Commission.

KEITH HOLMES
27 Dalebury Road, **London**
SW17 7HQ
TEL   081 672 4606
OPEN   8–8 Daily.

Specialise in restoring prints, drawings,
watercolours, watercolours on silk.

PROVIDE Home Inspections. Free
Estimates. Chargeable Local
Collection/Delivery Service.
SPEAK TO Keith Holmes.
Member of IIC. This workshop is
included on the register of conservators
maintained by the Conservation Unit of
the Museums and Galleries Commission.
SEE Books.

PENNY JENKINS
51 Wandsworth Common Westside,
London SW18 2EE
TEL   081 870 1503
OPEN   9–6 Mon–Fri By Appointment
        Only.

Specialise in restoring all works of art on
paper, including prints, drawings and
watercolours.

PROVIDE Home Inspections by
arrangement. Free Estimates.
Chargeable Local Collection/Delivery
Service.
SPEAK TO Penny Jenkins.
Member of UKIC, IIC, AIC and IPC.
This workshop is included on the register
of conservators maintained by the
Conservation Unit of the Museums and
Galleries Commission.

PH7 PAPER CONSERVATORS
Unit 210, The Business Village, 3–9
Broomhill Road, **London SW18 4JQ**
TEL   081 871 5075
FAX   081 877 1940
OPEN   9–5.30 Mon–Fri or By
        Appointment.

Specialise in restoring works of art on
paper, including watercolours, prints,
drawings.

PROVIDE Home Inspections. Free
Estimates. Free Collection/Delivery
Service.
SPEAK TO Victoria Pease.
Member of IPC, UKIC and IIC. This
workshop is included on the register of
conservators maintained by the
Conservation Unit of the Museums and
Galleries Commission.
SEE Books.

PLOWDEN AND SMITH LTD
190 St Ann's Hill, **London SW18 2RT**
TEL   081 874 4005
FAX   081 874 7248
OPEN   9–5.30 Mon–Fri.

Specialise in conserving and restoring
paintings.

PROVIDE Home Inspections. Free
Estimates. Free/Chargeable
Collection/Delivery Service.
SPEAK TO Bob Butler.
SEE Furniture, Porcelain, Silver, Display.

DIANA WASHINGTON
17 Cicada Road, **London SW18 2NN**
TEL   081 874 6223
OPEN   9–5 Mon–Fri By Appointment
Only.

Specialise in restoring all types of works
of art on paper, including prints,
drawings, watercolours and pastels.
Photographic and written records of
works carried out provided. Advice given
on maintenance and care of collections.

PROVIDE Home Inspections. Free
Estimates. Collection Delivery Service.
SPEAK TO Diana Washington.
Member of IPC, UKIC, IIC and AIC.
This workshop is included on the register
of conservators maintained by the
Conservation Unit of the Museums and
Galleries Commission.
SEE Picture Frames, Books.

R. M. S. SHEPHERD ASSOCIATES LTD
11 Berkley Place, **London SW19 4NN**
TEL   081 946 5293
FAX   081 946 5293
OPEN   9–6 Mon–Fri.

Specialise in restoring easel paintings.

PROVIDE Home Inspections. Free
Estimates. Chargeable
Collection/Delivery Service.
SPEAK TO Mr R. Shepherd.
Associate Member of ABPR and a Fellow
of the IIC.

HAMISH DEWAR
1st Floor, 9 Old Bond Street, **London
W1X 3TA**
TEL   071 629 0317
FAX   071 493 6390
OPEN   9–6 Mon–Fri.

Specialise in conserving and restoring
oil paintings.

PROVIDE Home Inspections.
Free/Refundable Estimates. Chargeable
Collection/Delivery Service.
SPEAK TO Hamish Dewar.

HAHN AND SON LTD
47 Albemarle Street, **London W1X 3FE**
TEL   071 493 9196
OPEN   9.30–5.30 Mon–Fri.

Specialise in conserving and restoring
oil paintings.

PROVIDE Home Inspections. Free
Estimates. Free Collection/Delivery
Service.
SPEAK TO Paul Hahn.
Established 1870.

PAUL MITCHELL LTD
99 New Bond Street, **London W1Y 9LF**
TEL   071 493 8732
FAX   071 409 7136
OPEN   9.30–5.30 Mon–Fri.

Specialise in the conservation and
restoration of paintings.

PROVIDE Home Inspections. Free
Estimates. Chargeable
Collection/Delivery Service.
Member of BADA, the Guild of Master
Craftsmen and IIC. Associate Member
of ABPR.
SPEAK TO Paul Mitchell.
SEE Picture Frames.

BOURLET
32 Connaught Street, **London W2 2AY**
TEL   071 724 4837
OPEN   11–5.30 Mon–Fri and most Sats.

Specialise in restoring oil paintings and
watercolours.

PROVIDE Home Inspections. Free
Estimates. Collection/Delivery Service.
SPEAK TO Gabrielle Rendell.
SEE Furniture, Picture Frames.

FENELLA HOWARD
14 Shaa Road, **London W3 7LN**
TEL   081 749 5656
OPEN   By Appointment.

Specialise in conserving and restoring
18th–20th century British and European
oil paintings.

PROVIDE Home Inspections. Free
Estimates. Chargeable
Collection/Delivery Service.
SPEAK TO Fenella Howard.

THE CONSERVATION STUDIO
The Studio, 107 Shepherds Bush Road,
London W6 7LP
TEL   071 602 0757
FAX   071 602 0757
OPEN   9–5 Mon–Fri.

Specialise in restoring items made from
paper, including Old Master drawings,
18th–20th century British and European
watercolours, prints and drawings and
Oriental prints and watercolours.
Posters, wallpaper screens and 19th and
20th century photographs are also
repaired.

PROVIDE Home Inspections. Free
Estimates. Chargeable
Collection/Delivery Service.
SPEAK TO Norma McCaw.
Has collection points in Hampshire and
Yorkshire.
Member of IPC and Worshipful
Company of Painter Stainers. This
workshop is included on the register of
conservators maintained by the
Conservation Unit of the Museums and
Galleries Commission.

DR POPPY COOKSEY
Aston House, 8 Lower Mall, **London
W6 9DJ**
TEL   081 846 9279
OPEN   By Appointment.

Specialise in cleaning and restoring oil
paintings watercolours.

PROVIDE Home Inspections. Free
Estimates in London. Chargeable
Collection/Delivery Service.
SPEAK TO Dr Poppy Cooksey.
SEE Picture Frames.

CLAUDIO ASTROLOGO
59–61 Kensington High Street, **London
W8 5ED**
TEL   071 937 7820
OPEN   By Appointment.

Specialise in restoring easel paintings,
paintings on panels and icons.

PROVIDE Chargeable Estimates. SPEAK TO
Claudio Astrologo.
Member of IIC and UKIC.
SEE Porcelain.

DAGGETT GALLERY
1st Floor, 153 Portobello Road, **London
W11 2DY**
TEL   071 229 2248
FAX   071 584 2950
OPEN   10–4 Mon–Fri; 9–4 Sat; By
            Appointment.

Specialise in restoring oil paintings,
lining etc.

PROVIDE Home Inspections.
Free/Chargeable Estimates. Chargeable
Collection/Delivery Service.
SPEAK TO Charles or Caroline Daggett.
Member of LAPADA.
SEE Picture Frames.

VICTORIA LEANSE
Studio Three, George and Dragon Hall,
Mary Place, **London W11 4PL**
TEL   071 229 5855
OPEN   9–5.30 Mon–Fri.

Specialise in restoring easel paintings.

PROVIDE Home Inspections. Estimates by
arrangement. Collection/ Delivery
Service by arrangement.
SPEAK TO Victoria Leanse.
Member of IIC, UKIC. Associate
Member of ABPR. This workshop is
included on the register of conservators
maintained by the Conservation Unit of
the Museums and Galleries Commission.

ROBERT O'RORKE
17 Lonsdale Road, **London W11 2BY**
TEL   071 229 2892
OPEN   10–5.30 Mon–Fri or By
            Appointment.

Specialise in restoring oil paintings and
can also copy paintings.

PROVIDE Local Home Inspections. Free

Estimates in studio. Free Local
Collection/Delivery Service.
SPEAK TO Robert O'Rorke.
Associate Member of ABPR. This
workshop is included on the register of
conservators maintained by the
Conservation Unit of the Museums and
Galleries Commission.

JOANNA PAYNE
14 Addison Avenue, **London W11 4QR**
TEL   071 602 5474
OPEN   9–6 By Appointment.

Specialise in restoring all works of art on
paper, including drawings, prints,
wallpapers.

PROVIDE Home Inspections. Free Local
Estimates. Collection/Delivery Service.
SPEAK TO Joanna Payne.
Member of IIC, UKIC and IPC. This
workshop is included on the register of
conservators maintained by the
Conservation Unit of the Museums and
Galleries Commission.

NICOLE RYDER
Studio Three, George and Dragon Hall,
Mary Place, **London W11 4PL**
TEL   071 229 5855
OPEN   By Appointment.

Specialise in restoring easel paintings.

PROVIDE Home Inspections. Free
Estimates. Free/Chargeable
Collection/ Delivery Service.
SPEAK TO Nicole Ryder.
Member of UKIC. Associate Member of
ABPR. This workshop is included on
the register of conservators maintained
by the Conservation Unit of the
Museums and Galleries Commission.

COUTTS GALLERIES
75 Blythe Road, **London W14 OHD**
TEL   071–602–3980
OPEN   10–5 Mon–Fri; By Appointment
         Sat.

Specialise in restoration of pictures.

PROVIDE Home Inspections. Free
Estimates. Free Collection/Delivery
Service.
SPEAK TO Seabury Burdett–Coutts.
SEE Furniture, Picture Frames.

GERALD H. MORRIS
2 Beaconsfield Terrace Road, **London
W14 0PR**
TEL   071 603 7838
OPEN   9–6.30 Mon–Sat.

Specialise in restoring and conserving
most paper–based articles, including
watercolours and prints.

PROVIDE Home Inspections. Free
Estimates. Free/Chargeable
Collection/Delivery Service.
SPEAK TO Gerald Morris.
Member of IPC.
SEE Books.

DIANA REEVES
24 Applegarth Road, **London
W14 0HY**
TEL   071 603 8603
OPEN   9–6 Mon–Fri and By
         Appointment.

Specialise in restoring oil paintings of all
ages on canvas or panel.

PROVIDE Chargeable Home Inspections.
Free/Chargeable Estimates. Chargeable
Local Collection/Delivery Service.
SPEAK TO Diana Reeves.
Full Member of ABPR and Fellow of IIC.
This workshop is included on the register
of conservators maintained by the
Conservation Unit of the Museums and
Galleries Commission.

ABBOTT & HOLDER
30 Museum Street, **London WC1A
1LH**
TEL   071 637 3981
OPEN   9.30–6 Mon–Fri.

Specialise in restoring watercolours,
drawings and pastels.

PROVIDE Inspections. Free Estimates.

SPEAK TO Susan C. Smith
Member of IPC. This workshop is included on the register of conservators maintained by the Conservation Unit of the Museums and Galleries Commission. SEE Books.

JENNIFER RICHENBERG
32 O'Donnell Court, Brunswick Square,
London WC1 1NX
TEL　　071 837 2307
　　　　ANS 071 837 2307
OPEN　By Appointment.

Specialise in restoring paintings in oil, acrylic or gouache on canvas or panel.

PROVIDE Home Inspections. Free Estimates. Free/Chargeable Collection/Delivery Service.
SPEAK TO Jennifer Richenberg.
Member of UKIC, IIC. Associate Member of ABPR.

UCL PAINTING ANALYSIS LTD
History of Art Department, University College London, 43 Gordon Square,
London WC1
TEL　　071 383 2090
OPEN　9.30–5.30 Mon–Fri By Appointment Only.

Specialise in the analysis of painting materials on paintings for dating or conservation purposes including pigment, cross–section analysis, x-ray, infra-red and u.v. photography.

PROVIDE Home Inspections. Free Estimates.
SPEAK TO Libby Sheldon or Catherine Hassall.
This workshop is included on the register of conservators maintained by the Conservation Unit of the Museums and Galleries Commission.

HENRY DONN GALLERY
138–142 Bury New Road, Whitefield,
Greater Manchester M25 6AD
TEL　　061 766 8819
OPEN　9.30–1, 2–5.15 Mon–Sat.

Specialise in restoring Modern British oils and pastels.

PROVIDE Home Inspections. Chargeable Estimates. Chargeable Collection/Delivery Service.
SPEAK TO H. or N. Donn. Mr Donn is Past Master of the FATG.

J. G. TREVOR–OWEN
181–193 Oldham Rd, Rochdale,
Greater Manchester OL16 5QZ
TEL　　0706 48138
OPEN　1.30–7 Mon–Fri or By Appointment.

Specialises in restoring paintings.

PROVIDE Home Inspections. Refundable Estimates.
SPEAK TO J. G. Trevor–Owen.
SEE Clocks, Collectors (Musical Instruments).

HARRIET OWEN HUGHES
41 Bluecoat Chambers, School Lane,
Liverpool, **Merseyside L1 3BX**
TEL　　051 708 6808
OPEN　9.30–5 By Appointment Only.

Specialise in restoring easel paintings (16th–20th century) as well as contemporary paintings.

PROVIDE Home Inspections. Free Estimates. Chargeable Collection/Delivery Service.
SPEAK TO Harriet Owen Hughes.
Full Member of ABPR.

LYVER & BOYDELL GALLERIES
15 Castle Street, Liverpool, **Merseyside L2 4SX**
TEL　　051 236 3256
OPEN　10–30–5.30 Mon–Fri; By Appointment Sat.

Specialise in restoring watercolours and prints.

PROVIDE Home Inspections. Free
Estimates.
SPEAK TO Paul or Gill Breen.
SEE Books, Picture Frames.

COLLERAN AND CIANTAR LTD

Hillingdon Studio, 80 Denecroft
Crescent, Hillingdon, **Middlesex
UB10 9HY**

TEL   0895 256410
FAX   0895 256410
OPEN   9-5.30 Mon–Fri.

Specialise in conserving and restoring
watercolours, drawings, prints and other
items on paper.

PROVIDE Home Inspections.
Free/Chargeable Estimates.
Free/Chargeable Collection/Delivery
Service.
SPEAK TO Marcel Ciantar.
Member of UKIC, IPC, AIC and IIC.
SEE Collectors (Paper).

MICHAEL AND ROSEMARY COOK AND EMMA COOK

7 Harwood Drive, Hillingdon,
Middlesex UB10 0BG

TEL   0895 255515
OPEN   9–6.30 Mon–Fri; Sat a.m.

Specialise in restoring paintings,
watercolours, drawings and prints.

PROVIDE Home Inspections. Free
Estimates. Free/Chargeable
Collection/Delivery Service.
SPEAK TO Michael or Rosemary Cook.
Member of UKIC, IPC and ABA.
Associate Member of ABPR.
SEE Picture Frames.

PATRICIA GARNER

The Studio, 55 Arragon Road,
Twickenham, **Middlesex TW1 3NG**

TEL   081 892 1819
FAX   081 891 0115
OPEN   By Appointment.

Specialise in conserving and restoring
oil paintings. Research service includes
technical studies in the fine arts.

PROVIDE Home Inspections. Chargeable
Estimates. Free Collection/Delivery
Service.
SPEAK TO Patricia Garner.
Member of UKIC. This workshop is
included on the register of conservators
maintained by the Conservation Unit of
the Museums and Galleries Commission.

THE HAMPTON HILL GALLERY

203 & 205 High Street, Hampton Hill,
Middlesex TW12 1NP

TEL   081 977 5273
OPEN   9–5 Tues–Sat.

Specialise in restoring 18th–20th
century watercolours, drawings and
prints. Oil painting restoration is also
undertaken.

PROVIDE Home Inspections. Free
Estimates.
SPEAK TO Tony Wilson.

ANN HORNE PAPER CONSERVATOR

36 Lebanon Park, Twickenham,
Middlesex TW1 3DG

TEL   081 892 0688
FAX   081 744 2177
OPEN   By Appointment Only.

Specialise in restoring prints, drawings
and watercolours.

PROVIDE Local Home Inspections. Free
Estimates. Free Local
Collection/Delivery Service.
SPEAK TO Ann Horne.
SEE Books.

MARIA J. LESIAK

Leliwa, 71 St. Anne's Avenue, Stanwell,
Staines, **Middlesex TW19 7RL**

TEL   0784 257401
FAX   0784 257401
OPEN   By Appointment.

Specialise in restoring oil paintings on canvas, panel and metal plate.

PROVIDE Home Inspections. Free Estimates. Free Local Collection/Delivery Service.
SPEAK TO Maria J. Lesiak.
Member of UKIC. Associate Member of ABPR. This workshop is included on the register of conservators maintained by the Conservation Unit of the Museums and Galleries Commission.
SEE Picture Frames, Furniture.

JOHN MALCOLM FINE ART RESTORATION
62 Linden Avenue, Ruislip, **Middlesex HA4 8UA**
TEL　0895 621616
OPEN　8.30–5 Mon–Fri or By Appointment.

Specialise in restoring oil paintings, works of art on paper and murals.

PROVIDE Home Inspections. Free Estimates. Free Collection/Delivery Service.
SPEAK TO John Malcolm.
SEE Picture Frames.

COLMORE GALLERIES
52 High Street, Henley–in–Arden, Solihull, **West Midlands B95 5AN**
TEL　0564 792938
OPEN　11–5.30 Mon–Fri; 11–4.30 Sat.

Specialise in restoring 19th and 20th century oils and watercolours.

PROVIDE Home Inspections. Refundable Estimates. Collection/Delivery Service Available.
SPEAK TO B. D. Jones.
SEE Picture Frames.

BARBARA CONWAY
155 Whoberley Avenue, Chapelfields, Coventry, **West Midlands CV5 8FB**
TEL　0203 678986
OPEN　By Appointment.

Specialise in restoring and conserving prints, drawings and watercolours.

PROVIDE Home Inspections. Free Estimates. Free Collection/Delivery Service.
SPEAK TO Mrs Barbara Conway. Member of IPC.

MOIRA TWIST
5 Percival Road, Edgbaston, Birmingham, **West Midlands B16 9SX**
TEL　021 429 8310
OPEN　By Appointment.

Specialise in conservation and restoration of oil paintings, mainly British 18th and 19th century, major European schools and modern contemporary work, including cleaning, varnish removal, restoration of paint loss. Work can be undertaken on site when necessary. Advice given on condition of paintings and long-term care of collections, detailed post-inspection reports on work and treatment recommended and full reports on work carried out.

PROVIDE Home Inspections. Free Estimates. Free Local Collection/Delivery Service.
SPEAK TO Moira Twist.
Member of IIC, UKIC and Associate Member of ABPR. This workshop is included on the register of conservators maintained by the Conservation Unit of the Museums and Galleries Commission.

THE BROTHERHOOD OF ST SERAPHIM
St Seraphims', Station Road, Little Walsingham, **Norfolk NR22 6DG**
TEL　0328 820610
OPEN　By Appointment.

Specialise in restoring icons.

PROVIDE Home Inspections.
Free/Chargeable Estimates.
Collection/Delivery Service by
arrangement.
SPEAK TO Leon Liddament.

PENNY LAWRENCE
Fairhurst Gallery, Bedford Street,
Norwich, **Norfolk NR2 1AS**
TEL   0603 632064
OPEN   9–5 Mon–Fri.

Specialise in restoring and conserving
oil paintings, watercolours and prints.

PROVIDE Home Inspections. Free
Estimates. Free/Chargeable
Collection/Delivery Service.
SPEAK TO Penny Lawrence.
This workshop is included on the register
of conservators maintained by the
Conservation Unit of the Museums and
Galleries Commission.
SEE Furniture, Picture Frames, Silver.

FRANK WASS FABPR
Cambridge Studio Workshop, Seafront,
Cromer, **Norfolk NR27 9HD**
TEL   0263 512085
OPEN   By Appointment.

Specialise in restoring easel paintings
(oil), panel or canvas. Comprehensive
lining service.

PROVIDE Home Inspections. Free
Estimates. Free Local
Collection/Delivery Service.
SPEAK TO Frank or Michael Wass.
Full Member of ABPR.

WESTCLIFFE GALLERY AND ART FRAMERS
2–8 Augusta Street, Sheringham,
Norfolk NR26 8LA
TEL   0263 824320
OPEN   9.30–5.30 Mon–Sat; closed
         Wed.

Specialise in oil, watercolour and print
restoration.

PROVIDE Home Inspections. Free
Estimates. Free/Chargeable
Collection/Delivery Service.
SPEAK TO Richard Parks.
SEE Picture Frames.

BROADWAY FINE ART
61 Park Avenue South, Abington,
Northampton, **Northamptonshire
NN3 3AB**
TEL   0604 32011
OPEN   By Appointment.

Specialise in restoring oil paintings.

PROVIDE Home Inspections. Estimates.
Collection/Delivery Service. All by
arrangement.
SPEAK TO Michael Robinson B.A. Fine
Art (Hons) A.T.D. M.A.
Mr Robinson is a Full Member of ABPR.

LYNNE BROWNE
High House, Leadgate Bank, Ninebanks,
Allendale, **Northumberland NDE47
9PDR**
TEL   0434 345387
OPEN   9–7 Mon–Sat.

Specialise in restoring easel paintings on
canvas or panel in acrylic, oil or mixed
media.

PROVIDE Home Inspections. Free
Estimates. Chargeable
Collection/Delivery Service.
SPEAK TO Lynne Brown.
Member of UKIC and IIC

FLORENCE CONSERVATION & RESTORATION
102 Nottingham Road, Long Eaton,
Nottingham, **Nottinghamshire
NG10 2BZ**
TEL   0602 733625
OPEN   8–5 Mon–Fri; 9–12 Sat.

Specialise in cleaning and restoring oil paintings, watercolours, pastels, drawings, prints and photographs.

PROVIDE Home Inspections. Refundable Estimates. Chargeable Collection/ Delivery Service.
SPEAK TO Ron Florence.
SEE Furniture, Porcelain.

DIAN HALL
The Church House, Thrumpton, **Nottinghamshire NG11 0AX**
TEL   0602 830446
OPEN   9–6 Mon–Fri or By Appointment.

Specialise in restoring easel paintings, drawings and watercolours, pastels and miniatures, wall and ceiling paintings.

PROVIDE Home Inspections. Free Estimates. Free Collection/Delivery Service.
SPEAK TO Dian Hall B.A. Dip. Cons. Member of UKIC. This workshop is included on the register of conservators maintained by the Conservation Unit of the Museums and Galleries Commission.

ANDREW HIRST
88 Gertrude Road, West Bridgeford, **Nottinghamshire NG2 5DB**
TEL   0602 814574
OPEN   9–5 Mon–Fri.

Specialise in restoring easel paintings on canvas, panel or copper.

PROVIDE Home Inspections. Free Estimates. Chargeable Collection/Delivery Service.
SPEAK TO Andrew Hirst. Member of UKIC. Associate Member of ABPR.
SEE Picture Frames.

BART LUCKHURST
The Gallery, 9 Union Street, Bingham, **Nottinghamshire NG13 8AD**
TEL   0949 837668
OPEN   9–5 Tues–Thur; 9.–1 Sat.

Specialise in restoring oils and watercolours, relining and handmade stretcher bars. Also restore old photographs.

PROVIDE Home Inspections. Free Estimates. Collection/Delivery Service by arrangement.
SPEAK TO Bart Luckhurst.
Member of FATG.
SEE Picture Frames.

MARK ROBERTS
1 West Workshops, Tan Gallop, Welbeck, Nr. Worksop, **Nottinghamshire S80 3LW**
TEL   0909 484270
OPEN   By Appointment.

Specialise in conserving and restoring European easel paintings.

PROVIDE Home Inspections. Refundable Estimates. Chargeable Collection/ Delivery Service.
SPEAK TO Mark or Diana Roberts.
SEE Picture Frames.

ARTHUR AND ANN RODGERS
7 Church Street, Ruddington, Nottingham, **Nottinghamshire NG11 6HA**
TEL   0602 216214
OPEN   9–5 Tues, Wed; 9–1 Thur, Fri; 9–5 Sat.

Specialise in hand-colouring, cleaning, restoring and repairing prints.

PROVIDE Home Inspections. Chargeable Estimates. Free Collection/Delivery Service.
SPEAK TO Arthur Rodgers.
SEE Books

BARBARA BIBB
149 Kingston Road, Oxford, **Oxfordshire OX2 6RP**
TEL   0865 56444
OPEN   9–5 Mon–Sat.

Specialise in restoring oil and easel paintings.

PROVIDE Home Inspections. Free Estimates. Free Local Collection/Delivery Service.
SPEAK TO Barbara Bibb.
Associate Member of ABPR. This workshop is included on the register of conservators maintained by the Conservation Unit of the Museums and Galleries Commission.
SEE Furniture, Picture Frames.

RUTH E. BUBB, CONSERVATION OF PAINTINGS

Poplars Farmhouse, 63 Main Road, Middleton Cheney, Banbury, **Oxfordshire OX17 2LU**
TEL   0295 711147
FAX   0295 711147
OPEN   By Appointment Only.

Specialise in restoring easel paintings on canvas and solid supports of all periods. Also offer surveys of collections and condition reports. All work is fully documented.

PROVIDE Home Inspections. Free Estimates. Chargeable Collection/Delivery Service.
SPEAK TO Ruth Bubb.
Associate Member of UKIC and ABPR. This workshop is included on the register of conservators maintained by the Conservation Unit of the Museums and Galleries Commission.

ANNA HULBERT

1 The Green, Childrey, Wantage, **Oxfordshire OX12 9UG**
TEL   0235 751 602
OPEN   By Appointment. It is best to write first of all.

Specialise in restoring Mediaeval panel paintings, wall paintings, architectural polychromy, including painted stone. Also 17th century wall paintings. Will work on site if required.

PROVIDE Home Inspections. Chargeable Estimates.

SPEAK TO Anna Hulbert.
Associate Member of ABPR. This workshop is included on the register of conservators maintained by the Conservation Unit of the Museum and Galleries Commission.

ANNE KENNETT

17 Greenmere, Brightwell–Cum–Stowell, **Oxfordshire OX10 0QN**
TEL   0491 834757
OPEN   9.30–6 Mon–Fri or By Appointment.

Specialise in restoring works of art on paper, mostly prints, drawings and watercolours.

PROVIDE Home Inspections. Free Estimates. Chargeable Collection/Delivery Service.
SPEAK TO Anne Kennett.
Member of IPC.
SEE Picture Frames.

OXFORD CONSERVATIONS

Full address witheld by request, **Oxfordshire**
TEL   0865 62614
FAX   0865 750311
OPEN   By Appointment Only.

Specialise in restoring paintings and can provide technical analysis, surveys, condition reports and other documentation and advice on exhibition, transport and storage.

PROVIDE Home Inspections. Free Estimates. Chargeable Collection/Delivery Service.
SPEAK TO Candy Kuhl, Chief Conservator.
Member of UKIC and IIC, Associate Memner of ABPR. This workshop is included on the register of conservators maintained by the Conservation Unit of the Museums and Galleries Commission.
SEE Picture Frames, Porcelain.

PICTURE CONSERVATION AND RESTORATION STUDIOS

40–41 Park End Street, Oxford,
Oxfordshire OX1 1JD
All correspondence to: Head Office,
7 Beech Close, Buckingham,
Buckinghamshire MK18 1PG
TEL   0865 200289
OPEN   9–5,30 Mon–Sat By
Appointment Only.

Specialise in the cleaning and restoration of oil paintings, watercolours and prints. Specialists in the lining of oil paintings.

PROVIDE Home Inspections. Chargeable Estimates. Chargeable Collection/ Delivery Service.
SPEAK TO Mr Garve Hessenberg BA.
SEE Picture Frames.

DIANNE BRITTON AND GRAEME STOREY

The Grange, Maesbrook, Oswestry,
Shropshire SY10 8QP
TEL   0691 85260
OPEN   By Appointment.

Specialise in restoring works on paper, oil paintings. Specialists in on–site work.

PROVIDE Home Inspections. Chargeable Estimates. Chargeable Collection/ Delivery Service.
SPEAK TO Dianne Britton or Graeme Storey.
Member of IIC, IPC and UKIC. This workshop is included on the register of conservators maintained by the Conservation Unit of the Museums and Galleries Commission.

MAUREEN A. BURD

Station House, Church Stretton,
Shropshire SY6 6AX
TEL   0694 722057
OPEN   By Appointment.

Specialise in restoring and conserving prints, drawings, watercolours, easel paintings, pastels.

PROVIDE Home Inspections. Free/Chargeable Estimates. Collection/Delivery Service by arrangement.
SPEAK TO Mrs Maureen Burd.
Member of IPC and IIC.

JULIET MARGUERITE CELIA GIBBS

The Old Vicarage, Stanton–Upon–Hine Heath, Shrewsbury, **Shropshire SY4 4LR**
TEL   0939 250881
OPEN   9–5 Mon–Fri or By
Appointment.

Specialise in restoring easel paintings, lining, blister laying, transfers, cleaning.

PROVIDE Home Inspections. Free Estimates. Collection/Delivery Service.
SPEAK TO Juliet Gibbs.
Established 1976. This workshop is included on the register of conservators maintained by the Conservation Unit of the Museums and Galleries Commission.

TIM EVERETT

Pitminster Studio, Taunton, **Somerset TA3 7AZ**
TEL   0823 42710
OPEN   By Appointment.

Specialise in conservation and restoration of oil paintings on canvas and panel. Also paper restoration.

PROVIDE Home Inspections. Free Estimates. Free Collection/Delivery Service.
SPEAK TO Tim Everett.
This workshop is included on the register of conservators maintained by the Conservation Unit of the Museums and Galleries Commission.
SEE Picture Frames.

THE ANTIQUE RESTORATION STUDIO

The Old Post Office, Haughton,
Staffordshire ST18 9JH
TEL 0785 780424
FAX 0785 780157
OPEN 9–5 Mon–Fri.

Specialise in restoring antique and modern paintings.

PROVIDE Home Inspections. Free Estimates. Free Collection/Delivery Service.
SPEAK TO D. P. Albright.
SEE Carpets, Furniture, Porcelain.

JESSE BRUTON

Park House, Codsall Wood,
Staffordshire WV8 1QR
TEL 0902 84 3055
OPEN 10–6 Mon–Fri or By Appointment.

Specialise in restoring easel paintings, including modern works.

PROVIDE Home Inspections. Chargeable Estimates. Chargeable Collection/Delivery Service.
SPEAK TO Jesse Bruton.
Member of UKIC, IIC. Associate Member of ABPR. This workshop is included on the register of conservators maintained by the Conservation Unit of the Museums and Galleries Commission. Restorer to the Midland Museum Service since 1969.

CONSULTANT CONSERVATORS OF FINE ART

Ramsor Farm, Ramshorn, Nr.
Oakamoor, **Staffordshire ST10 3BT**
TEL 0538 702928
OPEN By Appointment.

Specialise in restoring paintings, including multi media, multi supports, miniatures, watercolours and prints. Also, provide on–site radiography.

PROVIDE Home Inspections. Free Estimates. Free/Chargeable Collection/Delivery Service.
SPEAK TO Marilyn Jackson Mooney.
Member of UKIC and IIC. This workshop is included on the register of conservators maintained by the Conservation Unit of the Museums and Galleries Commission.

VICTORIA DES BEAUX ARTS LTD

11 Newcastle Street, Burslem, Stoke–on–Trent, **Staffordshire ST6 3QB**
TEL 0782 836490
OPEN 9–5 Mon–Sat.

Specialise in cleaning and restoring 17th–19th century oil paintings.

PROVIDE Home Inspections. Free/Chargeable Estimates. Free Collection/Delivery Service.
SPEAK TO Mrs Bryden.
SEE Picture Frames.

ROGER & SYLVIA ALLAN

The Old Red Lion, Bedingfield, Eye,
Suffolk IP23 7LQ
TEL 0728 628491
OPEN By Appointment.

Specialise in restoring oil paintings on panel or canvas and miniatures.

PROVIDE Home Inspections. Free Estimates.
SPEAK TO Roger Allan.
SEE Furniture, Silver.

PHILIPPA ELLISON

Fords Farm, Winston, Nr. Stowmarket,
Suffolk IP14 6BD
TEL 0728 860572
OPEN 9–5 Mon–Fri.

Specialise in restoring works of art on paper. Advice on general care available.

PROVIDE Home Inspections. Free Estimates. Collection/Delivery Service.
SPEAK TO Philippa Ellison.

Member of IPC. This workshop is
included on the register of conservators
maintained by the Conservation Unit of
the Museums and Galleries Commission.
SEE Books, Picture Frames.

JOHN GAZELEY
ASSOCIATES FINE ART
17 Fonnereau Road, Ipswich, **Suffolk
IP1 3JR**
TEL   0473 252420
OPEN   By Appointment.

Specialise in cleaning, relining and
restoring oil paintings, particularly 17th
and 18th century English portraits.

PROVIDE Free Estimates.
SPEAK TO Dr John Gazeley.
SEE Furniture, Picture Frames.

JUDITH GOWLAND MA
PhD
6 Duke Street, Haughley, **Suffolk
IP14 3QS**
TEL   0449 770181
OPEN   By Appointment.

Specialise in restoring watercolours,
prints and drawings.

PROVIDE Home Inspections. Chargeable
Estimates. Chargeable Collection/
Delivery Service.
SPEAK TO Judith Gowland.
Member of IPC.
SEE **North Yorkshire**
SEE Books.

C. W. P. KEYES
36 High Street, Debenham, Stowmarket,
Suffolk IP14 6QN
TEL   0728 860624
OPEN   10–3 Mon–Sat.

Specialise in restoration of watercolours,
prints, drawings, posters. Will provide
photographs and reports of work done.

PROVIDE Home Inspections. Chargeable
Estimates. Chargeable Collection/
Delivery Service.

SPEAK TO Charles Keyes. Member of IPC.
SEE Picture Frames, Books.

JANE McAUSLAND
Nether Hall Barn, Old Newton,
Stowmarket, **Suffolk IP14 4PP**
TEL   0449 673571
FAX   0449 770689
OPEN   9–6 Mon–Fri.

Specialise in restoring and conserving all
items considered to be art on paper. This
includes prints, drawings, watercolours,
pastels and artist photographs. All work
is carried out in a fully equipped, secure
studio. They also give advice on
preventative conservation for collections
and have a consultancy service one day a
week at 41 Lexington Street, London
W1R 3LG.
TEL   071 437 1070.

PROVIDE Home Inspections. Free
Estimates. Free Local
Collection/Delivery Service.
SPEAK TO Jane McAusland.
Fellow of the IIC, Founder Member of
IPC, member of UKIC and the AIC.
This workshop is included on the register
of conservators maintained by the
Conservation Unit of the Museums and
Galleries Commission.

PEASENHALL ART &
ANTIQUES GALLERY
Peasenhall, Nr. Saxmundham, **Suffolk
IP17 2HJ**
TEL   072 879 224
OPEN   9–6 Daily.

Specialise in cleaning and restoring oils,
watercolours and prints.

PROVIDE Local Home Inspections. Free
Estimates. Free Local Collection/
Delivery.
SPEAK TO Mike Wickins.
SEE Furniture

BOURNE GALLERY LIMITED
31–33 Lesbourne Road, Reigate, **Surrey RH2 7JS**
TEL   0737 241614
OPEN   10–1, 2–5.30 Mon–Sat; 10–1 Wed.

Specialise in restoring 19th and 20th century oil paintings.

PROVIDE Home Inspections. Free Estimates. Collection/Delivery Service by arrangement.
SPEAK TO John Robertson.

J. H. COOKE AND SONS LTD
Station Avenue, Kew, **Surrey TW9 3QA**
TEL   081 948 5644
FAX   081 332 2786
OPEN   9.30–5.30 Mon–Fri.

Specialise in restoring oil paintings.

PROVIDE Home Inspections. Free Estimates. Free Collection/Delivery Service.
SPEAK TO Philip Robinson, Michael Robinson or Jean Hudson.
They are Full Members of ABPR and Mr Philip Robonson is a Fellow of IIC.

S. A. ESDAILE
69 Farley Road, Selsdon, South Croydon, **Surrey CR2 7NG**
TEL   081 657 6708
OPEN   By Appointment.

Specialise in restoring works of art on paper, European and Oriental prints, drawings in different media, watercolours, ephemera on paper, posters. Surveys of collections undertaken.

PROVIDE Home Inspections. Free Estimates. Free Local Collection/Delivery Service.
SPEAK TO Sally Esdaile.
Member of IIC, UKIC, IPC. This workshop is included on the register of conservators maintained by the Conservation Unit of the Museums and Galleries Commission.

JOHN HILL
'Farthings', Trindles Road, South Nutfield, **Surrey RH1 4JG**
TEL   0737 823404
OPEN   9–5 Mon–Fri.

Specialise in restoring prints and watercolours. Provide conservation advice on all pictures.

PROVIDE Home Inspections. Free Estimates. Chargeable Collection/Delivery Service.
SPEAK TO John Hill.
Member of IPC.
SEE Books, Picture Frames.

KING'S COURT GALLERIES
54 West Street, Dorking, **Surrey RH4 1BS**
TEL   0306 881757
FAX   0306 75305
OPEN   9.30–5.30 Mon–Sat.

Specialise in paper conservation and restoration, including engravings, decorative and sporting prints.

PROVIDE Home Inspections. Free Estimates.
SPEAK TO Mrs J. Joel.
SEE **London SW6**
SEE Books.

LIMPSFIELD WATERCOLOURS
High Street, Limpsfield, **Surrey RH8 0DT**
TEL   0883 717010
OPEN   11–3 Tues; 10–2 Thur–Fri:10–3 Sat.

Specialise in conserving, cleaning and restoring prints and watercolours.

PROVIDE Local Home Inspections, Free Estimates.
SPEAK TO Christine Reason.
SEE Picture Frames.

JACK MAY
'Beukenhof', Hogs Back, Guildford,
Surrey GU3 1DD
TEL   0483 570615
OPEN   By Appointment Mon–Sat.

Specialise in restoration of watercolours
and prints and their presentation.

PROVIDE Home Inspections by
arrangement. Free Estimates. Free Local
Collection/Delivery Service.
SPEAK TO Jack May.
Full Member of ABPR. Established
1970.

**PETER NEWMAN
RESTORER**
The Studio, Newmans Lane, Surbiton,
Surrey KT6 4QQ
TEL   081 390 8672
OPEN   9.30–6 Mon–Fri.

Specialise in restoring Old Masters and
contemporary oil paintings. Specialist in
lining and panel work.

PROVIDE Home Inspections. Free
Estimates. Chargeable
Collection/Delivery Service.
SPEAK TO Peter Newman.
Full Member of ABPR.

MARNY PARK
Loseberry, 30 Hare Lane, Claygate,
Surrey KT10 9BU
TEL   0372 463628
FAX   0372 470140
OPEN   9–5 Mon–Fri.

Specialise in restoring art on paper,
including prints, drawings and
watercolours.

PROVIDE Home Inspections. Free
Estimates. Free Local
Collection/Delivery Service.
SPEAK TO Marny Park (Mrs Ann Margaret
Park).
Member of IPC.
SEE Books.

HILARY PINDER
1st Floor, St Kilda, The Hermitage,
Richmond, **Surrey TW10 6SH**
TEL   081 948 4426
OPEN   10–7 Daily.

Specialise in restoring icons and
paintings.

PROVIDE Home Inspections. Free
Estimates. Free Collection/Delivery
Service.
SPEAK TO Hilary Pinder.
Member of IIC. Associate Member of
ABPR. This workshop is included on the
register of conservators maintained by
the Conservation Unit of the Museums
and Galleries Commission.

PAULINE PLUMMER
19D Kew Gardens Road, Richmond,
Surrey TW9 3HD
TEL   081 940 9794
OPEN   By Appointment.

Specialise in restoring on–site paintings
and painted decoration, ceiling
paintings, murals, canvases fixed in situ,
painted screens and panelling of all
periods in oil or size tempera, not lime
tempera.

PROVIDE Home Inspections. Chargeable
Estimates.
SPEAK TO Pauline Plummer.
Fellow of IIC. Full Member of ABPR.
This workshop is included on the
register of conservators maintained by
the Conservation Unit of the Museums
and Galleries Commission.

CHARLES RAKE
7 Avonmore Avenue, Guildford, **Surrey
GU1 1TW**
TEL   0483 37211
OPEN   8.30–6.30 Mon–Sat.

Specialise in complete cleaning and
restoration of oil paintings on canvas and
panel.

PROVIDE Home Inspections. Free

Estimates. Free Collection/Delivery
Service.
SPEAK TO Charles Rake.
This workshop is included on the register
of conservators maintained by the
Conservation Unit of the Museums and
Galleries Commission.

SAGE ANTIQUES & INTERIORS
High Street, Ripley, **Surrey GU23 6BB**
TEL   0483 224396
FAX   0483 211996
OPEN   9.30–5.30 Mon–Sat.

Specialise in restoring oil paintings and
watercolours.

PROVIDE Free Estimates.
Collection/Delivery Service.
SPEAK TO Howard or Chrissie Sage.
Member of LAPADA and the Guild of
Master Craftsmen.
SEE Porcelain, Furniture.

S. & S. PICTURE RESTORATION STUDIOS
The Rookery, Frensham, Farnham,
Surrey GU10 3DU
TEL   0252 793673
OPEN   10–6 Mon–Fri.

Specialise in restoring oil paintings of all
periods.

PROVIDE Home Inspections.
Free/Chargeable Estimates.
Collection/Delivery Service by
arrangement.
SPEAK TO Roy Skelton.

R. SAUNDERS
71 Queens Road, Weybridge, **Surrey
KT13 9UQ**
TEL   0932 842601
OPEN   9.15–5 Mon–Sat; closed Wed.

Specialise in cleaning and restoring oil
paintings and watercolours.

PROVIDE Home Inspections. Free
Estimates. Free Collection/Delivery
Service.

SPEAK TO J. B. Tonkinson.
SEE Furniture, Porcelain, Silver.

NICHOLAS PETER SEVERSWAY
123 Weybourne Lane, Heath End,
Farnham, **Surrey GU9 9DD**
TEL   0252 28345
OPEN   10–1, 2–6 Tues–Fri; 9–4 Sat.

Specialise in restoring oil paintings,
prints and watercolours.

PROVIDE Home Inspections. Free
Estimates. Free Local
Collection/Delivery Service.
SPEAK TO Nick Seversway.
Member of UKIC and IPC. Associate
Member of ABPR.
SEE Picture Frames.

JULIAN SPENCER-SMITH
The Studio, 30A College Road, Woking,
Surrey GU22 8BU
TEL   0483 726070
OPEN   9–1, 2–5 Mon–Fri.

Specialise in all aspects of conservation
work to oil paintings such as their own
lining and panel work etc.

PROVIDE Home Inspections. Free
Estimates. Free Collection/Delivery
Service.
SPEAK TO Julian Spencer–Smith.
Full Member of ABPR.

THE CONSERVATION WORKSHOP
6 Green Man Yard, Boreham Street, Nr.
Herstmonceux, **East Sussex BN27 4SF**
TEL   0323 833842
OPEN   9.30–6 Mon–Fri or By
            Appointment.

Specialise in conserving works of art on
paper, photographs, modern media.
They run workshops on paper and
photographic conservation.

PROVIDE Home Inspections. Free
Estimates. Free Local
Collection/Delivery Service.
SPEAK TO Ian Maver or Corinne Hillman.
Member of IPC, UKIC, Royal
Photographic Society, Society of
Archivists and Wallpaper History Society.
This workshop is included on the register
of conservators maintained by the
Conservation Unit of the Museums and
Galleries Commission.
SEE Books.

JOHN DAY OF EASTBOURNE FINE ART
9 Meads Street, Eastbourne, **East Sussex BN20 7QY**
TEL   0323 725634 or 0860 466197
OPEN   10–5 Mon–Fri; closed Wed.

Specialise in cleaning, restoring and
relining oil paintings, particularly East
Anglian and Victorian Schools.

PROVIDE Home Inspections. Free
Estimates Chargeable
Collection/Delivery Service.
SPEAK TO John Day.

FIRELEAD LTD
Banff Farm, Upper Clayhill, Uckfield Rd,
Ringmer, Lewes, **East Sussex BN8 5RR**
TEL   0273 890918
FAX   0273 890691
OPEN   8–5.30 Mon–Fri By
           Appointment.

Specialise in restoring oil paintings and
watercolours.

PROVIDE Local Home Inspections. Local
Free Estimates. Chargeable
Collection/Delivery Service.
SPEAK TO David Gilbert.
SEE Furniture.

E. R. KINANE
R & K Enterprises, Old Brewery Centre,
Old Brewery Yard, High Street, Hastings,
East Sussex TN34 3ER
TEL   0424 446431 or 439261
OPEN   9–4 Mon–Fri; 10–1 Sat or By
           Appointment.

Specialise in restoring easel paintings
and murals.

PROVIDE Home Inspections. Free
Estimates. Free Collection/Delivery
Service.
SPEAK TO E. R. Kinane.
Associate Member of IIC, UKIC and
ABPR. This workshop is included on the
register of conservators maintained by
the Conservation Unit of the Museums
and Galleries Commission.

MICHAEL LESLIE FINE ARTS
The Garden Studio, Denniker Cottage,
Fletching, Nr. Uckfield, **East Sussex TN22 3SH**
TEL   0825 724176
FAX   0825 768410
OPEN   By Appointment.

Specialise in restoring all easel paintings
from mediaeval to 20th century. Also
large–scale paintings, if necessary on
location. They also specialise in fire and
water damaged pictures.

PROVIDE Home Inspections. Free
Estimates. Free Local
Collection/Delivery Service.
SPEAK TO Michael Leslie.
Mr Leslie is a Full Member of ABPR.

ADRIANNE MEAD
School Hill Studios, 204 High Street,
Lewes, **East Sussex BN7 2NS**
TEL   0273 476087
OPEN   9–5 Mon–Sat.

Specialise in restoring oils and
watercolours.

PROVIDE Home Inspections. Free
Estimates. Collection/Delivery Service.
SPEAK TO Adrianne Mead.
SEE Picture Frames.

G. MURRAY–BROWN PICTURE SERVICES
Silverbeach House, Norman Road,
Pevensey Bay, **East Sussex BN24 6JR**
TEL   0323 764298
OPEN   By Appointment.

Specialise in restoring oil and watercolour paintings and old prints.

PROVIDE Home Inspections. Free Estimates. Collection/Delivery Service.
SPEAK TO Geoffrey Murray–Brown.
SEE Picture Frames.

SOUTH EAST CONSERVATION CENTRE
5 North Street, St Leonards–on–Sea, **East Sussex TN38 OEY**
TEL   0424 431157
FAX   0424 431807
OPEN   9–5 Mon–Fri or By Appointment.

Specialise in restoring fine oil paintings on canvas or panel, gilding.

PROVIDE Home Inspections. Free Estimates. Chargeable Collection/Delivery Service.
SPEAK TO Rupert Smith.
This workshop is included on the register of conservators maintained by the Conservation Unit of the Museums and Galleries Commission.

STEWART GALLERY
48 Devonshire Road, Bexhill–on–Sea, **East Sussex TN40 1AX**
TEL   0424 223410
FAX   0323 29588
OPEN   9–5.30 Mon–Sat.

Specialise in restoring 19th and 20th century oil paintings and watercolours.

PROVIDE Home Inspections. Free Estimates. Free Collection/Delivery Service.
SPEAK TO Mrs L. Knight.

STEWART GALLERY
25 Grove Road, Eastbourne, **East Sussex BN20 4TT**
TEL   0323 29588
FAX   0323 29588
OPEN   9–5.30 Mon–Fri; 11–4 Sat.

Specialise in restoring 19th and 20th

century oil paintings and watercolours.

PROVIDE Home Inspections. Free Estimates. Free Collection/Delivery Service.
SPEAK TO S. A. Ettinger.

NATALIE COPELAND
39 Fairlea Close, Burgess Hill, **West Sussex RH15 8NW**
TEL   0444 248976
OPEN   9.30–5.30 Mon–Fri or By Appointment.

Specialise in conserving and restoring works of art on paper. Also do surveys of collections, give advice on storage mounting and framing and will give free written estimates detailing condition and work to be carried out backed up by photographic documentation.

PROVIDE Home Inspections. Free Estimates. Local Collection/Delivery Service.
SPEAK TO Mrs Natalie Copeland.
Member of IPCR and the American Institute of Conservation. Associate Member of ABPR. Mrs Copeland is a Visiting Lecturer at Camberwell College of Art.
This workshop is included on the register of conservators maintained by the Conservation Unit of the Museums and Galleries Commission.

RPM RESTORATIONS
7 Hurst Close, Amberley, **West Sussex BN18 9NX**
TEL   0798 831845
OPEN   By Appointment.

Specialise in paper conservation and restoring watercolours, drawings and prints.

PROVIDE Home Inspections. Free Estimates. Free Collection/Delivery Service.
SPEAK TO James Jacob.

JENNIFER RIDD FINE ART RESTORER

White Cat Cottage, Birch Grove, Horsted Keynes, Haywards Heath, **West Sussex RH17 7BU**
Tel 0825 740559
Open 9–6.30 Mon–Sat
By appointment.

Specialise in restoring fine oil or tempera paintings on a variety of supports, usually of canvas, wood or copper.
Thirty years' experience in the restoration of fine oil paintings. Collections a speciality. Advice given on hanging and framing.

PROVIDE Home Inspections. Free Estimates. Free Collection and Delivery service of canvasses under 50×40 in. Larger canvasses chargeable.

SPEAK TO Mrs Ridd.

FELLOW OF ABPR.

SURREY PRINT WATERCOLOUR CLEANING COMPANY
Mockingbird, Spy Lane, Loxwood, **West Sussex RH14 0SS**
TEL   0403 752097
OPEN   By Appointment.

Specialise in cleaning and restoring of works of art on paper, particularly watercolours and prints.

PROVIDE Free Estimates. Chargeable Collection/Delivery Service.
SPEAK TO Ken Downs.

SUSSEX CONSERVATION STUDIO
'Hill Bank', Broad Street, Cuckfield, **West Sussex RH17 5DX**
TEL   0444 451964
OPEN   8.30–5.30 Mon–Fri or By Appointment.

Specialise in restoring all types of works of art on paper, including prints, drawings, pastels, watercolours, etc. Cleaning, relining, repair work and retouching are all carried out to conservation standards using up-to-date techniques.

PROVIDE Free Estimates. Home Inspections by arrangement. Free Local Collection/Delivery Service.
SPEAK TO Reginald or Bernadette Selous. Member of IPC. This workshop is included on the register of conservators maintained by the Conservation Unit of the Museums and Galleries Commission.
SEE Books.

ANNE–NOELLE TAMPLIN
Hammerwood Park, Nr. East Grinstead, **West Sussex RH19 3QE**
TEL   0342 860594
FAX   0342 850594
OPEN   By Appointment.

Specialise in restoring oil paintings on canvas.

PROVIDE Home Inspections. Free
Estimates. Collection Delivery Service.
SPEAK TO Anne-Noelle Tamplin.
Member of UKIC. Associate Member of
ABPR.

MRS LINDSAY A. FARRIMOND

Studio Lamond, 22 Benton Bank,
Heaton, Newcastle–upon–Tyne,
Tyne & Wear NE7 7BE
TEL   091 265 9708
FAX   091 224 1130
OPEN   9.30–3.30 Mon–Fri.

Specialise in restoring prints, drawings,
watercolours, posters, pastels and
Modern. Will also undertake surveys of
collections. Full documentation and
photographs supplied if required.
PROVIDE Free Estimates.
SPEAK TO Mrs Lindsay A. Farrimond.
Member of IPC. This workshop is
included on the register of conservators
maintained by the Conservation Unit of
the Museums and Galleries Commission.

MACDONALD FINE ART

2 Ashburton Road, Gosforth, **Tyne &
Wear NE3 4XN**
TEL   091 2856188 or 2844214
OPEN   10–1, 2.30–5.30 Mon–Sat;
            closed Wed.

Specialise in restoring Victorian
watercolours and oil paintings.
PROVIDE Free Estimates. Free
Collection/Delivery Service.
SPEAK TO Tom MacDonald.
SEE Picture Frames.

SUSAN B. AIRY

The Old Barn, Radway, **Warwickshire
CV 35 0UF**
TEL   0295 87392
OPEN   8–8 Daily.

Specialise in restoring oil paintings on
canvas, panel paintings and icons.
PROVIDE Home Inspections. Free
Estimates. Chargeable
Collection/Delivery Service.
SPEAK TO Susan Airy.
Member of UKIC. This workshop is
included on the register of conservators
maintained by the Conservation Unit of
the Museums and Galleries Commission.
SEE Picture Frames, Furniture.

SIMON NEIL FOSTER

36 Grove Road, Stratford–upon–Avon,
Warwickshire CV37 6PB
TEL   0789 292156
OPEN   8.30–6 Mon–Sat.

Specialise in restoring easel paintings;
oil on canvas, board, panel and mixed
media.
PROVIDE Home Inspections. Collection
Delivery Service.
SPEAK TO Simon Foster. Member of
UKIC.

FOSTER RESTORERS

7 Rivermead Drive, Tiddington,
Stratrford–upon–Avon, **Warwickshire
CV37 7AL**
TEL   0789 204899
FAX   0789 267974
OPEN   10.30–5 Tues, Thur, Fri.

Specialise in restoring oil paintings,
watercolours and prints.
PROVIDE Home Inspections. Chargeable
Estimates. Free/Chargeable
Collection/Delivery Service. Packing
and Shipping Service.
SPEAK TO Jerrold E. F. Foster.
Member of UKIC and BAFRA. This
workshop is included on the register of
conservators maintained by the
Conservation Unit of the Museums and
Galleries Commission.
SEE Books

D. M. BEACH
52 High Street, Salisbury, **Wiltshire**
SP1 2PG
TEL   0722 333801
OPEN   9–5.30 Mon–Sat.

Specialise in restoring oils, watercolours
and prints.

PROVIDE Home Inspections. Free
Estimates. Free Local
Collection/Delivery Service.
SPEAK TO Anthony Beach.
SEE Books.

CHARLES BOOTH– JONES
Fox Conservation Studio, Hill Barn,
Monkton Deverill, Warminster,
Wiltshire BA12 7EY
TEL   0985 844479
OPEN   By Appointment.

Specialise in restoring fine oil paintings
of all periods.

PROVIDE Home Inspections. Free
Estimates. Chargeable
Collection/Delivery Service.
SPEAK TO Charles Booth–Jones.
This workshop is included on the register
of conservators maintained by the
Conservation Unit of the Museum and
Galleries Commission.

ANDREW FANE
Thistle Cottage, Great Bedwyn, Nr.
Marlborough, **Wiltshire SN8 3LH**
TEL   0672 870549
OPEN   8.30–5.30 Mon–Fri or By
       Appointment.

Specialise in restoring watercolours,
pastels, prints, drawings, posters.

PROVIDE Home Inspections. Free
Estimates. Free/Chargeable
Collection/Delivery Service.
SPEAK TO Andrew Fane.
Member of IPC.
This workshop is included on the register
of conservators maintained by the

Conservation Unit of the Museums and
Galleries Commission.
SEE Books.

ROGER PHIPPEN
The Corner, Pottle Street,
Horningsham, Warminster, **Wiltshire**
BA12 7LX
TEL   0985 844644
OPEN   9.30–6 Mon–Fri.

Specialise in restoring oil paintings and
easel paintings of all periods.

PROVIDE Home Inspections. Chargeable
Estimates. Chargeable Collection/
Delivery Service.
SPEAK TO Roger Phippen.
Full Member of ABPR.

WINSTANLEY SALISBURY BOOKBINDERS
213 Devizes Road, Salisbury, **Wiltshire**
SP2 9LT
TEL   0722 334998
OPEN   8.30–5.30 Mon–Fri.

Specialise in restoring prints and paper
conservation.

PROVIDE Free Estimates.
Collection/Delivery Service.
SPEAK TO Alan Winstanley.
SEE Books.

SARAH WITHEROW
Pinhills Farm, Bowood Estate, Calne,
Wiltshire SN11 0LY
TEL   0249 816848
FAX   0249 821174
OPEN   9–6 Mon–Sat.

Specialise in restoring Old Master
paintings and panels, oil on paper.

PROVIDE Home Inspections. Free
Estimates. Free/Chargeable
Collection/Delivery Service.
SPEAK TO Sarah Witherow.
Full Member of ABPR.

STEPHEN AND PAMELA ALLEN

St Andrew's Cottage, Constable Burton, Leyburn,
North Yorkshire DL8 5RG
TEL   0677 50295
OPEN   By Appointment.

Specialise in restoring works on paper, including watercolours, prints and drawings.

PROVIDE Home Inspections. Free Estimates. Chargeable Collection/Delivery Service.
SPEAK TO Stephen Allen or Pamela Allen
Member of IPC. This workshop is included on the register of conservators maintained by the Conservation Unit of the Museums and Galleries Commission.
SEE Books.

RICHARD BENNETT

18 Kirkgate, Thirsk, **North Yorkshire YO7 1PQ**
TEL   0845 524085
OPEN   By Appointment.

Specialise in restoring and conserving oil paintings.

PROVIDE Chargeable Estimates. Collection/Delivery Service by arrangement.
SPEAK TO Richard Bennett.
Associate Member of ABPR.
SEE Picture Frames.

JUDITH GOWLAND MA PhD

East Ayrlow Banks, East Hauxwell, Leyburn, **North Yorkshire DL8 5NJ**
TEL   0677 50364
OPEN   By Appointment.

Specialise in restoring watercolours, prints and drawings.

PROVIDE Home Inspections. Chargeable Estimates. Chargeable Collection/Delivery Service.
SPEAK TO Judith Gowland.

Member of IPC.
SEE **North Yorkshire**
SEE Books.

AMELIA RAMPTON

29 Portland Stret, York, **North Yorkshire YO3 7EH**
TEL   0904 628048
OPEN   9–6 Mon–Fri By Appointment Only.

Specialise in conserving and restoring prints, drawings and watercolours.

PROVIDE Home Inspections. Free/Chargeable Estimates. Free Collection/Delivery Service.
SPEAK TO Amelia Rampton.
Member of IPC and UKIC. This workshop is included on the register of conservators maintained by the Conservation Unit of the Museums and Galleries Commission.
SEE Books.

THE DAVIE GALLERY

8 Castlegate, Tickhill, Doncaster, **South Yorkshire DN11 9QU**
TEL   0302 751199
OPEN   9.30–5 Mon–Sat; closed Wed.

Specialise in conservation and restoration of paintings.

PROVIDE Home Inspections. Free Estimates. Free Collection/Delivery Service.
SPEAK TO Ian Davie.
Member of FATG.
SEE Picture Frames.

KIERAN CULLIVAN

25 Cathedral Road, Cavan, **Co. Cavan**
TEL   049 31254
OPEN   By Appointment.

Specialise in restoring oil paintings on canvas.

PROVIDE Home Inspections. Free

Estimates. Collection/Delivery Service by arrangement.
SPEAK TO Kieran Cullivan
Member of IPCRA.

PHYLLIS ARNOLD GALLERY ANTIQUES
Hoops Courtyard, Greyabbey, **Co. Down BT22 2NE**
TEL   02477 88199
      ANS 0247 853322
OPEN   11–5 Wed, Fri, Sat.

Specialise in restoring watercolours and portrait miniatures.

PROVIDE Free Estimates.
Collection/Delivery Service by arrangement.
SPEAK TO Phyllis Arnold.
Member of the Royal Society of Miniature Painters.
SEE Picture Frames.

BARBARA BEST
9 Acton Road, Poyntzpass, Newry, **Co. Down BT35 6TB**
TEL   0762 86727
OPEN   By Appointment.

Specialise in conserving oil paintings.

PROVIDE Home Inspections. Free Estimates. Chargeable Collection/Delivery Service.
SPEAK TO Barbara Best. Member of IPCRA.
SEE Picture Frames.

SERGIO BENEDETTI
National Gallery of Ireland, Merrion Square West. Dublin 2, **Co. Dublin**
TEL   01 6615133
OPEN   By Appointment.

Specialise in restoring and conserving oil paintings.

PROVIDE Free/Chargeable Estimates.
SPEAK TO Sergio Benedetti.

SUSAN CORR
Paper Conservation Studio, 48 Woodley Park, Dundrum, Dublin 14. **Co. Dublin**
TEL   01 2987661
OPEN   By Appointment.

Specialise in conservation of watercolours, prints, drawings and pastels.

PROVIDE Home Inspections. Free Estimates. Collection/Delivery Service by arrangement.
SPEAK TO Susan Corr.
Member of IPCRA and IPC.
SEE Books.

JAMES A. GORRY
20 Molesworth Street, Dublin 2, **Co. Dublin**
TEL   01 6795319
FAX   01 6795319
OPEN   10–6 Mon–Fri.

Specialise in restoring oil paintings.

PROVIDE Home Inspections.
SPEAK TO James Gorry.
SEE Picture Frames.

ROLAND HULME– BEAMAN
30 Leeson Park Avenue, Dublin 6, **Co. Dublin**
TEL   01 6604850
OPEN   By Appointment.

Specialise in restoring easel paintings, mainly Irish, European and American 18th to 20th century.

PROVIDE Chargeable Home Inspections. Free/Chargeable Estimates.
SPEAK TO Roland Hulme–Beaman.
Member of IPCRA.

LARKIN STUDIO
2 Stoneview Place, Dun Laoghaire, Dublin, **Co. Dublin**
TEL   01 2805030
OPEN   By Appointment.

Specialise in restoring 19th and 20th century easel paintings, wax relining.

PROVIDE Home Inspections. Free Estimates.
SPEAK TO Elizabeth Larkin.
Member of IPCRA.

PATRICK McBRIDE
Paper Conservation Studio, IDA Tower Complex, Pearse Street, Dublin 2, **Co. Dublin**
TEL   01 775656
FAX   01 775487
OPEN   By Appointment.

Specialise in restoring works of art on paper, watercolours, prints and drawings.

PROVIDE Home Inspections. Chargeable Estimates. Free Collection/Delivery Service.
SPEAK TO Patrick McBride.
Member of IPCRA, IPC and ICOM.
SEE Books.

ANDREW O'CONNOR
National Gallery of Ireland, Merrion Square West, Dublin 2, **Co. Dublin**
TEL   01 615133
OPEN   By Appointment.

Specialise in restoring and conserving oil paintings.

PROVIDE Free/Chargeable Estimates.
SPEAK TO Andrew O'Connor.
Member of IPCRA.

KAREN REIHILL
30 Hollybank Avenue, Lower Ranelagh, Dublin 6, **Co Dublin**
TEL   01 962462
OPEN   By Appointment.

Specialise in restoring and conserving works of art on paper, including watercolours, pastels, prints and drawings.

PROVIDE Free/Chargeable Estimates.

SPEAK TO Karen Reihill.
Member of IPCRA.
SEE Books.

THOMAS IRISH
Newcastle Upper, Crossabeg, Wexford, **Co. Wexford**
TEL   053 28232
OPEN   By Appointment.

Specialise in restoring oil paintings.

PROVIDE Home Inspections. Free Estimates. Free Collection/Delivery Service.
SPEAK TO Thomas Irish. Member of IPCRA and the Guild of Glass Engravers.

PAINTINGS CONSERVATION LTD
Penny Craig Cottage, Pen–Y–Craig Avenue, St Helier, Jersey, **Channel Islands JE2 3GN**
TEL   0534 74591
OPEN   8–8 Mon–Sat By Appointment.

Specialise in restoring paintings in oil on any support.

PROVIDE Home Inspections. Free Estimates. Collection Delivery Service.
SPEAK TO Ian Rolls BA (Hons), Fine Art, Dip Cons.
Member of UKIC and Associate Member of ABPR.
SEE Picture Frames

JAMES FLAVELL BOOKBINDER AND RESTORER
26 Foreland Road, Bembridge, **Isle of Wight PO35 5XW**
TEL   0983 872856
OPEN   9–5.30 Mon–Fri; 9–12.30 Sat.

Specialise in restoring prints.

PROVIDE Home Inspections. Free Estimates. Free Collection/Delivery Service.

SPEAK TO James Flavell.
Mr Flavell is City and Guilds qualified, Member of Society of Bookbinders, Associate Member of Designer Bookbinders. This workshop is included on the register of conservators maintained by the Conservation Unit of the Museums and Galleries Commission.
SEE Books, Furniture.

THE SHANKLIN GALLERY

67 Regent Street, Shanklin, **Isle Of Wight PO37 7AE**
TEL   0983 863113
OPEN   9–5 Mon–Sat.

Specialise in restoring all types of pictures, including oils, watercolours, pastels and prints.

PROVIDE Home Inspections. Free Estimates. Collection/Delivery Service.
SPEAK TO Mr Campbell.
Member of Fine Art Trade Guild.
SEE Picture Frames.

BLACKWOOD FINE ARTS GALLERY

10–11 Bourtree Terrace, Hawick, Roxburghshire, **Borders TD9 9HN**
TEL   0450 78547
FAX   0450 77780
OPEN   9.30–5.30 Mon–Fri; 10–2 Sat.

Specialise in restoring art works on canvas, panel, paper, in oil, tempera, watercolour, gouache, pastel, charcoal, pencil.

PROVIDE Home Inspections. Free Estimates. Chargeable Collection/Delivery Service.
SPEAK TO Carol Sutherland.
Member of SSCR. This workshop is in the Scottish Conservation Directory.
SEE Picture Frames.

VALENTINE WALSH

Caldra, Fogo, Duns, Berwickshire, **Borders**
TEL   071 261 1691
FAX   071 401 9049
OPEN   By Appointment.

Specialise in restoring easel paintings from 1400 to 1950, particularly paintings on panel and can also accommodate very large paintings.

PROVIDE Home Inspections. Free/Chargeable Estimates. Free/Chargeable Collection/Delivery Service.
SPEAK TO Valentine Walsh.
Member of UKIC. This workshop is included on the register of conservators maintained by the Conservation Unit of the Museums and Galleries Commission.
SEE **London SE1**

RILEY, DUNN & WILSON LTD

Bellevue Bindery, Glasgow Road, Camelon, Falkirk, **Central FK1 4HP**
TEL   0324 21591
FAX   0324 611508
OPEN   8.30–5 Mon–Fri.

Specialise in restoring prints and drawings.

PROVIDE Home Inspections. Free Estimates. Free Collection/Delivery Service.
SPEAK TO John Penman.
SEE **London EC1, West Yorkshire**.
SEE Books.

JOSEPH SCHERRER

30 Harbour Street, Creetown, Wigtownshire, **Dumfries & Galloway DG8 7JJ**
TEL   067182 268
OPEN   10–5 Mon–Sat or By Appointment.

Specialise in restoring paintings on

canvas, panel and paper. Has worked in France and can advise.

PROVIDE Home Inspections. Free Estimates.
SPEAK TO Joseph Scherrer.
This workshop is in the Scottish Conservation Directory.
SEE Picture Frames.

JAMES ANDERSON RITCHIE
Art Restoration Service, 6 Woodhill Place, Aberdeen, **Grampian AB2 4LF**
TEL   0224 310491
OPEN   9–5.30 or By Appointment.

Specialise in restoring oil paintings, watercolours and prints.

PROVIDE Local Home Inspections. Free Estimates. Chargeable Collection/ Delivery Service.
SPEAK TO J. Anderson Ritchie.
This workshop is in the Scottish Conservation Directory.
SEE Carpets, Picture Frames.

ALDER ARTS
57 Church Street, Inverness, **Highland IV1 1DR**
TEL   0463 243575
OPEN   9–5.30 Mon–Sat.

Specialise in cleaning and restoring 17th–19th century oil paintings.

PROVIDE Home Inspections. Free/Chargeable Estimates. Free Collection/ Delivery Service.
SPEAK TO Ken Hardiman.
SEE Picture Frames.

ORBOST GALLERY
Bolvean, Isle of Skye, **Highland IV55 8ZB**
TEL   047 022 207
OPEN   By Appointment.

Specialise in repairing and restoring oil paintings as well as wood and marble finishes for interior restoration,

presentation calligraphy and illumination.

PROVIDE Home Inspections. Free/Chargeable Collection/Delivery Service.
SPEAK TO Dr David L. Roberts MA FSA (Scotland).
This workshop is in the Scottish Conservation Directory.
SEE Picture Frames.

THURSO ANTIQUES
Drill Hall, 21 Sinclair Street, Thurso, **Highland**
TEL   0847 63291 or 05934 276
FAX   0847 62824
OPEN   10–5 Mon–Fri; 10–1 Sat.

Specialise in cleaning and restoring oil paintings and watercolours.

PROVIDE Free Estimates. Collection/Delivery Service by arrangement.
SPEAK TO G. Atkinson.
SEE Silver.

CELIA BLAIR
The Studio, Cramond Brig Farm, Edinburgh, **Lothian EH4 6DY**
TEL   031 339 6502
OPEN   By Appointment.

Specialise in conservation and restoration of easel paintings and carrying out conservation surveys.

PROVIDE Home Inspections. Free/Chargeable Estimates. Free/Chargeable Collection/Delivery Service.
SPEAK TO Celia Blair.
This workshop is in the Scottish Conservation Directory.

BOURNE FRAMES AND RESTORATION LTD
4 Dundas Street, Edinburgh, **Lothian EH3 6HZ**
TEL   031 557 4874
FAX   031 557 8382
OPEN   10–6 Mon–Fri; 10–1 Sat.

Specialise in restoring paintings.

PROVIDE Home Inspections. Free Estimates. Free/Chargeable Collection/Delivery Service.
SPEAK TO Susan Heys.
This workshop is in the Scottish Conservation Directory.
SEE Picture Frames.

CHRISTINE BULLICK
5 Belford Terrace, Edinburgh, **Lothian EH4 3DQ**
TEL   031 332 6948
OPEN   By Appointment.

Specialise in restoring early panel painting, Elizabethan and Jacobean and also contemporary painting.

PROVIDE Home Inspections. Free/Chargeable Estimates.
SPEAK TO Christine Bullick.
Member of IIC, UKIC and SSCR. This workshop is in the Scottish Conservation Directory.

MALCOLM INNES GALLERY
67 George Street, Edinburgh, **Lothian EH2 2JG**
TEL   031 226 4151
FAX   031 226 4151
OPEN   9.30–6 Mon–Fri.

Specialise in restoring oils, watercolours and prints especially natural history, Scottish and sporting subjects.

PROVIDE Home Inspections. Free Estimates. Free/Chargeable Collection/Delivery Service.
SPEAK TO Anthony Woodd.
SEE **London SW3**
SEE Picture Frames.

CLARE MEREDITH
Conservation Studio, Hopetoun House, South Queensferry,
West Lothian EH30 9SL
TEL   031 331 2003
OPEN   By Appointment Only.

Specialise in the conservation and restoration of easel paintings and condition surveys of collections.

PROVIDE Inspections on site. Chargeable Estimates.
SPEAK TO Clare Meredith.
Member of SSCR, UKIC, IIC and the Museums Association. Full Member of ABPR. This workshop is in the Scottish Conservation Directory. This workshop is included on the register of conservators maintained by the Conservation Unit of the Museums and Galleries Commission.

PARKES & BORDONE
Unit 01, St Mary's Workshops, Henderson Street, Leith, Edinburgh **Lothian EH6 6DD**
TEL   031 553 5111
FAX   031 555 1211
OPEN   9–5 Mon–Fri or By Appointment.

Specialise in conserving, cleaning, lining and restoring oil paintings, as well as some frame repairs. They also do surveys of collections.

PROVIDE Home Inspections. Free Estimates. Collection/Delivery Service by arrangement.
SPEAK TO Jane Hutchison.
This workshop is in the Scottish Conservation Directory.

FIONA BUTTERFIELD
Overhall, Kirkfieldbank, Lanark, **Strathclyde ML11 9TZ**
TEL   0555 666291
OPEN   By Appointment.

Specialise in conserving paper, prints, watercolours and drawings.

PROVIDE Home Inspections. Free/Chargeable Estimates.
SPEAK TO Fiona Butterfield.
Member of IPC, UKIC, IIC and SSCR. This workshop is in the Scottish Conservation Directory.

DAPHNE FRASER
Glenbarry, 58 Victoria Road, Lenzie, Glasgow, **Strathclyde G66 5AP**
TEL   041 776 1281
OPEN   By Appointment.

Specialise in restoring antique oil paintings.

PROVIDE Free Estimates.
SPEAK TO Daphne Fraser.
SEE Collectors (Dolls; Toys), Furniture, Picture Frames. This workshop is in the Scottish Conservation Directory.

McIAN GALLERY
10 Argyll Square, Oban, **Strathclyde PA34 4AZ**
TEL   0631 66755
OPEN   9–5.30 Mon–Sat.

Specialise in fine art restoration.

PROVIDE Chargeable Collection/Delivery Service.
SPEAK TO Rory Campbell–Gibson.
SEE Picture Frames.

KENNETH McKENZIE
91 Hyndland Street, Glasgow, **Strathclyde G11 5PU**
TEL   041 339 6408
OPEN   Mon–Fri By Appointment.

Specialise in lining and restoration of oil paintings.

PROVIDE Home Inspections. Free Estimates. Free Collection/Delivery Service.
SPEAK TO Kenny McKenzie. Member of SSCR. This workshop is in the Scottish Conservation Directory.
SEE Picture Frames.

JOHN MELROSE
74 Manse Road, Motherwell, **Strathclyde ML1 2PT**
TEL   0698 64249
OPEN   By Appointment.

Specialise in restoring easel paintings.

PROVIDE Home Inspections. Free/Chargeable Estimates. Chargeable Collection/Delivery Service.
SPEAK TO John Melrose.

Associate Member of ABPR and the IIC. This workshop is included on the register of conservators maintained by the Conservation Unit of the Museums and Galleries Commission.
This workshop is in the Scottish Conservation Directory.

WESTPORT GALLERY
3 Old Hawkhill, Dundee, **Tayside DD1 5EU**
TEL   0382 21751
OPEN   9–5 Mon–Fri.

Specialise in cleaning oil paintings and framing.

PROVIDE Free Estimates. Chargeable Collection/Delivery Service.
SPEAK TO Neil Livingstone.
SEE Arms, Furniture, Picture Frames, Silver

CARL UTTERIDGE
Capel Bethel, Dinas Mawddwy, Machynlleth, **Powys SY20 9JA**
TEL   0650 531432
OPEN   9–6 Mon–Sat.

Specialise in restoring oil paintings on canvas, board and panels, prints and watercolours.

PROVIDE Home Inspections. Free Estimates. Free Local Collection/Delivery Service.
SPEAK TO Carl Utteridge or Jennifer A'Brook.
Member of UKIC. This workshop is included on the register of conservators maintained by the Conservation Unit of the Museums and Galleries Commission.
SEE Books.

MANOR HOUSE FINE ARTS

73 Pontcanna Street, Cardiff, **South Glamorgan CF1 9HS**
TEL   0222 227787
OPEN   10.30–5.30 Tues, Thur, Fri, Sat or By Appointment.

Specialise in restoring and conserving oil paintings, watercolours and prints.

PROVIDE Home Inspections. Free Estimates at the gallery. Chargeable Collection/Delivery Service.
SPEAK TO Steven Denley–Hill.
SEE Picture Frames

PICTURE FRAMES

ADAM GALLERY
13 John Street, Bath, **Avon BA1 2JL**
TEL   0225 480406
OPEN   9.30–5.30 Mon–Sat.

Specialise in framing of oil paintings, watercolours and drawings.

PROVIDE Home Inspections. Free Estimates. Collection/Delivery Service by arrangement.
SPEAK TO Paul or Philip Dye.
SEE Oil Paintings.

ANTHONY REED
94–96 Walcot Street, Bath, **Avon BA1 5BG**
TEL   0225 461969 or 0272 333595
OPEN   9–6 Mon–Sat.

Specialise in restoring picture frames, including gilding.

PROVIDE Home Inspections. Chargeable Estimates. Chargeable Local Collection/Delivery Service.
SPEAK TO Anthony Reed.
Member of the IIC.
SEE Furniture, Oil Paintings.

SUSAN CLOWES LAMBERT
E. Becker Ltd, Unit 4, Cherrycourt Way, Stanbridge Road, Leighton Buzzard, **Bedfordshire LU7 6UH**
TEL   0525 853033
FAX   0525 853032
OPEN   9–5 Mon–Fri By Appointment.

Specialise in conservation mounting and framing.

PROVIDE Home Inspections. Free Estimates. Chargeable Collection/Delivery Service.
SPEAK TO Susan Clowes Lambert and David Lambert.
Member of IPC and UKIC.
SEE Oil Paintings.

HERON PICTURES
High Street, Whitchurch–on–Thames, Reading, **Berkshire RG8 7EX**
TEL   0734 843286
OPEN   10–7 Tues–Sat.

Specialise in cleaning and restoring frames as well as gilding.

PROVIDE Home Inspections. Free Estimates. Free Local Collection/Delivery Service.
SPEAK TO George Duckett.
SEE Oil Paintings.

LEADON FINE ARTS
134 Silverdale Road, Earley, Reading, **Berkshire RG6 2LX**
TEL   0734 264999
OPEN   By Appointment.

Specialise in renovating frames.

PROVIDE Home Inspections. Free Estimates. Collection/Delivery Service.
SPEAK TO D. J. Dodds.
SEE Oil Paintings.

JOCK HOPSON CONSERVATION SERVICE
Holes Lane, Olney, **Buckinghamshire MK46 4BX**
TEL   0234 712306
FAX   0234 241634
OPEN   By Appointment.

Specialise in gilding and carving picture frames.

PROVIDE Home Inspections. Free/Chargeable Estimates. Chargeable Collection/Delivery Service.
SPEAK TO Jock Hopson.
Member of UKIC. This workshop is included on the register of conservators maintained by the Conservation Unit of the Museums and Galleries Commission.
SEE Furniture, Arms.

ELIZABETH WINTGENS GALLERY
96 High Street, Marlow, **Buckinghamshire SL7 1AQ**
TEL   0628 482759
FAX   0628 898186
OPEN   9.30–5.30 Mon–Sat.

Specialise in complete care and conservation service for old frames.

PROVIDE Home Inspections. Free Estimates. Free Local Collection/Delivery Service.
SPEAK TO Michael Wintgens.
Member of IIC and Fine Art Trade Guild.
SEE Oil Paintings.

WENDY A. CRAIG
Cambridge Conservation Studio, Balsham Road, Linton, Cambridge, **Cambridgeshire CB2 6LE**
TEL   0223 881295
FAX   0223 894056
OPEN   9–6 Mon–Sat.

Specialise in conservation mounting.

PROVIDE Home Inspections. Free Estimates. Free/Chargeable Collection/Delivery Service.
SPEAK TO Wendy Ann Craig.
This workshop is included on the register of conservators maintained by the Conservation Unit of the Museums and Galleries Commission.
SEE Oil Paintings.

JULIE CRICK
Studio 5, Hope Street Yard, Cambridge, **Cambridgeshire CB1 3NA**
TEL   0223 410586
OPEN   By Appointment.

Specialise in restoring picture frames.

PROVIDE Home Inspections. Free Estimates. Free/Chargeable Collection/Delivery Service.
SPEAK TO Julie Crick.
Member of UKIC, Associate Member of ABPR, Diploma in Conservation. This workshop is included on the register of conservators maintained by the Conservation Unit of the Museums and Galleries Commission.
SEE Oil Paintings.

FRANK GOODINGHAM
Studio 3, Hope Street Yard, Hope Street, Cambridge, **Cambridgeshire**
CB1 3NA
TEL   0223 410702
OPEN   10–6 Mon–Fri.

Specialise in restoring 18th and 19th century gilded work, including composition or carved frames.

PROVIDE Home Inspections. Refundable Estimates. Collection/Delivery by arrangement.
SPEAK TO Frank Goodingham.
SEE Furniture.

A. ALLEN ANTIQUE RESTORERS
Buxton Rd, Newtown, Newmills, Via Stockport, **Cheshire SK12 3JS**
TEL   0663 745274
OPEN   8–5 Mon–Fri; 9–12 Sat.

Specialise in restoring picture frames and gilding.

PROVIDE Home Inspections. Free/Chargeable Estimates. Free Collection/Delivery Service.
SPEAK TO Tony Allen.
SEE Clocks, Furniture, Silver.

DEBBIE COLEMAN
Watchtower Studio, Church End, East Looe, **Cornwall PL13 1BX**
TEL   0503 263232 or 263344
OPEN   10.30–5 Mon–Sat or By Appointment.

Specialise in restoring gilt frames.

PROVIDE Home Inspections. Free Estimates. Collection/Delivery Service.
SPEAK TO Debbie Coleman. Associate Member of ABPR. This workshop is included on the register of conservators maintained by the Conservation Unit of the Museums and Galleries Commission.
SEE Oil Paintings.

ACORN STUDIO
Ghylwood House, Gosforth, **Cumbria**
CA20 1AH
TEL   09467 25516
OPEN   By Appointment.

Specialise in conservation framing, especially of needlework.

PROVIDE Home Inspections. Free Estimates.
SPEAK TO Rodney Mostyn.
Member of the Fine Art Trade Guild and IPC.

GALERIE LAFRANCE
647 Wimborne Road, Winton, Bournemouth, **Dorset BH9 2AR**
TEL   0202 522313
OPEN   8.30–1, 2–5.30 Mon–Fri; 9–1 Sat.

Specialise in cleaning and restoring picture frames. Gesso and composition replaced, gilding as necessary.

PROVIDE Home Inspections. Free Estimates. Free/Chargeable Collection/Delivery Service.
SPEAK TO Pierre Lafrance.
SEE Oil Paintings.

MRS CATHERINE MATHEW
Kiwi Cottage, Maperton Road, Charlton Horethorne, Sherborne, **Dorset**
DT9 4NT
TEL   0963 220595
OPEN   9–6 Mon–Fri or By Appointment.

Specialise in cleaning picture frames to leave the original gold, regilding where new moulding has been applied or where necessary.

PROVIDE Home Inspections. Free Estimates. Free Collection/Delivery Service.
SPEAK TO Catherine Mathew.
SEE Furniture.

CLAIRE TIMINGS GILDING

Unit 4, Westhill Barns, Evershot, Dorchester, **Dorset DT2 0LD**
TEL   0975 83267
FAX   0935 83574
OPEN   9.30–4 By Appointment.

Specialise in restoring gilded picture frames.

PROVIDE Home Inspections. Free/Chargeable Estimates. Chargeable Collection/Delivery Service.
SPEAK TO Claire or Simon Timings. Member of UKIC and SSCR. This workshop is included on the register of conservators maintained by the Conservation Unit of the Museums and Galleries Commission.
SEE Furniture.

ALLYSON McDERMOTT (INTERNATIONAL CONSERVATION CONSULTANTS)

Lintz Green Conservation Centre, Lintz Green House, Lintz Green, Rowlands Gill, **Durham NE39 1NL**
TEL   0207 71547 or 0831 104145 or 0831 257584
FAX   0207 71547
OPEN   9–5.30 Mon–Fri.

Specialise in conservation mounting and framing to museum standards, including gilding.

PROVIDE Home Inspections. Free Estimates. Chargeable Collection/Delivery Service.
SPEAK TO Allyson Mc Dermott or Gillian Lee. They have a Southern Regional Office at 45 London Road, Cheltenham, **Gloucestershire**.
SEE Art Researchers, Carpets, Lighting, Oil Paintings, Specialist Photographers.

TERRY HILLIARD

The Barn, Master Johns, Thoby Lane, Mountnessing, Brentwood, **Essex CM15 0JY**
TEL   0277 354717
OPEN   By Appointment.

Specialise in restoring gilded picture frames and carving and gilding, including making reproduction frames.

PROVIDE Home Inspections. Free Estimates. Free Collection/Delivery Service.
SPEAK TO Terry Hilliard. Member of the Guild of Master Craftsmen.
SEE Furniture.

RICHARD ILES GALLERY

10 Northgate Street, Colchester **Essex CO1 1HA**
TEL   0206 577877
OPEN   9.30–4.30 Mon–Sat.

Specialise in picture framing.

PROVIDE Free Estimates.
SPEAK TO Richard Iles.
SEE Oil Paintings.

MILLSIDE ANTIQUE RESTORATION

Parndon Mill, Parndon Mill Lane, Harlow, **Essex CM20 2HP**
TEL   0279 428148
FAX   0279 415075
OPEN   10–5 Mon–Fri.

Specialise in restoring picture frames.

PROVIDE Home Inspections. Free/Chargeable Estimates. Chargeable Collection/Delivery Service.
SPEAK TO David Sparks or Angela Wickliffe-Philp.
SEE Oil Paintings, Porcelain, Silver.

PEARLITA FRAMES LTD

30 North Street, Romford, **Essex RM11 2LB**
TEL   0708 760342
OPEN   9–5.30 Mon–Sat.

Specialise in picture framing.

PROVIDE Home Inspections. Free
Estimates. Free Collection/Delivery
Service.
SPEAK TO Trevor Woodward.
SEE Oil Paintings

ASTLEY HOUSE FINE ART

Astley House, High Street, Moreton–in–
Marsh, **Gloucestershire GL56 0LL**
TEL   0608 50601
FAX   0608 51777
OPEN 9–5.30 Mon–Sat; closed Wed.

Specialise in framing.

PROVIDE Free Estimates. Chargeable
Collection/Delivery Service.
SPEAK TO David or Nanette Glaisyer.
SEE Oil Paintings.

CLEEVE PICTURE FRAMING

Coach House Workshops, Stoke Road,
Bishops Cleeve, Cheltenham,
Gloucestershire GL52 4RP
TEL   0242 672785
FAX   0242 676827
OPEN 9–1, 2–5.30 Mon–Fri; 9–1 Sat.

Specialise in restoring and conserving
picture frames as well as bespoke framing
and decorative mounts.

PROVIDE Home Inspections. Free
Estimates. Free Collection/Delivery
Service.
SPEAK TO James Gardner.
SEE Oil Paintings.

CRISPIN ART SERVICES

68 Crispin Road, Winchcombe,
Cheltenham, **Gloucestershire
GL54 5JX**
TEL   0242 602947
FAX   0242 603723
OPEN 9–5 Mon–Sat or By
       Appointment.

Specialise in restoring gilt frames,
repairing and refinishing. Missing
decoration can be cast and replaced. They
also carry out bronze powder and gold
gilding, gesso and polychrome work. All
types of decorated and washline mounts
for watercolours supplied.

PROVIDE Home Inspections. Free
Estimates. Chargeable
Collection/Delivery Service.
SPEAK TO Mr R. E. Holness.

A. J. PONSFORD ANTIQUES

51–53 Dollar Street, Cirencester,
Gloucestershire GL7 2AS
TEL   0285 652355
OPEN 8.30–5.30 Mon–Fri.

Specialise in restoring picture frames.

PROVIDE Home Inspections. Free
Estimates. Free Collection/Delivery
Service.
SPEAK TO A. J. Ponsford.
SEE Furniture, Oil Paintings.

GRAINNE WHITTLEY CONSERVATION AND RESTORATION OF WORKS OF ART ON PAPER

2 Durban Villas, Bath Road, Nailsworth,
Gloucestershire GL6 0HJ
TEL   0453 833687
OPEN 9–6 Mon–Sat.

Specialise in conservation mounting and
framing.

PROVIDE Home Inspections. Free
Estimates. Free Collection/Delivery
Service.
SPEAK TO Grainne Whittley (Miss).
Member of UKIC and IPC. BA (Hons)
in Conservation from Camberwell
College of Arts and Crafts.
SEE Oil Paintings, Books.

CORFIELD RESTORATIONS LTD

120 High Street, Lymington,
Hampshire SO41 9AQ
TEL 0590 673532
OPEN 9.15–5.30 Mon–Sat.

Specialise in picture mounting and framing.

PROVIDE Home Inspections. Free Estimates. Local Free Collection/Delivery Service.
SPEAK TO Alan Bloomfield or Michael Corfield.
Also at Setters Farm, Lymington. 0590 671977.
SEE Furniture, Oil Paintings.

EDWIN COLLINS

Coltsfoot Gallery, Hatfield, Leominster,
Hereford & Worcester
HR6 0SF (Please use Herefordshire if writing).
TEL 056 882 277
OPEN By Appointment.

Specialise in a mounting and framing service.

PROVIDE Free Estimates.
SPEAK TO Edwin Collins.
Member of IPC.
SEE Oil Paintings.

T. M. HUGUENIN

20 Albany Terrace, Worcester,
Hereford & Worcester WR1 3DU
TEL 0905 28133
OPEN Mon–Sat By Appointment.

Specialise in conservation mounting and framing of works of art on paper, prints, drawings, watercolours.

PROVIDE Home Inspections. Free Estimates. Chargeable Collection/Delivery Service.
SPEAK TO T. M. Huguenin.
Member of UKIC and IPC. This workshop is included on the register of conservators maintained by the Conservation Unit of the Museums and Galleries Commission.
SEE Oil Paintings.

JENNINGS & JENNINGS

30 Bridge Street, Leominster,
Hereford & Worcester HR6 9JQ
TEL 0568 512946
OPEN 10–5.30 Mon–Sat.

Specialise in conserving and restoring gilded picture frames.

PROVIDE Home Inspections. Free Estimates. Free/Chargeable Collection/Delivery Service.
SPEAK TO Sabina Jennings.
SEE Furniture.

EUGENE B. OKARMA

Brobury House Gallery, Brobury,
Hereford & Worcester HR3 6BS
TEL 09817 229
OPEN 9–4 Mon–Sat.

Specialise in restoring frames.

PROVIDE Local Home Inspections.
SPEAK TO Mr Okarma.
SEE Oil Paintings.

HERTFORDSHIRE CONSERVATION SERVICE

Seed Warehouse, Maidenhead Yard, The Wash, Hertford, **Hertfordshire SG14 1PX**
TEL 0992 588966 or 0992 504662
    ANS 0992 588966
FAX 0992 503184
OPEN 9–6 Mon–Fri By Appointment.

Specialise in repair, restoration or replacement of picture frames.

PROVIDE Home Inspections. Free/Chargeable Estimates. Chargeable Collection/Delivery Service.
SPEAK TO J. M. Macqueen.
This workshop is included on the register of conservators maintained by the

Conservation Unit of the Museums and Galleries Commission.
SEE Collectors (Dolls), Furniture, Lighting, Porcelain, Oil Paintings, Carpets.

CHARLOTTE HOOKER
Jasmine Cottage, Front Street, Laxton, Nr. Goole, **North Humberside DN14 7TS**
TEL   0430 430681
OPEN   8.30–5.30 Mon–Fri.

Specialise in a full restoration service for picture frames.

PROVIDE Home Inspections. Free/Chargeable Estimates.
SPEAK TO Charlotte Hooker. Member of UKIC.
SEE Oil Paintings.

CASTLE FINE ART STUDIO
26 Castle Street, Dover, **Kent CT16 1PW**
TEL   0304 206360
OPEN   10–1, 2–5.30 Mon–Fri; 10–1 Sat.

Specialise in a conservation quality framing service for trade, museum and private clients.

PROVIDE Home Inspections. Free Estimates. Free Local Collection/Delivery Service.
SPEAK TO Ms Deborah Colam. Member of IPC. This workshop is included on the register of conservators maintained by the Conservation Unit of the Museums and Galleries Commission.
SEE Books, Oil Paintings.

CLARE GALLERY
21 High Street, Royal Tunbridge Wells, **Kent TN1 1UT**
TEL   0892 538717
FAX   0323 729588
OPEN   9–5.30 Mon–Sat

Specialise in a framing service.

PROVIDE Home Inspections. Free Estimates. Chargeable Collection/Delivery Service.
SPEAK TO M. Ettinger.
SEE Oil Paintings.

ROGER GREEN FINE ART
Hales Place Studio, High Halden, Nr. Ashford, **Kent TN26 3JQ**
TEL   0233 850716
FAX   0233 850219
OPEN   9–5 Mon–Sat.

Specialise in conservation quality mounting and framing plus hand-finishing of frames, including gilding.

PROVIDE Local Home Inspections. Free Estimates.
SPEAK TO Roger Green or Ellen Green.
SEE Oil Paintings.

FRANCIS ILES FINE PAINTINGS
Rutland House, 103 High Street, Rochester. **Kent ME1 1LX**
TEL   0634 843081
FAX   0474 822403
OPEN   9–5.30 Mon–Sat.

Specialise in a framing service for all mediums, including early samplers and needlepoint.

PROVIDE Home Inspections. Free Estimates. Free Collection/Delivery Service.
SPEAK TO Jeanette or Lucy Iles.
SEE Oil Paintings.

LIBRARY CONSERVATORS
'Draycott', Green Lane, Temple Ewell, **Kent CT16 3AR**
TEL   0304 823060 or 206360
OPEN   10–5.30 Mon–Sat.

Specialise in framing all works of art on paper.

PROVIDE Home Inspections.

Free/Chargeable Estimates.
Free/Chargeable Collection/Delivery
Service.
SPEAK TO Louise Drover or Deborah
Colam.
Memner of IPC. This workshop is
included on the register of conservators
maintained by the Conservation Unit of
the Museums and Galleries Commission.
SEE Oil Paintings, Books.

W. J. MORRILL
437 Folkestone Road, Dover, **Kent
CT17 9JX**
TEL   0304 201989
OPEN   8–5 Mon–Thur; 8.30–1 Fri.

Specialise in making both wood and
composition period frames.

PROVIDE Home Inspections. Free
Collection/Delivery Service.
SPEAK TO Mr Barnes.
SEE Oil Paintings.

BARBARA WILDMAN
9 Woodside Terrace, Nelson, **Lancashire
BB9 7TB**
TEL   0282 699679
OPEN   By Appointment.

Specialise in restoring gilt frames, gesso
work and gold leaf.

PROVIDE Home Inspections. Free
Estimates. Chargeable
Collection/Delivery Service.
SPEAK TO Barbara Wildman.
SEE Oil Paintings.

RICHARD ZAHLER
Lane House, Fowgill, Bentham,
Lancaster, **Lancashire LA2 7AH**
TEL   05242 61998
OPEN   9–6 Mon–Fri or By
Appointment.

Specialise in restoring frames, water and
oil gilding.
SPEAK TO Richard Zahler.
Member of UKIC and the Guild of

Master Craftsmen. This workshop is
included on the register maintained by
the Conservation Unit of the Museums
and Galleries Commission.
SEE Books, Oil Paintings, Furniture.

W. F. GADSBY LTD
22 Market Place, Leicester,
Leicestershire LE1 5GF
TEL   0533 622410
OPEN   9–5 Mon–Sat.

Specialise in framing oils, watercolours
etc.

PROVIDE Free Estimates. Free Local
Collection/Delivery Service.
SPEAK TO Mr K. Platt.

THE OLD HOUSE GALLERY
13–15 Market Place, Oakham,
Leicestershire LE15 6DT
TEL   0572 755538
OPEN   10–5 Mon–Fri; 10–4 Sat; closed
Thur p.m.

Specialise in a framing service and
restoration of old frames.

PROVIDE Home Inspections. Free Local
Collection/Delivery Service.
SPEAK TO Richard Clarke.
SEE Oil Paintings.

BURGHLEY FINE ART CONSERVATION LTD
Burghley House, Stamford,
Lincolnshire PE9 3JY
TEL   0780 62155
OPEN   By Appointment.

Specialise in conserving and restoring
picture frames and gilding.

PROVIDE Home Inspections. Free
Estimates. Chargeable
Collection/Delivery Service.
SPEAK TO Michael Cowell.
Any work undertaken is fully
documented.
SEE Furniture, Oil Paintings.

W. F. GADSBY LTD
277 High Street, Lincoln, **Lincolnshire
LN2 1SG**
TEL   0522 527487
OPEN   9–5 Mon–Sat.

Specialise in framing oils, watercolours etc.

PROVIDE Free Estimates. Free Local Collection/Delivery Service.
SPEAK TO Ms S. Gadsby.

HIRST CONSERVATION
Laughton Hall Farmhouse, Laughton, Sleaford, **Lincolnshire NG34 0HE**
TEL   05297 449
FAX   05297 518
OPEN   9–5 Mon–Fri.

Specialise in restoring picture frames and gilding.

PROVIDE Home Inspections.
Free/Chargeable Estimates. Chargeable Collection/Delivery Service.
SPEAK TO Elizabeth Hirst.
Member of UKIC, IIC, Stone Federation. This workshop is included on the register of conservators maintained by the Conservation Unit of the Museums and Galleries Commission.
SEE Oil Paintings, Porcelain.

MICHAEL PARFETT
Unit 407, Clerkenwell Workshops, 31 Clerkenwell Close, **London EC1R 0AT**
TEL   071 490 8768
OPEN   By Appointment.

Specialise in all aspects of restoration to picture frames.

PROVIDE Home Inspections. Free Estimates. Local Free Collection/Delivery Service.
SPEAK TO Michael Parfett.
Licenciate of the City and Guilds of London, Member of UKIC. This workshop is included on the register of conservators maintained by the

Conservation Unit of the Museums and Galleries Commission.
SEE Collectors (Musical Instruments), Furniture.

F. A. POLLAK LTD PICTURE FRAMES
3–4 Faulkener's Alley, Cowcross Street, **London EC1M 6DD**
TEL   071 490 4406
OPEN   7.30–1, 2–5 Mon–Fri.

Specialise in restoring frames, including gilding.

PROVIDE Home Inspections. Free Estimates.
SPEAK TO Mrs E. M. Pollak or Mr J. Roeder.

PRUDENCE SEWARD
30 Sekforde Street, **London EC1R 0HH**
TEL   071 251 8152
OPEN   By Appointment.

Specialise in mounting and framing works on paper.

PROVIDE Home Inspections. Free Estimates. Chargeable Collection/Delivery Service.
SPEAK TO Prudence Seward.
Member of UKIC. This workshop is included on the register of conservators maintained by the Conservation Unit of the Museums and Galleries Commission.
SEE Oil Paintings.

PETER CHAPMAN ANTIQUES
Incorporating CHAPMAN RESTORATIONS
10 Theberton Street, **London N1 0QX**
TEL   071 226 5565
FAX   081 348 4846
OPEN   9.30–6 Mon–Sat.

Specialise in repairing carved wood, gesso and composition frames.

PROVIDE Home Inspections. Refundable

Estimates. Chargeable
Collection/Delivery Service.
SPEAK TO Peter Chapman or Tony
Holohan.
SEE Furniture, Oil Paintings, Porcelain,
Silver.

JOHN JONES FRAMES LTD
4 Morris Place, off Stroud Green Road,
London N4 3JG
TEL   071 281 5439
FAX   071 281 5956
OPEN   8–6 Mon–Fri; 9–2 Sat; 12–4
       Sun.

Specialise in providing the most
comprehensive framing service in the
UK., including restoration. They design,
manufacture and finish their own
mouldings on the premises.

PROVIDE Free Estimates. Chargeable
Collection/Delivery Service.
SPEAK TO John Jones, John Dawson or
Nick Hawker.
SEE Oil Paintings, Specialist
Photographers.

ALEXANDER LEY AND SON
13 Brecknock Rd, **London N7 OBL**
TEL   071 267 3645
FAX   071 267 4462
OPEN   8–6 Mon–Fri.

Specialise in restoring antique frames.
Also reproduction carving and gilding.

PROVIDE Home Inspections. Free
Estimates. Free Collection/Delivery
Service.
SPEAK TO Alexander or Anthony Ley.
SEE Furniture.

SUDBURY–JONES
44–48 Birkbeck Road, **London
N12 8DZ**
TEL   081 446 3164
OPEN   9–6 Mon–Sat; 10–2 Sun.

Specialise in picture framing and also

produce many specialised hand finishes,
including gilding and staining.

PROVIDE Home Inspections. Free
Estimates. Collection/Delivery Service.
SPEAK TO Tom Jones or Chris Frost.
SEE Oil Paintings.

THE PAINTING CONSERVATION STUDIO
Address withheld by request.
TEL   071 281 9997
OPEN   10–5 By Appointment.

Specialise in restoring frames.

PROVIDE Home Inspections.
Free/Chargeable Estimates. Chargeable
Collection/Delivery Service.
SPEAK TO Anne Ablett.
This workshop is included on the register
of conservators maintained by the
Conservation Unit of the Museums and
Galleries Commission.
SEE Oil Paintings.

DEANSBROOK GALLERY
134 Myddleton Road, **London
N22 4NQ**
TEL   081 889 8389
OPEN   10–5 Tues–Sat.

Specialise in framing oil paintings and
prints.

PROVIDE Home Inspections. Free
Estimates. Chargeable
Collection/Delivery Service.
SPEAK TO Anthony Edmunds.
SEE Oil Paintings.

JOHN DENHAM GALLERY
50 Mill Lane, **London NW6 1NJ**
TEL   071 794 2635
OPEN   11–5 Sun, Tues, Wed, Thur, Fri.

Specialise in picture framing.

PROVIDE Home Inspections. Free
Estimates. Free Collection/Delivery
Service.

SPEAK TO John Denham.
SEE Oil Paintings.

SOPHIE LEVENE GILDING AND RESTORATION
63A Cheltenham Road, **London SE15 3AF**
TEL   071 639 5735
FAX   081 299 0923
OPEN   10–6 Mon–Fri.

Specialise in restoring all styles of gilded decoration to period frames. They also provide a range of services including repair and reproduction of composition mouldings, carving and paint finishes carried out on site or in their London studio.

PROVIDE Home Inspections. Free Estimates. Chargeable Collection/Delivery Service.
SPEAK TO Sophie Levene. Member of UKIC. This workshop is included on the register of conservators maintained by the Conservation Unit of the Museums and Galleries Commission.
SEE Furniture.

THE O'SHEA GALLERY
89 Lower Sloane Street, **London SW1W 8DA**
TEL   071 730 0081
FAX   071 730 1386
OPEN   9.30–6 Mon–Fri; 9.30–1 Sat.

Specialise in framing 15th–19th century maps and prints.

PROVIDE Home Inspections. Free/Chargeable Estimates. Collection/Delivery Service.
SPEAK TO Raymond O'Shea.

ARNOLD WIGGINS AND SONS LTD
4 Bury Street, **London SW1Y 6AB**
TEL   071 925 0195
FAX   071 839 6928
OPEN   9.30–5.30 Mon–Fri.

Specialise in conserving and restoring period picture frames. Also picture frame makers.

PROVIDE Home Inspections. Free Estimates. Chargeable Collection/Delivery Service.
SPEAK TO Michael Gregory. Members of BADA, the Master Woodcarvers Association and the Society of Gilders.
SEE Furniture.

JOHN CAMPBELL PICTURE FRAMES LTD
164 Walton Street, **London SW3 2JL**
TEL   071 584 9268
FAX   071 581 3499
OPEN   9.30–5.30 Mon–Fri; 10–5 Sat.

Specialise in restoring period and contemporary picture frames.

PROVIDE Home Inspections. Free Estimates. Free Collection/Delivery Service.
SPEAK TO Roy Hogben. Member of the Guild of Master Craftsmen.
SEE Oil Paintings.

P. DOWLING
Chenil Galleries, 181–183 Kings Road, **London SW3 5EB**
TEL   071 376 5056
FAX   071 493 9344
OPEN   10–6 Mon–Sat.

Specialise in framing and mounting antique pictures.

PROVIDE Free Estimates.
SPEAK TO P. Dowling.
SEE Oil Paintings.

M. P. GERVAL & ASSOCIATES
28 Cheyne Walk, **London SW3 5HH**
TEL   071 351 2840
FAX   071 351 5374
OPEN   9.30–6 By Appointment.

Specialise in restoring carved,

composition and other types of frames, gilt or otherwise finished.

PROVIDE Home Inspections. Free Estimates. Free Local Collection/Delivery Service. SPEAK TO Marie–Pierre Gerval. Member of UKIC. This workshop is included on the register of conservators maintained by the Conservation Unit of the Museums and Galleries Commission. SEE Furniture.

GREEN AND STONE
259 Kings Road, **London SW3 5EL**
TEL   071 352 6521
FAX   071 351 1098
OPEN   9–5.30 Mon–Fri; 9.30–6 Sat.

Specialise in restoring antique frames, including gilding and veneer work. They also offer a picture framing service.

PROVIDE Local Home Inspections. Free Estimates. Free Local Collection/Delivery Service. SPEAK TO Mrs Hiscott or Miss Moore. SEE Oil Paintings, Lighting.

MALCOLM INNES GALLERY
172 Walton Street, **London SW3 2JL**
TEL   071 584 0575
OPEN   9.30–6 Mon–Fri; 10–1 Sat.

Specialise in framing oil paintings.

PROVIDE Free Estimates. Chargeable Collection/Delivery Service. SPEAK TO Malcolm Innes or Emma Shelton–Agar. SEE **Lothian.** SEE Oil Paintings.

SARAH SPICER
122 Marlborough, 61 Walton Street, **London SW3 2JZ**
TEL   071 581 3577
FAX   0359 30393
OPEN   9 6 Wed or By Appointment.

Specialise in conservation mounting and framing.

PROVIDE Home Inspections. Free Estimates. Free/Chargeable Collection/Delivery Service. SPEAK TO Sarah Spicer. Member of IPC.

COOPER FINE ARTS LTD
768 Fulham Road, **London SW6 5SJ**
TEL   071 731 3421
OPEN   10–7 Mon–Fri; 10–4 Sat.

Specialise in framing oil paintings and watercolours.

PROVIDE Free Estimates. SPEAK TO Jonathan Hill-Reid. SEE Oil Paintings.

PIERS FEETHAM GALLERY
475 Fulham Road, **London SW6 1HL**
TEL   071 381 5958
OPEN   10–1, 2–6 Mon–Fri; 2–6 Sat.

Specialise in framing works on paper to conservation standard and general framing.

PROVIDE Home Inspections. Free Estimates. SPEAK TO Piers Feetham.

ROY FRANDSEN
7 Lillie Yard, **London SW6 1HB**
TEL   071 385 9930
OPEN   8–5 Mon–Fri.

Specialise in restoring antique picture frames and manufacturing period and modern frames.

PROVIDE Home Inspections. Free Local Estimates. Free Local Collection/Delivery Service. SPEAK TO Derek Tanous or Jimmy Greenland.

GILT EDGE
275 Wandsworth Bridge Road, **London SW6 2TX**
TEL   071 731 7703
OPEN   10–6 Tues–Fri; 10–4 Sat.

Specialise in picture framing.

PROVIDE Free Estimates.
SPEAK TO Richard Pitt.
Member of the Guild of Master
Craftsmen.

PETER L. JAMES
681 Fulham Road, **London SW6 5PZ**
TEL   071 736 0183
OPEN   7.30–5.30 Mon–Fri.

Specialise in restoring lacquer, painted
and gilded frames.

PROVIDE Home Inspections. Refundable
Estimates. Chargeable
Collection/Delivery Service.
SPEAK TO Peter L. James.
SEE Furniture.

MICHAEL MARRIOTT
LTD
588 Fulham Road, **London SW6 5NT**
TEL   071 736 3110
FAX   071 731 2632
OPEN   9.30–5.30 Mon–Fri.

Specialise in mounting and framing of
prints.

PROVIDE Home Inspections. Free
Estimates. Collection/Delivery Service.
SPEAK TO Jean Marriott.
SEE Furniture.

JOHN TANOUS LTD
115 Harwood Road, **London SW6
4QL**
TEL   071 736 7999
FAX   071 371 5237
OPEN   9–1, 2–5 Mon–Fri.

Specialise in making and restoring
picture frames and gilding.

PROVIDE Free Estimates.
SPEAK TO Peter Copcutt.
Established 1913.

20th CENTURY GALLERY
821 Fulham Road, **London SW6 5HG**
TEL   071 731 5888
OPEN   10–6 Mon–Fri; 10–1 Sat.

Specialise in bespoke framing.

PROVIDE Free Estimates.
SPEAK TO Erika Brandl.
SEE Oil Paintings.

CAMILLA REDFERN
32 Abbey Business Centre, Ingate Place,
London SW8 3NS
TEL   071 627 0935
FAX   071 498 0144
OPEN   8.30–6 Mon–Fri or By
            Appointment.

Specialise in restoring all antiques of a
gilded parcel, including picture frames.

PROVIDE Home Inspections. Free
Estimates. Chargeable
Collection/Delivery Service.
SPEAK TO Camilla Redfern.
Member of UKIC and IIC. This
workshop is included on the register of
conservators maintained by the
Conservation Unit of the Museums and
Galleries Commission.
SEE Furniture.

CALLANAN LTD
Unit 7, Parkfields Industrial Estate,
Culvert Place, Culvert Road, **London
SW11 5BA**
TEL   071 828 7577
OPEN   9–6.30 Mon–Fri.

Specialise in restoring picture frames.
They have a large stock of period frames
of all types: washline, eglomisé, sanded
mounts. They will also copy period
frames.

PROVIDE Home Inspections. Free
Estimates. Chargeable
Collection/Delivery Service.
SPEAK TO David Callanan.
SEE Furniture.

HELEN DE BORCHGRAVE

Fine Art Restorer, 103 Albert Bridge Road, **London SW11 4PF**
TEL   071 738 1951
OPEN   By Appointment.

Specialise in restoring picture frames.

PROVIDE Home Inspections. Free Local Estimates. Collection/Delivery Service.
SPEAK TO Helen de Borchgrave.
Member of UKIC, IIC and ABPR. This workshop is included on the register of conservators maintained by the Conservation Unit of the Museums and Galleries Commission.
SEE Oil Paintings.

TREVOR CUMINE

133 Putney Bridge Road, **London SW15 2PA**
TEL   081 870 1525
OPEN   By Appointment.

Specialise in antique frames and making gilt frames for 20th century pictures.
SPEAK TO Trevor Cumine.
SEE Oil Paintings.

SERENA CHAPLIN

32 Elsynge Road, **London SW18 2HN**
TEL   081 870 9455
FAX   081 877 0943
OPEN   By Appointment.

Specialise in restoring gilded picture frames.

PROVIDE Free Estimates within the London area.
SPEAK TO Serena Chaplin.
Ms Chaplin also runs five day introductory courses in gilding and lacquer.
SEE Furniture.

DIANA WASHINGTON

17 Cicada Road, **London SW18 2NN**
TEL   081 874 6223
OPEN   9–5 Mon–Fri By Appointment Only.

Specialise in conservation mounting and framing.

PROVIDE Home Inspections. Free Estimates. Collection/Delivery Service.
SPEAK TO Diana Washington.
Member of IPC, UKIC, IIC and AIC.
This workshop is included on the register of conservators maintained by the Conservation Unit of the Museums and Galleries Commission.
SEE Oil Paintings, Books.

COURT PICTURE FRAMERS

8 Bourdon Street, **London W1Y 9AD**
TEL   071 493 3265
OPEN   9.30–5 Mon–Fri.

Specialise in carrying out all kinds of framing, including hand-gilded, limed, stained and painted mouldings, and conservation mounting and mount decoration.

PROVIDE Free Estimates. Free Collection/Delivery Service (for orders over £100 in London area).
SPEAK TO Andrew Butwright.
Member of the Fine Art Trade Guild.

RICCARDO GIACCHERINI FINE FRAMES

39 Newman Street, **London W1P 3PG**
TEL   071 580 1783
FAX   071 637 5221
OPEN   9.30–6 Mon–Fri or By Appointment.

Specialise in providing fine quality carved and gilded antique frames (not composition).

PROVIDE Local Home Inspections. Free Estimates. Chargeable Collection/Delivery Service.
SPEAK TO Louise Liddell or Riccardo Giaccherini.

TONY GUEST FRAMING

10 Ogle Street, **London W1P 7LQ**
TEL   071 580 8786
OPEN   8–5 Mon–Fri.

Specialise in restoring antique picture frames and are frame makers.

PROVIDE Home Inspections. Free Estimates. Collection/Delivery Service by arrangement.
SPEAK TO Tony Guest or David Duncan.
SEE Furniture.

PAUL MITCHELL LTD
99 New Bond Street, **London W1Y 9LF**
TEL   071 493 8732
FAX   071 409 7136
OPEN   9.30–5.30 Mon–Fri.

Specialise in antique picture frames, supplying hand-carved replica frames and the conservation and restoration of antique picture frames.

PROVIDE Home Inspections. Free Estimates. Chargeable Collection/Delivery Service. Member of BADA, the Guild of Master Craftsmen, and the IIC. Associate Member of ABPR.
SPEAK TO Paul Mitchell.
SEE Oil Paintings.

STEPHEN WELLS
1A Silver Place, **London W1R 3LL**
TEL   071 734 4660
OPEN   8.30–5.30 Mon–Fri.

Specialise in restoring picture frames.

PROVIDE Home Inspections. Free Estimates. Chargeable Collection/Delivery Service.
SPEAK TO Stephen Wells. Member of the Guild of Master Craftsmen and Conservation Mount Makers. This workshop is included on the register of conservators maintained by the Conservation Unit of the Museums and Galleries Commission.

BOURLET
32 Connaught Street, **London W2 2AY**
TEL   071 724 4837
OPEN   11–5.30 Mon–Fri; By Appointment Sat.

Specialise in restoring picture frames.

PROVIDE Home Inspections. Free Estimates. Collection/Delivery Service.
SPEAK TO Gabrielle Rendell.
SEE Oil Paintings, Furniture.

C. J. G. GILDERS & CARVERS
Unit 10, Sandringham Mews, **London W5 5DF**
TEL   081 579 2341
OPEN   10–5 Mon–Sat.

Specialise in restoring antique picture frames.

PROVIDE Home Inspections. Free Estimates. Free Local Collection/Delivery Service.
SPEAK TO Chris Gostomski.
SEE Furniture.

DR POPPY COOKSEY
Aston House, 8 Lower Mall, **London W6 9DJ**
TEL   081 846 9279
OPEN   By Appointment.

Specialise in picture frame repairs.

PROVIDE Home Inspections. Free Estimates in London. Chargeable Collection/Delivery Service.
SPEAK TO Dr Poppy Cooksey.
SEE Oil Paintings.

PORCELAIN AND PICTURES LTD
The Studio, 1B Gastein Road, **London W6 8LT**
TEL   071 385 7512
OPEN   9–5.30 Mon–Sat.

Specialise in framing pictures of any medium to full conservation standard, lining, colour washing plus a wide selection of moulding from antique to modern.

PROVIDE Home Inspections. Free Estimates. Free Local Collection/Delivery Service.

SPEAK TO David or Edward Toms.
Member of the Fine Art Trade Guild.
SEE Porcelain.

THE ROWLEY GALLERY LTD
115 Kensington Church Street, **London W8 7LN**
TEL   071 727 6495
OPEN   9–5 Mon–Fri; 9–7 Thur.

Specialise in restoring antique picture frames, bespoke framing, gilding and veneering.

PROVIDE Home Inspections. Free Estimates. Free Collection/Delivery
SPEAK TO A. J. Savill.
This firm was founded in 1898.

DAGGETT GALLERY
1st Floor, 153 Portobello Road, **London W11 2DY**
TEL   071 229 2248
FAX   071 584 2950
OPEN   10–4 Mon–Fri; 9–4 Sat; By Appointment.

Specialise in restoring frames, gilding and cutting down.

PROVIDE Home Inspections.
Free/Chargeable Estimates. Chargeable Collection/Delivery Service.
SPEAK TO Charles or Caroline Daggett.
Member of LAPADA.
SEE Oil Paintings.

THE CORK STREET FRAMING COMPANY LTD
8 Bramber Road, **London W14 9PB**
TEL   071 381 9211
FAX   071 381 9034
OPEN   10–6 Mon–Fri; By Appointment Sat.

Specialise in supplying hand–finished frames, including gilding, metal leaf and decorative paint effects and restoration of frames.

PROVIDE Home Inspections. Free

Estimates. Free Collection/Delivery Service.
SPEAK TO Gabrielle Coles.

COUTTS GALLERIES
75 Blythe Road, **London W14 OHD**
TEL   071 602 3980
OPEN   10–5 Mon–Fri; By Appointment Sat.

Specialise in restoration of antique frames.

PROVIDE Home Inspections, Free Estimates, Free Collection/Delivery Service.
SPEAK TO Seabury Burdett-Coutts.
SEE Furniture, Oil Paintings.

FELLOWES AND SAUNDERSON
116 Blythe Road, **London W14 0UH**
TEL   071 603 7475
OPEN   9.30–5.30 Tues–Fri; 10–4 Sat.

Specialise in restoration of antique frames and all aspects of framing and conservation mounting. They have their own range of gilded and hand–finished frames.

PROVIDE Home Inspections. Free Estimates. Free Collection/Delivery Service.
SPEAK TO Joan Saunderson.
SEE Furniture.

PHOEBE MASON
17 Russell Road, **London W14 8HU**
TEL   071 602 5694
OPEN   By Appointment Only.

Specialise in restoring picture frames, including gilding, ornamentation and plasterwork.

PROVIDE Home Inspections.
Free/Chargeable Estimates.
Free/Chargeable Collection/Delivery Service.
SPEAK TO Phoebe Mason.
SEE Furniture, Silver.

PAUL FERGUSON
Unit 20, 21 Wren Street, **London**
WC1X OHF
TEL   071 278 8759
FAX   071 278 8759
OPEN   9–5.30 Mon–Fri.

Specialise in restoring carved and gilded picture frames.

PROVIDE Home Inspections by arrangement. Free Estimates. Collection/Delivery Service by arrangement.
SPEAK TO Paul Ferguson.
SEE Furniture.

LYVER & BOYDELL GALLERIES
15 Castle Street, Liverpool, **Merseyside**
L2 4SX
TEL   051 236 3256
OPEN   10.30–5.30 Mon–Fri; By
        Appointment Sat.

Specialise in framing watercolours and prints.

PROVIDE Home Inspections. Free Estimates.
SPEAK TO Paul or Gill Breen.
SEE Books, Oil Paintings.

WELLINGTON CRAFTS (1980)
123 St John's Road, Waterloo, Liverpool, **Merseyside L22 9QE**
TEL   051 920 5511
OPEN   9.30–5 Mon–Sat.

Specialise in a full picture–framing service.

PROVIDE Home Inspections. Refundable Estimates. Chargeable Collection/Delivery Service.
SPEAK TO Neville Hymus.
SEE Furniture.

MICHAEL AND ROSEMARY COOK AND EMMA COOK
7 Harwood Drive, Hillingdon, **Middlesex UB10 0BG**
TEL   0895 255515
OPEN   9–6.30 Mon–Fri; Sat a.m.

Specialise in mounting and framing, gilding and compo (gesso).

PROVIDE Home Inspections. Free Estimates. Free/Chargeable Collection/Delivery Service.
SPEAK TO Michael or Rosemary Cook.
Member of UKIC, IPC and ABA.
Associate Member of ABPR.
SEE Oil Paintings.

MARIA J. LESIAK
Leliwa, 71 St Anne's Avenue, Stanwell, Staines, **Middlesex TW19 7RL**
TEL   0784 257401
FAX   0784 257401
OPEN   By Appointment.

Specialise in restoring antique gilt picture frames.

PROVIDE Home Inspections. Free Estimates. Free Local Collection/Delivery Service.
SPEAK TO Maria J. Lesiak.
Ms Lesiak is a Full Member of UKIC and an Associate Member of ABPR. This workshop is included on the register of conservators maintained by the Conservation Unit of the Museums and Galleries Commission.
SEE Oil Paintings, Furniture.

JOHN MALCOLM FINE ART RESTORATION
62 Linden Avenue, Ruislip, **Middlesex HA4 8UA**
TEL   0895 621616
OPEN   8.30–5 Mon–Fri or By
        Appointment.

Specialise in framing oil paintings and works of art on paper.

PROVIDE Home Inspections. Free Estimates. Free Collection/Delivery Service.
SPEAK TO John Malcolm.
SEE Oil Paintings.

COLMORE GALLERIES
52 High Street, Henley–in–Arden, Solihull, **West Midlands B95 5AN**
TEL   0564 792938
OPEN   11–5.30 Mon–Fri; 11–4.30 Sat.

Specialise in picture framing, gilding.
PROVIDE Home Inspections. Refundable Estimates. Collection/Delivery Service Available.
SPEAK TO B. D. Jones.
SEE Picture Frames.

W. F. GADSBY LTD
9 Bradford Street, Walsall, **West Midlands WS1 1TB**
TEL   0922 23104
OPEN   9–5 Mon–Sat.

Specialise in framing oils, watercolours etc.
PROVIDE Free Estimates. Free Local Collection/Delivery Service.
SPEAK TO Mr S. Roberts.

HAMPTON UTILITIES (B'HAM) LTD
15 Pitsford Street, Hockley, Birmingham, **West Midlands B18 6LJ**
TEL   021 554 1766
OPEN   8–4 Mon–Fri.

Specialise in restoring and repairing picture frames, including gilding.
PROVIDE Free Estimates.
SPEAK TO C.Harrison.
SEE Furniture, Silver.

CATHERINE MEADS
37 Cadbury Road, Moseley, Birmingham, **West Midlands B13 9BH**
TEL   021 449 4840
OPEN   9–7 Mon–Fri.

Specialise in picture frame restoration, including gilding.
PROVIDE Home Inspections. Free Estimates. Free Local Collection/Delivery Service.
SPEAK TO Catherine Meads.
Member of UKIC. This workshop is included on the register of conservators maintained by the Conservation Unit of the Museums and Galleries Commission.
SEE Silver.

PENNY LAWRENCE
Fairhurst Gallery, Bedford Street, Norwich, **Norfolk NR2 1AS**
TEL   0603 632064
OPEN   9–5 Mon–Fri.

Specialise in restoring and conserving picture frames.
PROVIDE Home Inspections. Free Estimates. Free/Chargeable Collection/Delivery Service.
SPEAK TO Penny Lawrence.
This workshop is included on the register of conservators maintained by the Conservation Unit of the Museums and Galleries Commission.
SEE Furniture, Oil Paintings, Silver.

WESTCLIFFE GALLERY AND ART FRAMERS
2–8 Augusta Street, Sheringham, **Norfolk NR26 8LA**
TEL   0263 824320
OPEN   9.30–5.30 Mon–Sat; closed Wed.

Specialise in conservation mounting, gilding, period frame restoration.
PROVIDE Home Inspections. Free Estimates. Free/Chargeable Collection/Delivery Service.
SPEAK TO Richard Parks.
SEE Oil Paintings.

J. A. & T. HEDLEY
3 St Mary's Chare, Hexham,
Northumberlandshire NE46 1NQ
TEL   0434 602317
OPEN   9–5 Mon–Sat; 9–12 Thur.

Specialise in picture framing.

PROVIDE Free Estimates. Chargeable
Collection/Delivery Service.
SPEAK TO D. Hall or W. H. Jewitt.
SEE Furniture.

ANDREW HIRST
88 Gertrude Road, West Bridgeford,
Nottinghamshire NG2 5DB
TEL   0602 814574
OPEN   9–5 Mon–Fri.

Specialise in restoring picture frames,
including gesso, composition and
gilding.

PROVIDE Home Inspections. Free
Estimates. Chargeable
Collection/Delivery Service.
SPEAK TO Andrew Hirst.
Member of UKIC and ABPR.
SEE Oil Paintings.

BART LUCKHURST
The Gallery, 9 Union Street, Bingham,
Nottinghamshire NG13 8AD
TEL   0949 837668
OPEN   9–5 Tues–Thur; 9–1 Sat.

Specialise in restoring period frames.

PROVIDE Home Inspections. Free
Estimates. Collection/Delivery Service
by arrangement.
SPEAK TO Bart Luckhurst.
Member of FATG.
SEE Oil Paintings.

MARK ROBERTS
1 West Workshops, Tan Gallop, Welbeck,
Nr. Worksop, **Nottinghamshire
S80 3LW**
TEL   0909 484270
OPEN   By Appointment.

Specialise in conserving and restoring
gilded frames.

PROVIDE Home Inspections. Refundable
Estimates. Chargeable
Collection/Delivery Service.
SPEAK TO Mark or Diana Roberts.
SEE Oil Paintings.

BARBARA BIBB
149 Kingston Road, Oxford,
Oxfordshire OX2 6RP
TEL   0865 56444
OPEN   9–5 Mon–Sat.

Specialise in restoring gilded frames.

PROVIDE Home Inspections. Free
Estimates. Free Local
Collection/Delivery Service.
SPEAK TO Barbara Bibb.
Member of ABPR. This workshop is
included on the register of conservators
maintained by the Conservation Unit of
the Museums and Galleries Commission.
SEE Furniture, Oil Paintings.

ANNE KENNETT
17 Greenmere, Brightwell–Cum–
Stowell, **Oxfordshire OX10 0QN**
TEL   0491 834757
OPEN   9.30–6 Mon–Fri or By
       Appointment.

Specialise in conservation quality
mounting and framing.

PROVIDE Home Inspections. Free
Estimates. Chargeable
Collection/Delivery Service.
SPEAK TO Anne Kennett.
Member of IPC.
SEE Oil Paintings.

OXFORD CONSERVATIONS
Full address witheld by request,
Oxfordshire
TEL   0865 62614
FAX   0865 750311
OPEN   By Appointment Only.

Specialise in restoring picture frames.

PROVIDE Home Inspections. Free
Estimates. Chargeable
Collection/Delivery Service.
SPEAK TO Candy Kuhl, Chief
Conservator.
Member of UKIC and IIC, Associate
Member of ABPR. This workshop is
included on the register of conservators
maintained by the Conservation Unit of
the Museums and Galleries Commission.
SEE Oil Paintings, Porcelain.

PICTURE CONSERVATION AND RESTORATION STUDIOS

40–41 Park End Street, Oxford,
Oxfordshire OX1 1JD
All correspondence to: Head Office, 7
Beech Close, Buckingham,
Buckinghamshire MK18 1PG
TEL   0865 200289
OPEN   9–5,30 Mon–Sat By
Appointment Only.

Specialise in the cleaning and restoration
of old gilded frames.

PROVIDE Home Inspections. Chargeable
Estimates. Chargeable
Collection/Delivery Service.
SPEAK TO Mr Garve Hessenberg BA.
SEE Oil Paintings.

SWALLOWS

16 Main Road, East Hagbourne,
Oxfordshire OX11 9LN
TEL   0235 818273
OPEN   9–5.30 Mon–Fri or By
Appointment.

Specialise in all mediums of framing with
particular attention to conservation
framing and preservation of artworks.
Also specialise in mount decoration
including washline and applied
decoration of all kinds.

PROVIDE Home Inspections. Free
Estimates. Chargeable
Collection/Delivery Service.
SPEAK TO Jennie Kuca.

TIM EVERETT

Pitminster Studio, Taunton, **Somerset
TA3 7AZ**
TEL   0823 42710
OPEN   By Appointment.

Specialise in conservation and
restoration of picture frames.

PROVIDE Home Inspections. Free
Estimates. Free Collection/Delivery
Service.
SPEAK TO Tim Everett.
This workshop is included on the register
of conservators maintained by the
Conservation Unit of the Museums and
Galleries Commission.
SEE Oil Paintings.

VICTORIA DES BEAUX ARTS LTD

11 Newcastle Street, Burslem, Stoke–on–
Trent,
Staffordshire ST6 3QB
TEL   0782 836490
OPEN   9–5 Mon–Sat.

Specialise in framing paintings.

PROVIDE Home Inspections.
Free/Chargeable Estimates. Free
Collection/Delivery Service.
SPEAK TO Mrs Bryden.
SEE Oil Paintings.

PHILIPPA ELLISON

Fords Farm, Winston, Nr. Stowmarket,
Suffolk IP14 6BD
TEL   0728 860572
OPEN   9–5 Mon–Fri.

Specialise in advice on framing works of
art on paper.

PROVIDE Home Inspections. Free
Estimates. Collection/Delivery Service.
SPEAK TO Philippa Ellison.
Member of IPC. This workshop is
included on the register of conservators

maintained by the Conservation Unit of the Museum and Galleries Commission. SEE Oil Paintings, Books.

JOHN GAZELEY ASSOCIATES FINE ART
17 Fonnereau Road, Ipswich, **Suffolk IP1 3JR**
TEL   0473 252420
OPEN   By Appointment.

Specialise in gilding and repairing of picture frames as well as making reproduction frames.

PROVIDE Free Estimates.
SPEAK TO Dr John Gazeley.
SEE Furniture, Oil Paintings.

C. W. P. KEYES
36 High Street, Debenham, Stowmarket, **Suffolk IP14 6QN**
TEL   0728 860624
OPEN   10–3 Mon–Sat.

Specialise in framing and mounting prints, drawings, watercolours and posters.

PROVIDE Home Inspections. Chargeable Estimates. Chargeable Collection/Delivery Service.
SPEAK TO Charles Keyes.
Member of IPC.
SEE Oil Paintings, Books.

JOHN HILL
"Farthings", Trindles Road, South Nutfield, **Surrey RH1 4JG**
TEL   0737 823404
OPEN   9–5 Mon–Fri.

Specialise in a conservation framing service.

PROVIDE Home Inspections. Free Estimates. Chargeable Collection/Delivery Service.
SPEAK TO John Hill.
Member of IPC.
SEE Books, Oil Paintings.

LIMPSFIELD WATERCOLOURS
High Street, Limpsfield, **Surrey RH8 0DT**
TEL   0883 717010
OPEN   11–3 Tues; 10–2 Thur–Fri; 10–3 Sat.

Specialise in full framing service and conservation framing.

PROVIDE Local Home Inspections. Free Estimates.
SPEAK TO Christine Reason.
SEE Oil Paintings.

MANOR ANTIQUES AND RESTORATIONS
2 New Shops, High Street, Old Woking, **Surrey GU22 9JW**
TEL   0483 724666
MOB 0860 851956
FAX   0483 750366
OPEN   10–5 Mon–Fri; 10–4.30 Sat.

Specialise in picture framing.

PROVIDE Home Inspections. Free Estimates. Collection/Delivery Service.
SPEAK TO Alan Wellstead.
Member of the Guild of Master Craftsmen.
SEE Clocks, Furniture.

CHARLES OWEN RESTORATIONS (GILDER)
The Studio, 1 Hillrise, Shere Road, West Horsley, **Surrey KT24 6EF**
TEL   0483 285271
OPEN   By Appointment.

Specialise in restoring picture frames.

PROVIDE Home Inspections. Free Estimates.
SPEAK TO Charles Owen.
SEE Furniture.

DAVID SAMUELS
Carters Framing Service, The Old Forge, 35 High Street, Godstone, **Surrey RH9 8LS**
TEL   0883 742457
OPEN   9–5 Mon–Fri.

Specialise in picture framing to the trade and public.

PROVIDE Free Estimates. Collection/Delivery Service.
SPEAK TO David Samuels.

NICHOLAS PETER SEVERSWAY
123 Weybourne Lane, Heath End, Farnham, **Surrey GU9 9DD**
TEL   0252 28345
OPEN   10–1, 2–6 Tues–Fri; 9–4 Sat.

Specialise in conservation framing.

PROVIDE Home Inspections. Free Estimates. Free Local Collection Delivery Service.
SPEAK TO Nick Seversway.
Member of UKIC and IPC. Associate Member of ABPR.
SEE Oil Paintings.

SHAUN VICKERS
Foxgloves, Clock Barn Lane, Busbridge, Godalming, **Surrey GU8 4AZ**
TEL   0483 429964
FAX   0483 424360
OPEN   9–6 Mon–Fri.

Specialise in restoring picture frames, including gilding.

PROVIDE Home Inspections. Free Estimates. Free Local Collection/Delivery Service.
SPEAK TO Shaun Vickers.
SEE Furniture, Clocks.

JUDITH WETHERALL
trading as J.B. SYMES
28 Silverlea Gardens, Horley, **Surrey RH6 9BB**
TEL   0293 775024
OPEN   8.30–5.30 Daily By Appointment Only.

Specialise in restoring gilded picture frames, including carving.

PROVIDE Free Local Home Inspections.

Free Estimates. Chargeable Collection/Delivery Service.
SPEAK TO Judith Wetherall.
Member of UKIC and IIC. This workshop is included on the register of conservators maintained by the Conservation Unit of the Museums and Galleries Commission.
SEE Clocks, Furniture, Porcelain.

ADRIANNE MEAD
School Hill Studios, 204 High Street, Lewes, **East Sussex BN7 2NS**
TEL   0273 476087
OPEN   9–5 Mon–Sat.

Specialise in restoring antique frames.

PROVIDE Home Inspections. Free Estimates. Collection/Delivery Service.
SPEAK TO Adrianne Mead.
SEE Oil Paintings.

G. MURRAY–BROWN PICTURE SERVICES
Silverbeach House, Norman Road, Pevensey Bay, **East Sussex BN24 6JR**
TEL   0323 764298
OPEN   By Appointment.

Specialise in restoring old frames.

PROVIDE Home Inspections. Free Estimates. Collection/Delivery Service.
SPEAK TO Geoffrey Murray–Brown.
SEE Oil Paintings.

SOUTH DOWN FINE ART LTD
28 Western Road, Hove, **East Sussex BN3 1HF**
TEL   0273 723760
OPEN   9.30–5 Mon–Fri; 9–5.30 Sat; closed Wed p.m.

Specialise in framing in both traditional swepts and modern metal, customised mounting, washlines, marble mounts.

PROVIDE Home Inspections. Free

Estimates. Free Collection/Delivery
Service.
SPEAK TO John Fobester.
Member of the Fine Art Trade Guild and
the Guild of Master Craftsmen.

STEWART GALLERY
48 Devonshire Road, Bexhill–on–Sea,
East Sussex TN40 1AX
TEL   0424 223410
FAX   0323 29588
OPEN   9–5.30 Mon–Sat.

Specialise in a framing service.

PROVIDE Home Inspections. Free
Estimates. Free Collection/Delivery
Service.
SPEAK TO Mrs L. Knight.
SEE Oil Paintings.

STEWART GALLERY
25 Grove Road, Eastbourne, **East
Sussex BN20 4TT**
TEL   0323 29588
FAX   0323 29588
OPEN   9–5.30 Mon–Fri; 11–4 Sat.

Specialise in a framing service.

PROVIDE Home Inspections. Free
Estimates. Free Collection/Delivery
Service.
SPEAK TO S. A. Ettinger.
SEE Oil Paintings.

CAROL BANKS AND SON
September Cottage, 88 Victoria Road,
Shoreham–by–Sea, **West Sussex
BN4 5WS**
TEL   0273 461647.
OPEN   By Appointment

Specialise in conservation and
restoration of carved and gilded finished
picture frames.

PROVIDE Local Home Inspections. Free
Estimates.
SPEAK TO Carol Banks.
Member of UKIC.
SEE Furniture, Porcelain.

DAVID WESTON
East Lodge, Woldringfold, Lower
Beeding, Horsham, **West Sussex
RH13 6NJ**
TEL   0403 891617
OPEN   By Appointment.

Specialise in restoring composition
frames and gilding and make
reproduction composition frames.

PROVIDE Free Estimates.
SPEAK TO David Weston.
SEE Furniture.

MACDONALD FINE ART
2 Ashburton Road, Gosforth, **Tyne and
Wear NE3 4XN**
TEL   091 285 6188 or 091 284 4214
OPEN   10–1, 2.30–5.30 Mon–Sat;
           closed Wed.

Specialise in framing Victorian
watercolours and paintings.

PROVIDE Free Estimates. Free
Collection/Delivery Service.
SPEAK TO Tom MacDonald.
SEE Oil Paintings.

SUSAN B. AIRY
The Old Barn, Radway, **Warwickshire
CV 35 0UF**
TEL   0295 87392
OPEN   8–8 Daily.

Specialise in restoring gilded frames.

PROVIDE Home Inspections. Free
Estimates. Chargeable
Collection/Delivery Service.
SPEAK TO Susan Airy.
Member of UKIC. This workshop is
included on the register of conservators
maintained by the Conservation Unit of
the Museums and Galleries Commission.
SEE Oil Paintings, Furniture.

ROOTHS OF BRADFORD-ON-AVON
18 Market Street, Bradford–on–Avon, **Wiltshire BA15 1LL**
TEL   0225 864191
FAX   0225 868782
OPEN   9.30–1.00, 2.15–6 Mon–Sat.

Specialise in conservation and restoration of all types of picture frames. Full bespoke and conservation framing service also available.

PROVIDE Home Inspections. Free Estimates. Collection/Delivery Service.
SPEAK TO Edward Rooth or Julia Rooth.
Member of the Guild of Mater Craftsmen, IPC and UKIC.

RICHARD BENNETT
18 Kirkgate, Thirsk, **North Yorkshire YO7 1PQ**
TEL   0845 524085
OPEN   By Appointment.

Specialise in framing oil paintings.

PROVIDE Chargeable Estimates. Collection/Delivery Service by arrangement.
SPEAK TO Richard Bennett.
Asssociate Member of ABPR.
SEE Oil Paintings.

W. C. GREENWOOD FINE ART
The Gallery, Oakdene Burneston, Nr. Bedale, **North Yorkshire DL8 2JE**
TEL   0677 424830 and 423217
OPEN   By Appointment.

Specialise in restoring old frames.

PROVIDE Home Inspections. Chargeable Collection/Delivery Service.
SPEAK TO William Greenwood.

THE DAVIE GALLERY
8 Castlegate, Tickhill, Doncaster, **South Yorkshire DN11 9QU**
TEL   0302 751199
OPEN   9.30–5 Mon–Sat; closed Wed.

Specialise in conservation and restoration of antique frames, will also supply hand–carved replica frames and sell antique picture frames.

PROVIDE Home Inspections. Free Estimates. Free Collection/Delivery Service.
SPEAK TO Ian Davie.
Member of the Fine Art Trade Guild.
SEE Oil Paintings.

W. F. GADSBY LTD
33 New Briggate. Leeds, **West Yorkshire LS2 8JD**
TEL   0532 455326
OPEN   9–5.30 Mon–Sat.

Specialise in framing oils, watercolours etc.

PROVIDE Free Estimates. Free Local Collection/Delivery Service.
SPEAK TO Mr K. Crossland.

PHYLLIS ARNOLD GALLERY ANTIQUES
Hoops Courtyard, Greyabbey, **Co. Down BT22 2NE**
TEL   02477 88199
ANS   0247 853322
OPEN   11–5 Wed, Fri, Sat.

Specialise in conservation framing.

PROVIDE Free Estimates. Collection/Delivery Service by arrangement.
SPEAK TO Phyllis Arnold.
Member of the Royal Society of Miniature Painters.
SEE Oil Paintings.

BARBARA BEST
9 Acton Road, Poyntzpass, Newry, **Co. Down BT35 6TB**
TEL   0762 86727
OPEN   By Appointment.

Specialise in restoring picture frames, including gilding.

PROVIDE Home Inspections. Free Estimates. Chargeable Collection/Delivery Service.
SPEAK TO Barbara Best. Member of IPCRA.
SEE Furniture.

JAMES A. GORRY
20 Molesworth Street, Dublin 2, **Co. Dublin**
TEL   01 6795319
OPEN   10–6 Mon–Fri.

Specialise in restoring frames.

PROVIDE Home Inspections.
SPEAK TO James Gorry.
SEE Oil Paintings.

JENNY SLEVIN
9 Innisboffin, Bailey View, Harbour Road, Dalkey, **Co. Dublin**
TEL   01 280 3429
OPEN   By Appointment.

Specialise in cleaning and repairing picture frames.

PROVIDE Home Inspections. Free/Chargeable Estimates. Collection/Delivery Service by arrangement.
SPEAK TO Jenny Slevin.
Member of IPCRA.
SEE Carpets, Furniture, Porcelain, Collectors (Wax).

SUSAN MULHALL
Blackwood, Robertstown, Naas, **Co. Kildare**
TEL   01 045 60336
OPEN   By Appointment.

Specialise in restoring picture frames, including gilding and gessowork.

PROVIDE Home Inspections.
Free/Chargeable Estimates.
Collection/Delivery Service by arrangement.
SPEAK TO Susan Mulhall.
Member of IPCRA.
SEE Furniture.

WLODEK SZUSTKIEWICZ
Stacumny House, Celbridge, **Co. Kildare**
TEL   01 628 8345 ex. 10
OPEN   By Appointment.

Specialise in restoring picture frames, including carving and gilding, gesso work.

PROVIDE Home Inspections. Free Estimates. Free Collection/Delivery Service.
SPEAK TO Wlodek Szustkiewicz.
Member of IPCRA.
SEE Furniture.

EMILY NAPER
Loughcrew, Oldcastle, **Co. Meath**
TEL   049 41356
FAX   049 41722
OPEN   By Appointment.

Specialise in restoring water and oil gilded picture frames.

PROVIDE Home Inspections. Free Estimates. Chargeable Local Collection/Delivery Service.
SPEAK TO Emily Naper.
Member of IPCRA.
SEE Furniture.

VALERIE McCOY
Fan–na–Greine, Glendalough, **Co. Wicklow**
TEL   0404 45125
OPEN   By Appointment.

Specialise in restoring and gilding picture frames.

PROVIDE Home Inspections. Free Estimates. Free Collection/Delivery Service.
SPEAK TO Valerie McCoy.
Member of IPCRA.
SEE Furniture, Porcelain.

PAINTINGS CONSERVATION LTD

Penny Craig Cottage, Pen–Y–Craig Avenue, St Helier, Jersey, **Channel Islands JE2 3GN**
TEL　0534 74591
OPEN　8–8 Mon–Sat By Appointment.

Specialise in basic repair work on picture frames.

PROVIDE Home Inspections. Free Estimates. Collection/Delivery Service.
SPEAK TO Ian Rolls BA (Hons), Fine Art, Dip Cons.
Member of UKIC and Associate Member of ABPR.
SEE Oil Paintings.

THE SHANKLIN GALLERY

67 Regent Street, Shanklin, **Isle Of Wight PO37 7AE**
TEL　0983 863113
OPEN　9–5 Mon–Sat.

Specialise in all aspects of picture frames.

PROVIDE Home Inspections. Free Estimates. Collection/Delivery Service.
SPEAK TO Mr Campbell.
Member of Fine Art Trade Guild.
SEE Oil Paintings.

BLACKWOOD FINE ARTS GALLERY

10–11 Bourtree Terrace, Hawick, Roxburghshire, **Borders TD9 9HN**
TEL　0450 78517
FAX　0450 77780
OPEN　9.30–5.30 Mon–Fri; 10–2 Sat.

Specialise in framing and mounting and restoring gilt frames, including gilding and carving.

PROVIDE Home Inspections. Free Estimates. Chargeable Collection/Delivery Service.
SPEAK TO Carol Sutherland.
Member of SSCR. This workshop is in the Scottish Conservation Directory.
SEE Oil Paintings.

LYNWOOD REPRODUCTIONS

Lynwood, Eskdalemuir, Langholm, Dumfriesshire, **Dumfries & Galloway DG13 0QH**
TEL　03873 73211
OPEN　9–6 Mon–Fri.

Specialise in restoring carved and gilded wood frames. They also have the facility to make copies of most woodcarvings and can undertake gilding of any sort.

PROVIDE Home Inspections. Free Estimates. Chargeable Collection/Delivery Service.
SPEAK TO John or Nancy Chinnery.
Member of SSCR and the Guild of Master Craftsmen.
SEE Furniture.

JOSEPH SCHERRER

30 Harbour Street, Creetown, Wigtownshire, **Dumfries & Galloway DG8 7JJ**
TEL　067182 268
OPEN　10–5 Mon–Sat or By Appointment.

Specialise in restoring and reproducing picture frames, including mouldings of all dimensions and periods. They also make up their own frames and water gild, carve and polish. Has worked in France and can advise.

PROVIDE Home Inspections. Free Estimates.
SPEAK TO Joseph Scherrer.
This workshop is in the Scottish Conservation Directory.
SEE Oil Paintings.

JAMES ANDERSON RITCHIE

Art Restoration Service, 6 Woodhill Place, Aberdeen, **Grampian AB2 4LF**
TEL   0224 310491
OPEN   9–5.30 or By Appointment.

Specialise in restoring picture frames and also provide a framing service.

PROVIDE Local Home Inspections. Free Estimates. Chargeable Collection/Delivery Service.
SPEAK TO J. Anderson Ritchie.
This workshop is in the Scottish Conservation Directory. Member of SSCR.
SEE Carpets, Oil Paintings.

ALDER ARTS

57 Church Street, Inverness, **Highland IV1 1DR**
TEL   0463 243575
OPEN   9–5.30 Mon–Sat.

Specialise in framing 17th–19th century oil paintings.

PROVIDE Home Inspections. Free/Chargeable Estimates. Free Collection/ Delivery Service.
SPEAK TO Ken Hardiman.
SEE Oil Paintings.

ORBOST GALLERY

Bolvean, Isle of Skye, **Highland IV55 8ZB**
TEL   047 022 207
OPEN   By Appointment.

Specialise in repairing and restoring ornate Victorian frames, also framed presentation calligraphy and illumination.

PROVIDE Home Inspections. Free/Chargeable Collection/Delivery Service.
SPEAK TO Dr David L. Roberts MA FSA (Scotland).

This workshop is in the Scottish Conservation Directory.
SEE Oil Paintings.

BOURNE FRAMES AND RESTORATION LTD

4 Dundas Street, Edinburgh, **Lothian EH3 6HZ**
TEL   031 557 4874
FAX   031 557 8382
OPEN   10–6 Mon–Fri; 10–1 Sat.

Specialise in restoring and gilding antique frames. They also keep a large stock of antique frames.

PROVIDE Home Inspections. Free Estimates. Free/Chargeable Collection/Delivery Service.
SPEAK TO Susan Heys.
This workshop is in the Scottish Conservation Directory.
SEE Oil Paintings.

MALCOLM INNES GALLERY

67 George Street, Edinburgh, **Lothian EH2 2JG**
TEL   031 226 4151
FAX   031 226 4151
OPEN   9.30–6 Mon–Fri.

Specialise in framing pictures.

PROVIDE Home Inspections. Free Estimates. Free/Chargeable Collection/Delivery Service.
SPEAK TO Anthony Woodd.
SEE London SW3.
SEE Oil Paintings.

DAPHNE FRASER

Glenbarry, 58 Victoria Road, Lenzie, Glasgow, **Strathclyde G66 5AP**
TEL   041 776 1281
OPEN   By Appointment.

Specialise in restoring ornate picture frames.

PROVIDE Free Estimates.
SPEAK TO Daphne Fraser.

SEE Collectors (Dolls, Toys), Furniture, Oil Paintings.

McIAN GALLERY
10 Argyll Square, Oban, **Strathclyde PA34 4AZ**
TEL 0631 66755
OPEN 9–5.30 Mon–Sat.

Specialise in picture framing.

PROVIDE Chargeable Collection/Delivery Service.
SPEAK TO Rory Campbell-Gibson.
SEE Oil Paintings.

KENNETH McKENZIE
91 Hyndland Street, Glasgow, **Strathclyde G11 5PU**
TEL 041 339 6408
OPEN Mon–Fri By Appointment.

Specialise in repair and re–gilding of frames.

PROVIDE Home Inspections. Free Estimates. Free Collection/Delivery Service.
SPEAK TO Kenny McKenzie. Member of SSCR. This workshop is in the Scottish Conservation Directory.
SEE Oil Paintings.

WESTPORT GALLERY
3 Old Hawkhill, Dundee, **Tayside DD1 5EU**
TEL 0382 21751
OPEN 9–5 Mon–Fri.

Specialise in framing paintings.

PROVIDE Free Estimates. Chargeable Collection/Delivery Service.
SPEAK TO Neil Livingstone.
SEE Arms, Furniture, Oil Paintings, Silver.

MANOR HOUSE FINE ARTS
73 Pontcanna Street, Cardiff, **South Glamorgan CF1 9HS**
TEL 0222 227787
OPEN 10.30–5.30 Tues, Thur, Fri, Sat or By Appointment.

Specialise in a bespoke framing service.

PROVIDE Home Inspections. Free Estimates at the gallery. Chargeable Collection/Delivery Service.
SPEAK TO Steven Denley–Hill.
SEE Oil Paintings.

PORCELAIN, GLASS AND SCULPTURE

DO

Always use both hands when lifting – never lift by handles
Remove lids before lifting
Interleave stacked plates with clean paper, and never stack them more than six deep
Avoid using force to release jammed decanter stoppers: try immersing in warm water,
and gradually adding hot water to increase the temperature
Avoid displaying ceramics at floor level

DON'T

Hang plates by spring-clip wallhangers which are not plastic covered
Stack plates flat when transporting them
Stack cups or glasses inside one another
Leave tea or coffee in cups for long periods
Use adhesive tape or sticky labels, especially on gilding
Put anything old in a microwave
Put flowerpots or containers directly on to plates or dishes
Keep wine for long in decanters
Store wineglasses with rims touching
Use more than a drop of detergent when washing
Warm old plates in the oven
Wear loose-sleeved clothes when arranging on shelves

STEPHEN BUSHELL
108 Walcot Street, Bath, **Avon
BA1 5BG**
TEL   0225 444404 ex.43
FAX   0225 448163
OPEN   8.30–5.30 Mon–Fri; By
       Appointment Sat.

Specialise in restoring sculptural and
architectural stonework of all types.

PROVIDE Home Inspections. Free Local
Estimates.
Free Local Collection/Delivery Service.
SPEAK TO Stephen Bushell.
Member of UKIC.

JANE WAY
RESTORATIONS
(Ceramic Restorer), 26 Foxcombe Road,
Weston, Bath, **Avon BA1 3ED**
TEL   0225 446770
OPEN   10–5 Mon–Fri By Appointment.

Specialise in restoring all types of
ceramics, especially Meissen, 18th and
19th century Chinese and English
porcelain.

PROVIDE Free/Chargeable Estimates.
SPEAK TO Jane Way.
Member of UKIC. This workshop is
included on the register of conservators
maintained by the Conservation Unit of
the Museums and Galleries Commission.

SAFAVID CERAMIC
RESTORATIONS
29 Blacksmiths Lane, Prestwood, Great
Missenden, **Buckinghamshire
HP16 0AP**
TEL   02406 5231
OPEN   By Appointment.

Specialise in restoring ceramics,
particularly English blue and white
transfer wares.

PROVIDE Home Inspections. Free
Estimates.
SPEAK TO Bridget Syms.

WILLIAM DAWSON
The Gatehouse, Buckden Towers,
Buckden, **Cambridgeshire PE18 9TA**
TEL   0480 811868
OPEN   By Appointment.

Specialise in repairing and restoring
ceramics, particularly Oriental and
English porcelain, as well as 19th and
20th century decorative pottery and
figures. Also ceramic gilding.

PROVIDE Home Inspections. Free
Estimates. Chargeable
Collection/Delivery Service.
SPEAK TO William Dawson.
In association with The China
Restoration Studio, Fulbeck Hall,
Grantham, **Lincolnshire**.

JOANNE McKINLEY
118 High Street, Norton, Stockton–on–
Tees, **Cleveland TS20 1DS**
TEL   0642 555033
OPEN   8.30–4.30 Mon–Fri; closed
       Thur; 9–12 Sat.

Specialise in restoring ceramics and
glass.

PROVIDE Chargeable Home Inspections.
Free Estimates.
SPEAK TO Joanne McKinley.
Member of UKIC. This workshop is
included on the register of conservators
maintained by the Conservation Unit of
the Museums and Galleries Commission.
SEE Furniture

JOHN AND ELIZABETH
CYNDDYLAN
Tre'staenog, Penbeagle Way, St. Ives,
Cornwall TR26 2EY
TEL   0736 797715
OPEN   9–5 Mon–Fri; 9–1 Sat.

Specialise in restoring oil and tempera
on sculpture.

PROVIDE Home Inspections. Free Local

Estimates. Free Local
Collection/Delivery Service.
SPEAK TO John or Elizabeth Cynddylan.
Member of UKIC and IIC.
SEE Oil Paintings

SPEAK TO Clare Spicer.
Ms Spicer also runs ceramic restoration
courses.
SEE Clocks

DOMINO RESTORATIONS

TEL   05394 45751
OPEN   By Appointment Only.

Specialise in restoring all classes of
ceramics, china, porcelain and glassware.

PROVIDE Home Inspections.
Free/Chargeable Estimates.
Free/Chargeable Collection/Delivery
Service.
SPEAK TO Roy or June Hargreaves.
SEE Silver.

KIRSTIE SESSFORD

The Vicarage, Preston Lane, Burton,
Christchurch, **Dorset BH23 7JU**
TEL   0202 484471
OPEN   9–5 Mon–Fri.

Specialise in restoring ceramics.

PROVIDE Home Inspections. Free
Estimates. Chargeable
Collection/Delivery Service.
SPEAK TO Kirstie Sessford.
Member of UKIC and IIC.

DIANA FRANCES DRYSDALE

4 Collipriest House, Tiverton, **Devon
EX16 4PT**
TEL   0884 258145
OPEN   10–6 Mon–Fri.

Specialise in restoring fine porcelain.

PROVIDE Home Inspections. Free
Estimates. Chargeable
Collection/Delivery Service.
SPEAK TO Diana Frances.
This workshop is included on the register
of conservators maintained by the
Conservation Unit of the Museum and
Galleries Commission.

GARY NICHOLSON

26 Ruby Street, Darlington, **Durham
DL3 0EN**
TEL   0325 460319
OPEN   9–5 Mon–Fri By Appointment.

Specialise in restoring all makes, types
and styles of ceramics.

PROVIDE Free Estimates.
SPEAK TO Gary Nicholson.
Member of UKIC.

CLARE SPICER

The Old Hare and Hounds, Fore Street,
Witheridge, Tiverton, **Devon
EX16 8AH**
TEL   0884 860 135
OPEN   9–4 Mon–Fri.

Specialise in restoring and conserving
ceramics, glass and enamel.

PROVIDE Local Home Inspections. Free
Estimates.

CHARMAINE

Brentwood, **Essex CM15 9AP**
TEL   0277 224224
OPEN   9–5 Mon–Fri.

Specialise in mechanically polishing the
inside of hollow glass vessels (decanters,
vases, glasses) to remove the etched
surface which causes the glass to look
white.

PROVIDE Free Estimates.
SPEAK TO Charmaine Cox.

CHANDELIER CLEANING AND RESTORATION SERVICES LTD

Gypsy Mead, Fyfield, Essex CM5 0BB
Tel 0277 899444 FAX 0277 899642

Specialise in restoration of fine period chandeliers employing their own skilled glass blowers, glass cutters, gilders and metal finishers.
PROVIDE Home Inspections Free/Refundable Estimates. Free Collection/Delivery Service.
SPEAK TO Mr Stewart L. Nardi
Members of the Lighting Association and The British Glass Manufacturers Confederation. This workshop is included on the register of conservators maintained by the Conservation Unit of the Museums and Galleries Commission.

MILLSIDE ANTIQUE RESTORATION
Parndon Mill, Parndon Mill Lane, Harlow, **Essex CM20 2HP**
TEL   0279 428148
FAX   0279 415075
OPEN   10–5 Mon–Fri.

Specialise in restoring Oriental and European porcelain and coloured glass.

PROVIDE Home Inspections. Free/Chargeable Estimates. Chargeable Collection/Delivery Service.
SPEAK TO David Sparks or Angela Wickliffe–Philp.
Also provide tuition courses in china and porcelain restoration. Member of the Guild of Master Craftsmen.
SEE Oil Paintings, Picture Frames, Silver.

JANE W. PRETIOUS
580A Longbridge Road, Dagenham, **Essex RM8 2AR**
TEL   081 599 5942
OPEN   10–4 Daily By Appointment.

Specialise in restoring china, porcelain, ceramics and sometimes glass.

PROVIDE Home Inspections. Free Estimates.
SPEAK TO Jane Pretious.
Member of UKIC.

KEITH BAWDEN
Mews Workshop, Montpellier Retreat, Cheltenham, **Gloucestershire GL50 2XS**
TEL   0242 230320
OPEN   7–4.30 Mon–Fri.

Specialise in conserving and restoring all aspects of porcelain.

PROVIDE Free Estimates. Home Inspections. Local Collection/Delivery Service.
SPEAK TO Keith Bawden.
SEE Clocks, Silver, Furniture, Oil Paintings.

BROCKSTEAD CONSERVATION
c/o Ham Cottage, Station Road, South Cerney, Nr. Cirencester, **Gloucestershire GL7 5UE**
TEL   0285 860310
OPEN   9–5.30 Mon–Sat.

Specialise in restoring ceramics and glass.
PROVIDE Home Inspections. Free Estimates. Free Collection/Delivery Service.
SPEAK TO Clare Bradley or James Bradley. Member of UKIC and IIC.

ATELIER FINE ART CASTINGS LTD
Hulfords Lane, Nr. Hartley Wintney, **Hampshire RG27 8AG**
TEL   0252 844388
OPEN   8.30–5 Mon–Fri.

Specialise in restoring bronze art work and bronze casting. Restoration of most other metalwork undertaken.
PROVIDE Free Estimates. Chargeable Collection/Delivery Service.
SPEAK TO Valerie.
SEE Silver.

KATHARINE BEWES ANTIQUE CHINA RESTORATION
Mercury Yacht Harbour, Satchell Lane, Hamble, Southampton, **Hampshire SO3 5HQ**
TEL   0703 455056
OPEN   9–6.30 Mon–Thur.

Specialise in restoring and repairing all forms of china, including Meissen, Bow, Chelsea, Oriental, Belleek, Doulton and Parian ware.
PROVIDE Estimates.
SPEAK TO Katharine Bewes.
Also run china restoration courses.

PHILIPPA M. NELSON
China Fix, 4 Setters Workshops, Mount Pleasant Lane, Lymington, **Hampshire SO41 8LS**
TEL   0590 679869
OPEN   By appointment only.

Specialise in restoration of all types of ceramics, china, porcelain and pottery. The modelling of missing pieces is a speciality as well as colour matching and detail in finishing to highest standards.
PROVIDE Free Estimates.
SPEAK TO Philippa Nelson.

MARY ROSE WRANGHAM
Studio 304, Victory Business Centre, Somers Road North, Portsmouth, **Hampshire PO1 1PJ**
TEL   0705 829863
       ANS 0705 829863
OPEN   10–5 Daily.

Specialise in in restoring ceramics, including Oriental and Chinese style decorative repairs in gold leaf.
PROVIDE Chargeable Home Inspections. Chargeable Estimates. Chargeable Collection/Delivery Service.
SPEAK TO Mary Rose Wrangham
Also provide studio ceramic repair courses and have a 90 minute training video for beginners and a 110 minute video for advanced pupils

SHEILA DONALDSON
Old Bridge House, Headbrook, Kington, **Hereford & Worcester HR5 3DZ**
TEL   0544 231540
OPEN   10–6 Mon–Sat.

Specialise in restoring antique and decorative items in all kinds of pottery or porcelain.

PROVIDE Home Inspections. Free Estimates. Chargeable Collection/Delivery Service.
SPEAK TO Sheila Donaldson.
Member of UKIC.

PIPE ELM PORCELAIN
Pipe Elm, Leigh Sinton, Malvern, **Hereford & Worcester WR13 5EA**
TEL 0886 832492
OPEN By Appointment.

Specialise in restoring European and Oriental pottery and porcelain, including antiquities.

PROVIDE Home Inspections. Free Estimates. Free Collection/Delivery Service every two months at the IAC Fair, Newark.
SPEAK TO Fred or Maggie Covins

HERITAGE RESTORATIONS
24 Castle Street, Berkhamsted, **Hertfordshire HP4 2DU**
TEL 0442 873819
OPEN 10–5 Daily.

Specialise in restoring porcelain.

PROVIDE Free Estimates. Home Inspections.
SPEAK TO John Wilshire.
SEE Clocks, Furniture.

HERTFORDSHIRE CONSERVATION SERVICE
Seed Warehouse, Maidenhead Yard, The Wash, Hertford, **Hertfordshire SG14 1PX**
TEL 0992 588966 or 504662
ANS 0992 588966
FAX 0992 503184
OPEN 9–6 Mon–Fri By Appointment.

Specialise in restoring ceramic, glass and stone vessels and ornaments.

PROVIDE Home Inspections. Free/Chargeable Estimates. Chargeable Collection/Delivery Service.
SPEAK TO J. M. Macqueen.
This workshop is included on the register of conservators maintained by the Conservation Unit of the Museums and Galleries Commission.
SEE Carpets, Collectors (Dolls), Lighting, Furniture, Oil Paintings, Picture Frames.

WILLIAM H. STEVENS
8 Eton Avenue, East Barnet, **Hertfordshire EN4 8TU**
TEL 081 449 7956
OPEN 9–5.30 Mon–Fri.

Specialise in restoring Japanese and Chinese pottery.

PROVIDE Home Inspections. Free Estimates. Free Collection/Delivery Service.
SPEAK TO John, Robin or Daniel Stevens.
The fifth generation of a family firm founded in 1836.
SEE Silver.

A. & S. ALLEN
40 Clarendon Way, Chislehurst, **Kent BR7 6RF**
TEL 0689 826345
OPEN 9–5 Mon–Fri.

Specialise in restoring ceramics, European and Oriental porcelain and pottery, enamels.

PROVIDE Free Estimates. Collection/Delivery Service by arrangement.
SPEAK TO Adrian Allen.
SEE Clocks.

AUDREY BURFORD
North West Kent. (full address withheld by request)
TEL 081 467 9757
OPEN 9–5 Mon–Fri.

Specialise in restoring European ceramics, principally earthenware, tin–glaze and ironstone pieces.
PROVIDE Free Estimates. Collection/Delivery Service by arrangement.
SPEAK TO Audrey Burford.

HENWOOD DECORATIVE METAL STUDIOS
The Bayle, Folkestone, **Kent CT20 1SQ**
TEL   0303 250911 or 245730
FAX   0303 850224
OPEN   8.30–5 Mon–Fri.

Specialise in restoring small bronze statues.
PROVIDE Local Home Inspections. Free Estimates. Local Free Collection/Delivery Service.
SPEAK TO Mr P. J. Rose.
Member of UKIC, Federation of Master Craftsmen and National Church Craft Association.
SEE Silver.

SARGEANT RESTORATIONS
21 The Green, Westerham, **Kent TN16 1AX**
TEL   0959 62130
OPEN   8.30–5.30 Mon–Sat.

Specialise in restoration, cleaning and wiring of chandeliers, lustres, candelabra and general light fittings.
PROVIDE Home Inspections. Free Estimates. Chargeable Collection/Delivery Service.
SPEAK TO Ann, David or Denys Sargeant.
SEE Silver.

BROTHERIDGE CHANDELIERS
3 Maytree Walk, Woodley Park, Skelmersdale, **Lancashire WN8 6UP**
TEL   0695 26276
FAX   0695 35634
OPEN   By Appointment.

Specialise in conserving and restoring glass chandeliers.
PROVIDE Home Inspections. Free Estimates. Chargeable Collection/Delivery Service.
SPEAK TO Terry Brotheridge.

E. & C. ROYALL
10 Waterfall Way, Medbourne, Nr. Market Harborough, **Leicestershire LE15 8EE**
TEL   0858 83744
OPEN   8.30–5 Mon–Fri.

Specialise in restoring European bronzes, as well as Oriental ivories, bronzes and woodcarvings.
PROVIDE Home Inspections. Free Estimates. Chargeable Collection/Delivery Service.
SPEAK TO C. Royall.
SEE Furniture

THE CHINA RESTORATION STUDIO
Fulbeck Hall, Grantham, **Lincolnshire** (post code not known)
TEL   0636 701952 or 812307 or 0480 811868
OPEN   By Appointment.

Specialise in high quality repair and restoration work on glass, stoneware and porcelain, including gilding.
PROVIDE Free Estimates.
SPEAK TO Anna Hackett, Sue Machin or William Dawson.
Also run various restoration courses round the country.

HIRST CONSERVATION
Laughton Hall Farmhouse, Laughton, Sleaford, **Lincolnshire NG34 0HE**
TEL   05297 449
FAX   05297 518
OPEN   9–5 Mon–Fri.

Specialise in restoring polychromy on other substrates, including plaster and stone and monuments.

PROVIDE Home Inspections. Free/Chargeable Estimates. Chargeable Collection/Delivery Service. SPEAK TO Elizabeth Hirst. Member of UKIC, IIC, Stone Federation. This workshop is included on the register of conservators maintained by the Conservation Unit of the Museums and Galleries Commission. SEE Oil Paintings, Picture Frames.

LINCOLNSHIRE CONSERVATION STUDIO

c/o Museum of Lincolnshire Life, Burton Road, Lincoln, **Lincolnshire LN1 3LY**
TEL 0522 533207
OPEN 9–5 Mon–Fri.

Specialise in restoring ceramics, wood and metal statuary to museum conservation standards.

PROVIDE Home Inspections. Free/Chargeable Estimates. Chargeable Collection/Delivery Service. SPEAK TO Stephanie Margrett or David Fisher. Member of UKIC. This workshop is included on the register of conservators maintained by the Conservation Unit of the Museums and Galleries Commission. SEE Arms, Furniture, Lighting

KAREN ODINGA

5 Coningsby Gardens, **London E4 9BB**
TEL 081 527 0209
OPEN By Appointment Only.

Specialise in restoring pottery and porcelain.

PROVIDE Free Estimates. SPEAK TO Mrs Karen Odinga. Member of UKIC and GADR.

DAVID TURNER

4 Atlas Mews, Ramsgate Street, **London E8 2NA**
TEL 071 249 2379
OPEN 10–6 Mon–Fri.

Specialise in restoring glass light fittings and lamp conversions.

PROVIDE Home Inspections. Free Estimates. Free Collection/Delivery Service. SPEAK TO David Turner. SEE Furniture, Silver.

RUPERT HARRIS

Studio 5, 1 Fawe Street, **London E14 6PD**
TEL 071 987 6231 or 515 2020
FAX 071 987 7994
OPEN 9–6 Mon–Fri.

Specialise in restoring fine sculpture.

PROVIDE Home Inspections. Chargeable Estimates. Collection/Delivery Service by arrangement. SPEAK TO Rupert Harris. Member of UKIC and IIC. This workshop is included on the register of conservators maintained by the Conservation Unit of the Museums and Galleries Commission. SEE Silver.

PAOLA CAMUSSO

46 Pennybank Chambers, 33–35 St John's Square, **London EC1M 4DS**
TEL 071 250 3278
FAX 071 250 0297
OPEN 10–6 Mon–Fri.

Specialise in restoring polychrome wood sculptures.

PROVIDE Home Inspections. Free Estimates. Free Collection/Delivery Service. SPEAK TO Ms Paola Camusso. Associate of ABPR. This workshop is included on the register of conservators maintained by the Conservation Unit of the Museums and Galleries Commission. SEE Oil Paintings.

MARIA KELLER CONSERVATION AND RESTORATION

Unit 46, Pennybank Chambers, St John's Square, **London EC1M 4DS**

TEL   071 386 8723 or 071 250 3278
OPEN   10–7 Mon–Fri or By Appointment.

Specialise in restoring polychrome wood sculpture.

PROVIDE Home Inspections. Free Estimates. Chargeable Collection/Delivery Service.
SPEAK TO Maria Keller.
Member of ABPR and UKIC. This workshop is included on the register of conservators maintained by the Conservation Unit of the Museums and Galleries Commission.
SEE Oil Paintings.

CERAMIC RESTORATIONS

7 Alwyne Villas, **London N1 2HG**

TEL   071 359 5240
OPEN   By Appointment Only.

Specialise in all types of pottery and porcelain restoration, especially decorative items.

PROVIDE Home Inspections. Free/Chargeable Estimates. Collection/Delivery Service by arrangement.
SPEAK TO John Parker.
Member of UKIC. This workshop is included on the register of conservators maintained by the Conservation Unit of the Museums and Galleries Commission.

PETER CHAPMAN ANTIQUES

Incorporating CHAPMAN RESTORATIONS
10 Theberton Street, **London N1 0QX**

TEL   071 226 5565
FAX   081 348 4846
OPEN   9.30–6 Mon–Sat.

Specialise in repairing bronze and other metalwork.

PROVIDE Home Inspections. Refundable Estimates. Chargeable Collection/Delivery Service.
SPEAK TO Peter Chapman or Tony Holohan.
SEE Furniture, Oil Paintings, Picture Frames, Silver.

ROSS ANTHONY FULLER

23 Rosecroft Avenue, **London NW3 7QA**

TEL   071 435 4562
OPEN   Mon–Sat By Appointment.

Specialise in restoration and conservation of sculpture and three–dimensional works of art concentrating on wood carving and finishing, including polychromy.

PROVIDE Home Inspections. Free/Chargeable Estimates. Free Local Collection/Delivery Service.
SPEAK TO Ross Anthony Fuller.
This workshop is included on the register of conservators maintained by the Conservation Unit of the Museums and Galleries Commission.
SEE Furniture.

CHINA REPAIRERS

64 Charles Lane, **London NW8 7SB**

TEL   071 722 8407
OPEN   9.30–5.30 Mon–Thur; 9.30–4.30 Fri.

Specialise in conservation and restoration of all antique and modern ceramics. They use invisible and museum techniques with the modelling of missing parts being a speciality. Glass repairs are also undertaken.

PROVIDE Free Estimates.
SPEAK TO Virginia Baron.
Provide courses and individual tuition in restoration. Member of the Guild of Master Craftsmen.

WELLINGTON GALLERY
1 St John's Wood High Street, **London NW8 7NG**
TEL   071 586 2620
OPEN   10–5.30 Mon–Sat.

Specialise in restoring glass and European and Oriental porcelain.

PROVIDE Home Inspections. Free Estimates. Chargeable Collection/Delivery Service.
SPEAK TO Mrs Maureen Barclay or Mr K. J. Barclay.
Member of LAPADA.
SEE Silver, Oil Paintings, Furniture.

VOITEK
Conservation of Works of Art, 9 Whitehorse Mews, Westminster Bridge Road, **London SE1 7QD**
TEL   071 928 6094
FAX   071 928 6094
OPEN   10.30–5 Mon–Fri.

Specialise in conservation of sculpture in marble, stone, terracotta.

PROVIDE Home Inspections with advice on condition, display, damage assessments and conservation strategy subject to fee.
Chargeable Collection/Delivery Service.
SPEAK TO Wojtek Sobczynski.
SEE Oil Paintings.

WILKINSON PLC
5 Catford Hill, **London SE6 4NU**
TEL   081 314 1080
FAX   081 690 1524
OPEN   9–5 Mon–Fri.

Specialise in restoring glass chandeliers, decanters, glasses and stoppers. Will also make glass shades to match existing ones.

PROVIDE Home Inspections. Free Estimates. Chargeable Collection/Delivery Service.
SPEAK TO Peter Prickett, Jane Milnes or David Wilkinson.
SEE Silver.

ASHTON–BOSTOCK (CHINA REPAIRS)
21 Charlwood Street, **London SW1V 2EA**
TEL   071 828 3656
OPEN   9.30–1, 2–5.30 Tues–Thur.

Specialise in restoring fine porcelain.

PROVIDE Refundable Estimates.
SPEAK TO David Ashton–Bostock.

ELIZABETH HANLEY
35 Elizabeth Street, **London SW1W 9RP**
TEL   071 730 8480
FAX   071 259 9752
OPEN   9.30–5.30 Mon–Fri.

Specialise in restoring lamps, lampshades and porcelain.

PROVIDE Home Inspections. Free Estimates. Chargeable Collection/Delivery Service.
SPEAK TO Elizabeth Hanley.
SEE Silver.

GRANVILLE & BURBIDGE

111 Kingsmead Road, **London SW2 3HZ**
TEL   081 674 1969
OPEN   9–6 Mon–Sat.

Specialise in conserving and restoring sculpture, including polychrome, wood, stone, marble, terracotta, alabaster and plaster.

PROVIDE Home Inspections. Free Estimates in the London area.
Chargeable Collection/Delivery Service.
SPEAK TO John Burbidge.
Will also do condition surveys, environmental monitoring and historical research and provision and/or recommendations for maintenance, display facilities, packing and transport.

JOHN HEAP
No.1 The Polygon, **London SW4 OJG**
TEL   071 627 4498
OPEN   By Appointment.

Specialise in restoring terracotta figures, remodelling sculpture.

PROVIDE Home Inspections. Free Estimates. Free Collection/Delivery Service.
SPEAK TO John Heap.
SEE Furniture, Silver.

SALLY NICHOLSON AND SHIRLEY PAUL
34 Perrymead Street, **London SW6 3SP**
TEL   071 731 3226
OPEN   9–5 Mon–Fri.

Specialise in all china restoration especially antique porcelain.

PROVIDE Free Estimates.
SPEAK TO Sally Nicholson or Shirley Paul. This workshop is included on the register of conservators maintained by the Conservation Unit of the Museums and Galleries Commission.

SCULPTURE RESTORATIONS
1 Michael Road, Kings Road, **London SW6 2ER**
TEL   071 736 7292
OPEN   8–4.30 Mon–Fri.

Specialise in restoring, repairing and conserving all works under the general classification of sculpture; bronze, other metals, wood, ivory, stone, marble, also including works which are painted or gilded.

PROVIDE Home Inspections. Free Estimates. Chargeable Collection/Delivery Service.
SPEAK TO John Doubleday or Michael Gaskin.

CHRISTOPHER WRAY'S LIGHTING EMPORIUM
600 Kings Road, **London SW6 2DX**
TEL   071 736 8434
FAX   071 731 3507
OPEN   9.30–6 Mon–Sat.

Specialise in restoring original Victorian and Edwardian light fittings.

PROVIDE Free Estimates. Chargeable Collection/Delivery Service.
SPEAK TO Curos Khawlari.
SEE Silver.

H. W. POULTER & SON
279 Fulham Road, **London SW10 9PZ**
TEL   071 352 7268
FAX   071 351 0984
OPEN   9–5 Mon–Fri; 10–1 Sat.

Specialise in restoring antique marble and sculpture.

PROVIDE Home Inspections Refundable Estimates. Chargeable Collection/Delivery Service.
SPEAK TO Douglas Poulter.
Have a workshop at 1A Adelaide Grove, off Uxbridge Road, London W12.
TEL   081 749 4557;
OPEN   7.30–5.30 Mon–Fri.

GILLIAN QUARTLY– WATSON
Studio C, Warriner House, 140 Battersea Park Road, **London SW11 4NB**
TEL   071 498 5938
OPEN   9.30–5.30 Mon–Fri.

Specialise in restoring ceramics and glass.

PROVIDE Home Inspections. Free Estimates. Chargeable Collection/Delivery Service.
SPEAK TO Gillian Quartly–Watson.
Member of UKIC and BADA.

P & F BINNINGTON
Re–locating in S.W. London
TEL   081 977 2570
ANS   081 977 2570
OPEN   By Appointment.

Specialise in restoring verre eglomisé (gilt glass). They also make copies to commission, including table tops and wall panels.

PROVIDE Home Inspections. Free Local Estimates. Chargeable Collection/Delivery Service.
SPEAK TO Jane Bishop.
SEE Furniture.

SARAH BAKER
Studio 3F, London House, 68 Upper Richmond Road, **London SW15 2RP**
TEL　　081 877 3752
OPEN　　10–6 Mon–Fri.

Specialise in restoring ceramics, enamel and glass.

PROVIDE Free Estimates.
SPEAK TO Sarah Baker.
Member of UKIC.

JUDITH LARNEY
Unit 2, Fovant Mews, 12A Noyna Road, **London SW17 7PH**
TEL　　081 682 3781
OPEN　　9–5.30 Mon–Fri or By Appointment.

Specialise in restoring ceramics, enamels, terracotta and marble.

PROVIDE Free Estimates.
SPEAK TO Judith Larney.
Member of UKIC, IIC and Museums Association. This workshop is included on the register of conservators maintained by the Conservation Unit of the Museums and Galleries Commission.

PLOWDEN AND SMITH LTD
190 St Ann's Hill, **London SW18 2RT**
TEL　　081 874 4005
FAX　　081 874 7248
OPEN　　9–5.30 Mon–Fri.

Specialise in restoring and conserving bronze, stone, marble, ceramics, glass, ivory.

PROVIDE Home Inspections. Free Estimates. Free/Chargeable Collection/Delivery Service.
SPEAK TO Martin Baile.
SEE Oil Paintings, Furniture, Silver, Display.

GINA KELLAND
14 Luxborough House, Luxborough Street, **London W1M 3LE**
TEL　　071 486 8051
OPEN　　10–6 Mon–Fri.

Specialise in restoring pottery, porcelain and glass.
SPEAK TO Gina Kelland.
Member of UKIC.

BLOOMFIELD CERAMIC RESTORATIONS LTD
43 Portland Place, **London W1N 3AG**
TEL　　071 580 5761
FAX　　071 636 1625
OPEN　　By Appointment.

Specialise in restoring antique European/Oriental ceramics and bronzes also general ceramics, porcelain and ancient pottery, etc. Cleaning of all objects. Advice on invisible and non-invisible repairs.

PROVIDE Free Estimates (but home inspections chargeable).
SPEAK TO Steven P. Bloomfield.
SEE Silver.

W. SITCH & CO. LTD
48 Berwick Street, **London W1V 4JD**
TEL　　071 437 3776
OPEN　　8.30–5.30 Mon–Fri; 9–1 Sat.

Specialise in restoring late 19th century lighting.

PROVIDE Home Inspections. Free
Estimates. Free/Chargeable
Collection/Delivery Service.
SPEAK TO Ron Sitch.
SEE Silver.

HOLDEN CONSERVATION SERVICES

6 Warple Mews, Warple Way, **London W3 0RF**
TEL   081 740 1203
FAX   081 749 8356
OPEN   8–5 Mon–Fri.

Specialise in restoring stone, marble, terracotta, plaster and other non–metallic sculptures.

PROVIDE Home Inspections. Free
Estimates. Chargeable
Collection/Delivery Service.
SPEAK TO Martin Holden.
Member of UKIC and IIC. This
workshop is included on the register of
conservators maintained by the
Conservation Unit of the Museums and
Galleries Commission.

N. DAVIGHI

117 Shepherds Bush Road, **London W6**
TEL   071 603 5357
OPEN   9–5 Mon–Sat.

Specialise in gilding, polishing and repairing lighting, especially crystal and ormolu chandeliers.

PROVIDE Home Inspections. Free
Estimates. Chargeable
Collection/Delivery Dervice.
SPEAK TO Mr N. Davighi

PORCELAIN AND PICTURES LTD

The Studio, 1B Gastein Road, **London W6 8LT**
TEL   071 385 7512
OPEN   9–5.30 Mon–Sat.

Specialise in restoring porcelain.

PROVIDE Home Inspections. Free
Estimates.
SPEAK TO June Spinella.
Member of the FATG.
SEE Picture Frames.

CLAUDIO ASTROLOGO

59–61 Kensington High Street, **London W8 5ED**
TEL   071 937 7820
OPEN   By Appointment.

Specialise in restoring polychrome statues.

PROVIDE Chargeable Estimates.
SPEAK TO Claudio Astrologo.
Member of IIC and UKIC.
SEE Oil Paintings.

ROSEMARY COOK RESTORATION

78 Stanlake Road, **London W12 7HJ**
TEL   081 749 7977
OPEN   By Appointment.

Specialise in restoring statuary, including polychrome surfaces.

PROVIDE Home Inspections. Free
Estimates. Free Collection/Delivery
Service in London.
SPEAK TO Rosemary Cook.
SEE Furniture, Silver.

MRS F. E. ANDREWES

22 Milson Road, **London W14 0LJ**
TEL   071 602 0604
FAX   071 602 0604
OPEN   9–5 Mon–Fri.

Specialise in restoring ceramics and porcelain.

PROVIDE Home Inspections. Free
Estimates. Free Local
Collection/Delivery Service.
SPEAK TO Mrs Andrewes.

THE GLASSHOUSE
65 Long Acre, **London WC2E 9JH**
TEL   071 836 9785
FAX   071 240 7508
OPEN 10–6 Mon–Fri; 11–5 Sat.

Specialise in restoring both antique and contemporary glass, including making liners, shades and pieces for chandeliers.

PROVIDE Home Inspections.
SPEAK TO James Watts.

HELEN POTTER
Ivy Cottage, Grove Road, Wallasey, Wirral, **Merseyside L45 3HF**
TEL   051 639 2826
OPEN 9–5 Mon–Fri.

Specialise in all aspects of restoring ceramics, including gilding and modelling missing areas.

PROVIDE Home Inspections. Free Estimates. Chargeable Delivery Service.
SPEAK TO Helen Potter.
Member of Ceramic and Glass Conservation Group. This workshop is included on the register of conservators maintained by the Conservation Unit of the Museums and Galleries Commission.

ROBIN RILEY–DESIGN RESTORATION
45 Catharine Street, Liverpool, **Merseyside L8 7NE**
TEL   051 709 3784
OPEN 9–6.30 Mon–Fri.

Specialise in restoring mosaic and sculpture.

PROVIDE Home Inspections. Chargeable Collection/Delivery Service.
SPEAK TO Robin Riley.

MAUREEN ANN ROBSON
Dip Cons. CSD (Design Management)
Studio, 29 Park Avenue, Hockley, Birmingham, **West Midlands B18 5ND**
TEL   021 551 1937
OPEN By Appointment.

Specialise in restoring ceramics, glass, mosaics, freshly excavated artefacts and ethnographic material.

PROVIDE Free Estimates. Chargeable Collection/Delivery Service.
SPEAK TO Consultant Conservator.
SEE Silver.

MARIANNE MORRISH
South Cottage Studio, Union Lane, Wortham Ling, Diss, **Norfolk IP22 ISP**
TEL   0379 643831
OPEN 10–4 Mon–Fri.

Specialise in restoring 18th century porcelain and early Staffordshire.

PROVIDE Home Inspections. Free Estimates. Chargeable Collection/Delivery Service.
SPEAK TO Marianne Morrish.
Ms Morrish is a member of the Guild of Master Craftsmen; she gives three–week tuition courses in ceramic restoration.
SEE Silver.

SUSAN NOEL
The Studio, Roundways, Holt, **Norfolk NR25 6BN**
TEL   0263 711362
OPEN 10–4 Tues, Wed, Thur or By Appointment.

Specialise in restoring ceramic figures, bowls and vases, both European and Oriental.

PROVIDE Free Estimates. Free Collection/Delivery Service.
SPEAK TO Susan Noel.

BARRY PARTON
Dar–Es–Salaam, West Harling Road,
East Harling, Norwich, **Norfolk
NR16 2SL**
TEL   0953 717115
OPEN   9–5 Mon–Fri.

Specialise in restoring ceramics.

PROVIDE Free Estimates.
SPEAK TO Barry Parton.

CAROL GALVIN
The Old Forge Conservation
Workshops, Charwelton, Nr. Daventry,
Northamptonshire NN11 6YU
TEL   0327 60594
FAX   0327 60049
OPEN   8.30–6 Mon–Sat.

Specialise in restoring fine art sculpture,
including marble, terracotta, plaster and
amber. Also polychromed surfaces on any
of these materials.

PROVIDE Home Inspections. Free
Estimates. Chargeable
Collection/Delivery Service.
SPEAK TO Carol Galvin.
Member of UKIC and IIC. This
workshop is included on the register of
conservators maintained by the
Conservation Unit of the Museums and
Galleries Commission.

GIUDICI–MARTIN
The Old Chapel, Newtown Street,
Woodford, Kettering,
Northamptonshire NN14 4HW
TEL   0536 743787 or 745900
FAX   0536 745900
OPEN   By Appointment.

Specialise in conservation, restoration
and reproduction of all types of stone
sculpture.

PROVIDE Home Inspections. Refundable
Estimates. Chargeable
Collection/Delivery Service.
SPEAK TO Paul Giudici.

For conservation purposes they will
provide a detailed condition report with
recommendation, specification and
estimates.

SHEILA MAURICE
The Old School, Barrasford, Hexham,
Northumberland NE48 4AR
TEL   0434 681 348
OPEN   9.30–5 Sun–Sat; closed Thur
      a.m.

Specialise in restoring porcelain and
ceramics.

PROVIDE Home Inspections. Free
Estimates. Free/Chargeable
Collection/Delivery Service.
SPEAK TO Sheila Maurice.
Member of UKIC.

FLORENCE CONSERVATION & RESTORATION
102 Nottingham Road, Long Eaton,
Nottingham, **Nottinghamshire
NG10 2BZ**
TEL   0602 733625
OPEN   8–5 Mon–Fri; 9–12 Sat.

Specialise in repairing ceramics, bronzes
and marbles.

PROVIDE Home Inspections. Refundable
Estimates. Chargeable
Collection/Delivery Service.
SPEAK TO Ron Florence.
SEE Oil Paintings, Furniture.

ROGER HAWKINS
Top Hat Antique Centre, 66 Derby
Road, Nottingham, **Nottinghamshire
NG1 5FD**
TEL   0602 507589
OPEN   9.30–5 Mon–Fri.

Specialise in restoring pottery,
porcelain, some glass, alabaster, marble,
spelter.

PROVIDE Home Inspections. Free
Estimates. Chargeable
Collection/Delivery Service.
SPEAK TO Roger Hawkins.

THE CONSERVATION STUDIO

68 East Street, Thame, **Oxfordshire OX9 3JS**
TEL   0844 214498
OPEN   By Appointment.

Specialise in restoration of all types of
ceramics and glass (except stained glass),
faience and enamels.

PROVIDE Free/Chargeable Estimates.
Free Local Collection/Delivery Service.
SPEAK TO Sandra Davison.
Fellow of IIC. This workshop is included
on the register of conservators
maintained by the Conservation Unit of
the Museums and Galleries Commission.

OXFORD CONSERVATIONS

Full address witheld by request,
Oxfordshire
TEL   0865 62614
FAX   0865 750311
OPEN   By Appointment Only.

Specialise in restoring polychromed
wood sculpture and can provide
technical analysis, surveys, condition
reports and other documentation and
advice on exhibition, transport and
storage.

PROVIDE Home Inspections. Free
Estimates. Chargeable
Collection/Delivery Service.
SPEAK TO Candy Kuhl, Chief
Conservator.
Member of UKIC and IIC, Associate
Member of ABPR. This workshop is
included on the register of conservators
maintained by the Conservation Unit of
the Museums and Galleries Commission.
SEE Oil Paintings, Picture Frames.

JOANNA SEAWARD

Mulberry House Studio, Mulberry
House, The Ridings, Shotover,
Oxfordshire OX3 8TB
TEL   0865 61033
FAX   0865 791772
OPEN   9–5 Mon–Sat By Appointment.

Specialise in restoring in all types of
ceramics.

PROVIDE Free Estimates.
SPEAK TO Joanna Seaward.
Member of UKIC. This workshop is
included on the register of conservators
maintained by the Conservation Unit of
the Museums and Galleries Commission.

F. C. MANSER & SON LTD

53–54 Wyle Cop, Shrewsbury,
Shropshire SY1 1XJ
TEL   0743 351120
FAX   0743 271047
OPEN   9–5.30 Mon–Wed, Fri; 9–1
          Thur; 9–5 Sat.

Specialise in restoration of glass; chipped
glass repaired, decanter stoppers,
mirrors, light fittings, porcelain repairs,
specialists in Tunbridge ware.

PROVIDE Home Inspections. Free
Estimates. Chargeable
Collection/Delivery Service.
SPEAK TO Paul Manser.
Member of LAPADA and the Guild of
Master Craftsmen.
SEE Clocks, Silver.

G. J. DICK–READ

Duxhams, Dulverton, **Somerset
TA22 9EJ**
TEL   0398 23460
OPEN   By Appointment.

Specialise in a glass and china repair
service.

PROVIDE Home Inspections. Free Local

Estimates. Chargeable
Collection/Delivery Service.
SPEAK TO John Dick–Read.
This workshop is included on the register
of conservators maintained by the
Conservation Unit of the Museums and
Galleries Commission.
SEE Furniture.

THE ANTIQUE RESTORATION STUDIO
The Old Post Office, Haughton,
Staffordshire ST18 9JH
TEL   0785 780424
FAX   0785 780157
OPEN   9–5 Mon–Fri.

Specialise in restoring antique and
modern ceramics.

PROVIDE Home Inspections. Free
Estimates Free Collection/Delivery
Service.
SPEAK TO D. P. Albright.
SEE Furniture, Oil Paintings, Carpets.

CONSERVATION SPECIALISTS LTD
Workshop: Camelsdale Road,
Haslemere, **Surrey GU27 3RJ**
Office: 18 Alexandria Road, **London
W13 0NR**
TEL   0428 661981 or 081 840 3294
FAX   0428 661983
OPEN   8.30–5.30 Mon–Fri or By
        Appointment.

Specialise in restoring sculpture and
allied objects, including stone,
terracotta, plaster, wood and polychrome
surfaces.

PROVIDE Home Inspections. Chargeable
Collection/Delivery Service.
SPEAK TO Deborah Carthy.
Member of UKIC, IIC, SSCR and
ICOM. This workshop is included on
the register of conservators maintained
by the Conservation Unit of the
Museums and Galleries Commission.

MRS VALERIE ESPLEN
Alldens Cottage, Thorncombe Street,
Nr. Bramley, **Surrey GU5 0NA**
TEL   0483 893021
OPEN   9–5.30 Mon–Fri.

Specialise in restoring all decorative
pottery and porcelain.

PROVIDE Free Estimates. Local
Collection/Delivery Service.
SPEAK TO Mrs Valerie Esplen.
Member of UKIC.

NORMAN FLYNN RESTORATIONS
37 Lind Road, Sutton, **Surrey SM1 4PP**
TEL   081 661 9505
OPEN   7.45–3.30 Mon–Fri.

Specialise in restoring antique and
modern porcelain and pottery.

PROVIDE Home Inspections. Free
Estimates. Free Collection/Delivery
Service each week to London.
SPEAK TO Norman Flynn.
Member of the Guild of Master
Craftsmen.
SEE Silver.

SAGE ANTIQUES & INTERIORS
High Street, Ripley, **Surrey GU23 6BB**
TEL   0483 224396
FAX   0483 211996
OPEN   9.30–5.30 Mon–Sat.

Specialise in restoring English and
Oriental ceramics.

PROVIDE Free Estimates.
Collection/Delivery Service.
SPEAK TO Howard or Chrissie Sage.
Member of LAPADA and the Guild of
Master Craftsmen.
SEE Furniture, Oil Paintings.

R. SAUNDERS
71 Queens Road, Weybridge, **Surrey
KT13 9UQ**
TEL   0932 842601
OPEN   9.15–5 Mon–Sat; closed Wed.

Specialise in restoring English porcelain.

PROVIDE Home Inspections. Free Estimates. Free Collection/Delivery Service.

SPEAK TO J. B. Tonkinson.

SEE Silver, Furniture, Oil Paintings.

SIMPSON DAY RESTORATION

Studio 13, Acorn House, Cherry Orchard Road, Croydon, **Surrey CR0 6BA**

TEL 081 681 8339

OPEN 9.30–6 Mon–Fri

Specialise in restoring fine porcelain and pottery.

PROVIDE Free Estimates.

SPEAK TO Sarah Simpson or Sarah Day.

SEE Silver.

JUDITH WETHERALL
trading as J.B. SYMES

28 Silverlea Gardens, Horley, **Surrey RH6 9BB**

TEL 0293 775024

OPEN 8.30–5.30 Daily By Appointment Only.

Specialise in restoring polychromed sculpture.

PROVIDE Free Local Home Inspections. Free Estimates. Chargeable Collection/Delivery Service.

SPEAK TO Judith Wetherall.

Member of UKIC and IIC. This workshop is included on the register of conservators maintained by the Conservation Unit of the Museums and Galleries Commission. Teaches gilding on ceramics.

SEE Clocks, Furniture, Picture Frames

DAVID CRAIG

Toll Cottage, Station Road, Durgates, Wadhurst, **East Sussex TN5 6RS**

TEL 0892 782188

OPEN 9–5.30 Mon–Fri.

Specialise in restoring antique porcelain and pottery.

PROVIDE Free Estimates. Free Collection/Delivery Service in London area.

SPEAK TO David Sutcliffe.

SEE Silver.

SUSAN FASQUELLE

9A Lucerne Road, Brighton, **East Sussex BN1 6GH**

TEL 0273 509 071 (after 7 p.m.)

OPEN By Appointment.

Specialise in restoring all types of ceramics, including earthenware, porcelain, stoneware and some enamels.

PROVIDE Free Estimates.

SPEAK TO Susan Fasquelle.

Member of UKIC. This workshop is included on the register of conservators maintained by the Conservation Unit of the Museums and Galleries Commission.

SUZY SMITH

86 Upper North Street, Brighton, **East Sussex BN1 3FL**

TEL 0273 220460

OPEN 9.30–6.30 Mon–Sat.

Specialise in restoring china and ceramics.

PROVIDE Home Inspections. Free Estimates. Free Local Delivery Service.

SPEAK TO Suzy Smith.

Ms Smith trained at Sèvres and at West Dean and also teaches ceramic restoration.

CAROL BANKS AND SON

September Cottage, 88 Victoria Road, Shoreham–by–Sea, **West Sussex BN4 5WS**

TEL 0273 461647.

OPEN By Appointment.

Specialise in repair and restoration of most types of pottery and porcelain figures and animals, including objects sculptured in wood and metal.

PROVIDE Free Estimates.
SPEAK TO Carol Banks.
Ms Banks is Tutor of Ceramic
Restoration L.E.A. and a member of
UKIC.
SEE Furniture, Picture Frames.

DAVID FILEMAN ANTIQUES
Squirrels, Bayards, Steyning, **West Sussex BN44 3AA**
TEL   0903 813229
OPEN   By Appointment.

Specialise in restoring and repairing
18th and 19th century glass chandeliers
and candelabra. This includes cleaning
and repinning.
PROVIDES Home Inspections. Free
Estimates. Chargeable
Collection/Delivery Service.
SPEAK TO David Fileman.

FINER CHINA
St Beethas, College Hill, Steyning, **West Sussex BN44 3GB**
TEL   0903 815107
OPEN   10–5 Mon–Fri By Appointment.

Specialise in restoring ceramics,
including porcelain and pottery, also
crystal and glass.
PROVIDE Home Inspections. Free
Estimates. Free Collection/Delivery
Service.
SPEAK TO Margaret Emsley.
Established 1988.

GARNER & CO.
Stable Cottage, Steyning Road,
Westiston, **West Sussex BN44 3DD**
TEL   0903 814565
OPEN   By Appointment (Tel Mon–Fri
9–5.30)

Specialise in the conservation and repair
of lead and bronze sculpture and glass
chandeliers.
PROVIDE Home Inspections. Estimates.
SPEAK TO Sid Garner.
SEE Clocks, Furniture, Silver.

PATRICIA R. JACKSON
81 The Warren, West Dean, Chichester,
West Sussex PO18 0RP
TEL   0243 63466
OPEN   By Appointment Only.

Specialise in restoring ceramics, glass,
enamels, objets d'art and archaeological
material of all periods.
PROVIDE Home Inspections.
Free/Chargeable Collection/Delivery
Service.
SPEAK TO Patricia Jackson.
Member of UKIC and IIC. This
workshop is included on the register of
conservators maintained by the
Conservation Unit of the Museums and
Galleries Commission.

SHEILA SOUTHWELL
7 West Street, Burgess Hill, **West Sussex RH15 8NN**
TEL   0444 244307
OPEN   10–4 Mon–Fri By Appointment.

Specialise in restoring porcelain and all
ceramics, some glass repairs and
particularly Oriental vases.
PROVIDE Home Inspections. Free
Estimates. Free/Chargeable
Collection/Delivery Service.
SPEAK TO Sheila Southwell.
This workshop is included on the register
of conservators maintained by the
Conservation Unit of the Museums and
Galleries Commission.

WEST DEAN COLLEGE
West Dean, Chichester, **West Sussex PO18 00Z**
TEL   0243 63 301
FAX   0243 63 342
OPEN   9–5 Mon–Fri.

Specialise in training conservators and
restorers in the field of antique ceramics
and will also undertake restoration.
PROVIDE Local Home Inspections. Free
Estimates.
SPEAK TO Peter Sarginson.
SEE Books, Clocks, Furniture, Silver

ROBERT MILLAR CRAIG

Clock House Studio, 22A Stoneleigh
Road, Gibbet Hill, Coventry,
Warwickshire CV4 7AD
TEL 0203 410402
OPEN 8.30–5.30 Mon–Fri or By
Appointment.

Specialise in restoration and repair of
china and glass, including insurance
valuation and repairs.

PROVIDE Home Inspections. Free
Estimates. Free Local
Collection/Delivery Service.
SPEAK TO Robert Millar Craig.
Member of UKIC. This workshop is
included on the register of conservators
maintained by the Conservation Unit of
the Museums and Galleries Commission.

RENAISSANCE RESTORATION CO.

The Forge, Manor Farm, Offchurch, Nr.
Leamington Spa, **Warwickshire
CV33 9AG**
TEL 0926 450430
OPEN 9–4 Mon, Tues, Fri.

Specialise in restoring bronze and lead
statuary, including spelter.

PROVIDE Home Inspections. Free
Estimates. Collection/Delivery Service.
SPEAK TO John A. Lennox.
Member of UKIC.

GILLIAN ARENGO–JONES

Glebe House, Church Walk, Ashton
Keynes, **Wiltshire SN6 6PB**
TEL 0285 861443
OPEN By Appointment.

Specialise in restoring pottery and
porcelain.

PROVIDE Free Estimates.
SPEAK TO Mr or Mrs Arengo–Jones.
Member of UKIC. This workshop is

included on the register of conservators
maintained by the Conservation Unit of
the Museums and Galleries Commission.

DELOMOSNE & SON LTD

Court Close, North Wraxall,
Chippenham, **Wiltshire SN14 7AD**
TEL 0225 891505
FAX 0225 891907
OPEN 9.30–5.30 Mon–Fri; 9.30–1 Sat.

Specialise in restoring English period
glass light fittings.

PROVIDE Home Inspections. Free
Estimates. Collection/Delivery Service
available.
SPEAK TO Martin Mortimer or Timothy
Osborne.

ROD NAYLOR

208 Devizes Road, Hilperton,
Trowbridge, **Wiltshire BA14 7QP**
TEL 0225 754497
OPEN By Appointment.

Specialise in supplying hand–blown
glass caddy bowls.

PROVIDE Home Inspections. Free
Estimates. Free Local
Collection/Delivery Service.
SPEAK TO Rod Naylor.
SEE Lighting, Furniture.

RESTORATIONS UNLIMITED

Pinkney Park, Malmesbury, **Wiltshire
SN16 0NX**
TEL 0666 840888
OPEN 8.30–5 Mon–Fri; By
Appointment Sat & Sun.

Specialise in restoring European and
Oriental ceramics.

PROVIDE Home Inspections. Free
Estimates. Free Collection/Delivery
Service.
SPEAK TO Richard Pinchis.
SEE Furniture, Clocks.

JANE WINCH CHINA REPAIRS
Westport Granary, Malmesbury,
Wiltshire SN16 OAL
TEL　0666 822119
OPEN　10–5 Mon–Fri.

Specialise in restoring and repairing decorative ceramics, antique and modern.

PROVIDE Home Inspections. Free Estimates.
SPEAK TO Jane Winch or Pat Paterson. Member of UKIC.

NIDD HOUSE ANTIQUES
Nidd House, Bogs Lane, Harrogate,
North Yorkshire HG1 4DY
TEL　0423 884739
OPEN　9–5 Mon–Fri or By Appointment.

Specialise in repairing statues up to 24 inches high.

PROVIDE Home Inspections. Free Local Estimates. Chargeable Collection/ Delivery Service.
SPEAK TO Mr D. Preston.
Member of the Guild of Master Craftsmen and UKIC. This workshop is included on the register of conservators maintained by the Conservation Unit of the Museums and Galleries Commission.
SEE Collectors (Scientific Instruments), Furniture, Silver.

CHINA RESTORATION
Westleigh Coach House, 11 Stubley Lane, Dronfield, Sheffield, **South Yorkshire S18 6PE**
TEL　0246 417037
OPEN　9–5.30 Mon–Fri or By Appointment.

Specialise in restoring china, stone, alabaster and marble.

PROVIDE Free Estimates.
SPEAK TO Teresa Goodlad

ST JAMES'S GALLERY LTD
Smith Street, St Peter Port, **Guernsey, Channel Islands**
TEL　0481 720070
OPEN　9–5 Mon–Fri; 9–1 Sat or By Appointment.

Specialise in some porcelain restoration.

PROVIDE Home Inspections. Chargeable Estimates. Collection/Delivery Service by arrangement.
SPEAK TO Mrs Whittam.
SEE Clocks, Furniture

DUNLUCE ANTIQUES
33 Ballytober Road, Bushmills, **Co. Antrim BT57 8UU**
TEL　02657 31140
OPEN　10–6 Mon–Thur; 2–6 Sat.

Specialise in restoring European and Oriental porcelain.

PROVIDE Home Inspections. Free Estimates. Chargeable Collection/Delivery Service.
SPEAK TO Clare Ross.
Clare Ross is West Dean trained.

LEINSTER STUDIOS
10 Leinster Square, Dublin 6, **Co. Dublin**
TEL　01 974009
OPEN　10–5 Mon–Fri.

Specialise in restoring ceramics, enamel, glass, alabaster and marble.

PROVIDE Home Inspections by arrangement. Free Estimates. Collection/Delivery Service by arrangement.
SPEAK TO Eileen O'Leary or Anne Reeves–Smyth.
Member of IPCRA.

DESIREE SHORTT
38 North Great George Street, Dublin 1, **Co. Dublin**
TEL　01 8722285
OPEN　9.30–5 Mon–Fri or By Appointment Sat, Sun.

Specialise in restoring porcelain, jade, stone, plastic, ivory.

PROVIDE Local Home Inspections. Free Estimates.
SPEAK TO Desiree Shortt.
Member of IPCRA.

JENNY SLEVIN
9 Innisboffin, Bailey View, Harbour Road, Dalkey, **Co. Dublin**
TEL   01 280 3429
OPEN   By Appointment.

Specialise in restoring ceramics, glass, jade, ivory, marble.

PROVIDE Home Inspections. Free/Chargeable Estimates. Collection/Delivery Service by arrangement.
SPEAK TO Jenny Slevin.
Member of IPCRA.
SEE Carpets, Furniture, Picture Frames, Collectors (Wax).

VALERIE McCOY
Fan–na–Greine, Glendalough, **Co. Wicklow**
TEL   0404 45125
OPEN   By Appointment.

Specialise in restoring European and Oriental ceramics.

PROVIDE Home Inspections. Free Estimates. Free Collection/Delivery Service.
SPEAK TO Valerie McCoy.
Member of IPCRA.
SEE Furniture, Picture Frames.

HELEN WARREN
26 Forbes Road, Rosyth, Dunfermline, **Fife KY11 2AN**
TEL   0383 419564
OPEN   By Appointment.

Specialise in restoring European and Oriental pottery and porcelain.

PROVIDE Free Estimates.

SPEAK TO Helen Warren
Member of UKIC and SSCR.

ANNE AND JAMES DAVIDSON, SCULPTORS
15 Redmoss Park, Aberdeen, **Grampian AB1 4JF**
TEL   0224 871759
OPEN   By Appointment.

Specialise in restoring plaster statuary.

PROVIDE Home Inspections. Free Estimates. Chargeable Collection/Delivery Service.
SPEAK TO Anne Davidson or James Davidson.
Anne Davidson is a Member of the Royal Society of British Sculptors. This workshop is in the Scottish Conservation Directory.

BENITA MILLER
30 Wester Links, Fortrose, **Highland IV10 8RZ**
TEL   0381 20479
OPEN   By Appointment.

Specialise in restoring European and Oriental ceramics.

PROVIDE Home Inspections. Free/Chargeable Estimates. Chargeable Collection/Delivery Service.
SPEAK TO Benita Miller.
Member of SSCR. This workshop is in the Scottish Conservation Directory.

LUIGI M. VILLANI
Traditional Antique Restoration and Consultancy Service, The Stable, Altyre, Forres, **Highland IV36 OSH**
TEL   0309 672572
OPEN   8–10 Mon–Fri.

Specialise in repair and restoration of wooden sculpture and objets d'art, angels, candlesticks, cupids, crucifixes etc, including gilding.

PROVIDE Home Inspections. Estimates.

SPEAK TO Luigi M. Villani or Rosalie Stuart.
Run a consultancy and training service on restoration, wood stains and finishes and also give lectures.
SEE Furniture.

BEAVER GLASS RESTORATION

23 Hatton Place, Edinburgh, **Lothian EH9 1UB**
TEL   031 667 8996
FAX   031 667 8996
OPEN   9–5 Mon–Fri.

Specialise in restoring glass, including grinding and polishing. Able to de–cloud non–leaded decanters.

PROVIDE Free Estimates.
SPEAK TO Marilyn or Derek Beaver. Members of SSCR.

ELLEN BREHENY

Conservation Studio, Hopetoun House, South Queensferry,
West Lothian EH30 9SL
TEL   031 331 2003
OPEN   By Appointment.

Specialise in conservation and restoration of ceramics and vessel glass and condition surveys of collections.

PROVIDE On–site Inspections. Free/Chargeable Estimates. Free/Chargeable Collection/Delivery Service.
SPEAK TO Ellen Breheny.
Member of UKIC and SSCR. This workshop is in the Scottish Conservation Directory.

HOUNDWOOD ANTIQUES RESTORATION

7 West Preston Street, Edinburgh
Lothian EH8 9PX
TEL   031 667 3253
OPEN   By Appointment.

Specialise in restoring antique ceramics.

PROVIDE Home Inspections. Free Estimates. Chargeable Collection/Delivery Service.
SPEAK TO Mr A. Gourlay.
SEE Furniture, Silver.

G. & A. MURRAY

Millburn Cottage, Skelmorlie, Ayrshire, **Strathclyde PA17 5EZ**
TEL   0475 520251
OPEN   8.30–6 Mon–Sat or By Appointment.

Specialise in restoring porcelain, earthenware, ivory and some glass. They do not do domestic china.

PROVIDE Free Estimates.
SPEAK TO George or Aline Murray.
Established 1979. Member of UKIC, CGCG, SSCR. This workshop is in the Scottish Conservation Directory.

CATHERINE RITCHIE

72 Novar Drive, Glasgow, **Strathclyde G12 9TZ**
TEL   041 339 0331
OPEN   By Appointment.

Specialise in restoring European and Oriental ceramics.

PROVIDE Free Estimates.
SPEAK TO Catherine Ritchie.

PETER J. DAVID

(address withheld by request) Barry, **South Glamorgan CF62 7RG**
TEL   0446 748153
OPEN   By Appointment.

Specialise in restoring all types of ceramics and porcelain, particularly Welsh and early English.

PROVIDE Free Estimates.
SPEAK TO Peter David.
This workshop is included on the register of conservators maintained by the Conservation Unit of the Museums and Galleries Commission.

IRENA ANTIQUES
111 Broad Street, Barry, **South Glamorgan CF6 8SX**
TEL   0446 747626 or 732517
OPEN   10–4 Mon–Fri.

Specialise in restoring European and Oriental porcelain.

PROVIDE Free Estimates. Free Collection/Delivery Service.
SPEAK TO Irena Halabuda
SEE Furniture

FURNITURE AND
MIRRORS

DO

Keep (and label) any veneers or mouldings which become detached
Dust marquetry furniture very carefully
Always pull out bearers for bureau lids fully
Lift, rather than drag, when moving large pieces
Check annually for active woodworm
Lift antique chairs by the seat-rail, not the back

DON'T

Place flower vases on polished surfaces
Polish metal mounts with metal polish – use a dry, medium-hard toothbrush to remove
dust
Use spray or silicone polishes
Restore gilding with paint
Put furniture near radiators or under sunny windows
Tilt chests of drawers forwards when moving them
Allow chairs to be tilted on two legs

M. AND S. BRADBURY

The Barn, Hanham Lane, Paulton, **Avon BS18 5PF**
TEL   0761 418910
OPEN   8–5 Mon–Fri or By
        Appointment.

Specialise in restoring furniture from all periods.

PROVIDE Home Inspections. Free Estimates. Free Local Collection/Delivery Service.
SPEAK TO M. or S. Bradbury.
Member of BAFRA. This workshop is included on the register of conservators maintained by the Conservation Unit of the Museums and Galleries Commission.

LAWRENCE BRASS AND SON

93–95 Walcot Street, Bath, **Avon BA1 5BW**
TEL   0225 464057
OPEN   8–5 Mon–Fri; By Appointment
        Sat.

Specialise in restoring fine furniture, including metalwork, gilding, upholstery. They cast furniture mounts and do firegilt ormolu. They also specialise in 'impossible' commissions.

PROVIDE Home Inspections. Free/Chargeable Estimates. Free Collection/Delivery Service.
SPEAK TO Mr Brass.
Established twenty-five years. Member of BAFRA and UKIC. This workshop is included on the register of conservators maintained by the Conservation Unit of the Museums and Galleries Commission.
SEE **London W9**

D. J. DAVIS

13 Castle Street, Thornbury, Bristol, **Avon BS12 1HA**
TEL   0454 412430
OPEN   By Appointment.

Specialise in restoring smaller items of furniture, occasional tables, chairs, cabinets, trays, mirrors etc. All aspects of cleaning, polishing and finishing covered.

PROVIDE Home Inspections. Free Estimates. Free Local Collection/Delivery Service.
SPEAK TO David Davis.
Mr Davis is a member of the Guild of Master Craftsmen and a director of the local museum.
SEE Clocks.

T. H. DEWEY

The Cottage, Kelston, Bath, **Avon BA1 9AF**
TEL   0225 447944
OPEN   8–5 Mon–Fri or By
        Appointment.

Specialise in restoring antique period furniture, including metalwork, but will repair a kitchen chair if requested.

PROVIDE Home Inspections. Free Local Estimates. Free Local Collection/Delivery Service.
SPEAK TO Tim Dewey.

FRANK DUX ANTIQUES

33 Belvedere, Bath, **Avon BA1 5HR**
TEL   0225 312367
OPEN   10–6 Mon–Sat.

Specialise in restoring antique furniture, all cabinet work and polishing.

PROVIDE Home Inspections. Refundable Estimates. Free Collection/Delivery Service on small items.
SPEAK TO Frank Dux.
Member of the UKIC.

MICHAEL JEFFRIES UPHOLSTERY

3 Upper Lambridge Street, Larkhall, Bath, **Avon BA1 6RY**
TEL   0225 310417
FAX   0225 448103
OPEN   9–1 Mon, 9–5 Tues–Fri, 9–12
        Sat.

Specialise in restoring any item of upholstered furniture of any period using only the appropriate methods and best quality materials, frames and carving also undertaken.

PROVIDE Home Inspections. Free/Chargeable Collection Delivery Service.
SPEAK TO Michael Jeffries.
Member of UKIC. Fellow of Association of Master Upholsterers.

PENNARD HOUSE ANTIQUES
3/4 Piccadilly, London Road, Bath, **Avon BA1 6PL**
TEL   0225 313791
FAX   0225 448196
OPEN   9.30–5.30 Mon–Sat.

Specialise in restoring English and French country furniture. Also undertake upholstery work, rushing and caning.

PROVIDE Home Inspections. Free Estimates. Free Collection/Delivery Service.
SPEAK TO Martin Dearden.

ANTHONY REED
94–96 Walcot Street, Bath, **Avon BA1 5BG**
TEL   0225 461969 or 0272 333595
OPEN   9–6 Mon–Sat.

Specialise in cleaning, restoring and gilding mirror frames.

PROVIDE Home Inspections. Chargeable Estimates. Chargeable Local Collection/Delivery Service.
SPEAK TO Anthony Reed.
Member of the IIC.
SEE Oil Paintings, Picture Frames.

ALICE WATTS
11 Mivart Street, Easton, Bristol, **Avon BS5 6JF**
TEL   0272 354831
OPEN   By Appointment.

Specialise in restoring giltwood

furniture, including surface decoration and gilding.

PROVIDE Home Inspections. Chargeable Estimates.
SPEAK TO Alice Watts.
Member of UKIC.

D. M. E. RESTORATIONS LTD
11 Church Street, Ampthill, **Bedfordshire MK45 2PL**
TEL   0525 405819
OPEN   8–5.30 Mon–Fri; 8–1 Sat or By Appointment.

Specialise in restoring English furniture, including polishing and gilding.

PROVIDE Home Inspections. Free Estimates. Collection/Delivery Service by arrangement.
SPEAK TO Duncan Everitt.

THOMAS HUDSON
The Barn, 117 High Street, Odell, **Bedfordshire MK43 7AS**
TEL   0234 721133
OPEN   8–6 Mon–Fri; 8–12 Sat.

Specialise in restoring antique furniture and old woodwork sympathetically. Can also make chairs to match existing sets.

PROVIDE Home Inspections. Chargeable Estimates.
SPEAK TO Thomas Hudson.
Please ring to discuss your requirements or to make an appointment to visit the workshop.

DAVID MITCHELL
45 St. Michael's Road, Bedford, **Bedfordshire MK40 2LZ**
TEL   0234 359976
OPEN   9–6 Mon–Fri or By Appointment.

Specialise in restoring all items of wooden furniture, including decorative items. Other wooden items can also be

restored on a problem–solving basis.
PROVIDE Home Inspections.
Free/Chargeable Estimates.
Chargeable Collection/Delivery Service.
SPEAK TO David Mitchell.
Member of UKIC and BAFRA.
SEE Oil Paintings, Clocks.

J. MOORE RESTORATIONS
College Farmhouse Workshops,
Chawston, Bedford,
Bedfordshire MK44 3BH
TEL   0480 214165
OPEN   8.30–5.30 Mon–Fri.

Specialise in restoring antique furniture,
including carving, gilding, marquetry,
French and wax polishing. Chairs and
other furniture copied, distressed and
patinated.

PROVIDE Home Inspections. Free
Estimates. Free Collection/Delivery
Service locally.
SPEAK TO Mr John Moore.

SIMON PALLISTER
33 Albion Road, Luton, **Bedfordshire LU2 0DS**
TEL   0582 453292
OPEN   8.30–6 Mon–Fri.

Specialise in restoring antique English
and Continental furniture and passive
electronic security tagging.

PROVIDE Home Inspections. Free
Estimates. Free Collection/Delivery
Service.
SPEAK TO Simon Pallister.
Member of BAFRA.

WATERLOO HOUSE ANTIQUES
Unit 2/3 College Farm, High Street,
Pulloxhill, **Bedfordshire MK45 5HP**
TEL   0525 717786
OPEN   10.30–4 Mon–Fri; 10.30–12
       Sat; closed Tues.

Specialise in restoring and re-

upholstering Victorian and Edwardian
furniture by traditional methods.
Recaning service also available.

PROVIDE Home Inspections. Free Local
Estimates. Free Collection/Delivery
Service.
SPEAK TO Mr R. J. Jennings.

ALPHA (ANTIQUE) RESTORATIONS
High Street, Compton, Nr. Newbury,
Berkshire RG16 0NL
TEL   0635 578245 and 0860 575203
OPEN   7–4 Mon–Fri.

Specialise in fine furniture restoration,
both English and Continental,
veneering, inlaying, specialised copy
chair making.

PROVIDE Home Inspections.
Free/Chargeable Estimates. Chargeable
Collection/Delivery Service.
SPEAK TO Graham Childs.
Member of BAFRA.

ASHLEY ANTIQUES AND FURNITURE
Unit 43, Hungerford Arcade,
Hungerford, **Berkshire RG17 0DL**
TEL   0672 20481
       ANS 0672 20481
OPEN   9.30–5.30 Daily.

Specialise in restoring English and
Continental furniture and making
furniture to order.

PROVIDE Home Inspections. Free
Estimates. Free Local
Collection/Delivery Service.
SPEAK TO Robert Duff.
SEE Clocks.

HAMILTON HAVERS
58 Conisboro Avenue, Caversham
Heights, Reading, **Berkshire RG4 7JE**
TEL   0734 473379
OPEN   By Appointment.

Specialise in restoring Boulle, marquetry, ivory, tortoiseshell, mother-of-pearl, brass, lapis lazuli and malachite on furniture.
PROVIDE Free/Chargeable Estimates.
SPEAK TO Hamilton Havers.
Mr Havers has worked for the National Trust.
SEE Clocks, Silver.

J. J. ANTIQUE RESTORATION
Braemar, Waltham Road, White Waltham, **Berkshire SL9 3SH**
TEL   0628 823741
OPEN   8–5 Mon–Fri.

Specialise in restoring 17th–19th century furniture.
PROVIDE Home Inspections. Free Estimates. Free Collection/Delivery Service.
SPEAK TO John White.
Member of the Guild of Master Craftsmen.

BEN NORRIS
Knowl Hill Farm, Knowl Hill, Kingsclere, Newbury, **Berkshire RG15 8WY**
TEL   0635 297950
FAX   0635 299851
OPEN   8.30–5.30 Mon–Fri.

Specialise in restoring antique furniture pre–1830, gilding, architectural woodwork and supplying and restoring brass furniture fittings.
PROVIDE Home Inspections. Free/Refundable Estimates. Free Local Collection/Delivery Service and to London.
SPEAK TO Ben Norris.
Member of BAFRA.

JOHN ARMISTEAD
Malham Cottage, Bellingdon, Nr. Chesham, **Buckinghamshire HP5 2UR**
TEL   0494 758209
OPEN   9–5 Mon–Fri.

Specialise in repairing metalwork, including brass beds.
PROVIDE Home Inspections, Free Estimates. Collection/Delivery Service by arrangement.
SPEAK TO John Armistead.
Member of the Guild of Master Craftsmen and UKIC. This workshop is included on the register of conservators maintained by the Conservation Unit of the Museums and Galleries Commission.
SEE Silver.

BROWNS OF WEST WYCOMBE
Church Lane, West Wycombe, **Buckinghamshire HP14 3AH**
TEL   0494 524537
FAX   0494 439548
OPEN   8–6 Mon–Fri; 8–12 Sat.

Specialise in restoring antique furniture and will make chairs to match existing sets.
PROVIDE Home Inspections. Free/Refundable Estimates. Free Collection/Delivery Service.
SPEAK TO D. A. Hines.

CHESS ANTIQUE RESTORATIONS
85 Broad Street, Chesham, **Buckinghamshire HP5 3EF**
TEL   0494 783043
FAX   0494 791302
OPEN   8–5 Mon–Sat.

Specialise in restoration of furniture.
PROVIDE Home Inspections. Chargeable Estimates. Chargeable Collection/Delivery Service.
SPEAK TO T. F. Chapman.

CONY CRAFTS
Hale Acre Workshops, Watchet Lane, Nr. Great Missenden, **Buckinghamshire HP16 0DR**
TEL   02406 5668
ANS   02406 5668
OPEN   9–5.30 Mon–Fri.

Specialise in sympathetically restoring antique and modern furniture, including traditional upholstery work, wood–carving, chair–rushing, chair–caning and French polishing. Pieces can be made to individual commission. Chairs made to make up uneven sets, singles or carvers matched to originals of any period. Insurance work undertaken.

PROVIDE Home Inspections. Free Estimates. Inclusive Collection/Delivery Service.
SPEAK TO Mr Nowlan.
Member of the Guild of Master Craftsmen.

JOCK HOPSON CONSERVATION SERVICE

Holes Lane, Olney, **Buckinghamshire MK46 4BX**
TEL   0234 712306
FAX   0234 241634
OPEN   By Appointment.

Specialise in gilding and carving furniture and mirror frames. Also Japanese lacquer work.

PROVIDE Home Inspections. Free/Chargeable Estimates. Chargeable Collection/Delivery Service.
SPEAK TO Jock Hopson.
Member of UKIC. This workshop is included on the register of conservators maintained by the Conservation Unit of the Museums and Galleries Commission.
SEE Picture Frames, Arms.

PERIOD FURNITURE SHOWROOMS

49 London End, Beaconsfield, **Buckinghamshire HP9 2HW**
TEL   0494 674112
OPEN   9–5.30 Mon–Sat.

Specialise in restoring English furniture, including cabinetmaking, chair–making, polishing and upholstery.

PROVIDE Home Inspections. Free Estimates. Free Collection/Delivery Service.
SPEAK TO R. E. W. Hearne.

TINGEWICK ANTIQUES CENTRE

Main Street, Tingewick, **Buckinghamshire MK18 4PB**
TEL   0280 848219
OPEN   10–5.30 Mon–Sat; 11–5 Sun; closed Fri.

Specialise in restoring metalware on furniture.

PROVIDE Home Inspections. Free Estimates. Collection/Delivery Service by arrangement.
SPEAK TO Rosemarie or Barry Smith. SEE Clocks.

WYCOMBE CANE AND RUSH WORKS

Victoria Street, High Wycombe, **Buckinghamshire HP11 2LU**
TEL   0494 442429
OPEN   9–5 Mon–Fri.

Specialise in all types of canework, including spider and fan work patterns and blind or secret cane. Also carry out rush seating.

PROVIDE Local Home Inspections . Refundable Estimates.
SPEAK TO Peter Gilbert.
Established in 1880. Visitors are always welcome to come and see work being carried out.

GRAHAM BARNES

14 St Mary's Street, Ely, **Cambridgeshire CB7 4ES**
TEL   0353 665218
OPEN   By Appointment.

Specialise in restoring pre–1830 fine furniture, marquetry and brass inlay.

PROVIDE Free Estimates.
SPEAK TO Graham Barnes.
Member of BAFRA.

CLADGILD LTD
Vine House, Reach, Cambridge,
Cambridgeshire CB5 0JD
TEL   0638 741989
FAX   0953 885800
OPEN   By Appointment.

Specialise in restoring wood products, including antique furniture and panelling. Also offer an upholstery service. Replicas can be made to order.

PROVIDE Home Inspections. Free Collection/Delivery Service.
SPEAK TO Jo Ann Dudley.
Members of the Association of Master Upholsterers and the Guild of Master Craftsmen.

DODDINGTON HOUSE ANTIQUES
2 Benwick Road, Doddington, Nr. March, **Cambridgeshire PE15 OTG**
TEL   0354 740755
OPEN   10–6 Mon–Sat.

Specialise in restoring painted furniture, lacquer work, cane and rush work.

PROVIDE Refundable Estimates. Free Collection/Delivery Service.
SPEAK TO Brian or Lynette Frankland.
SEE Clocks.

A. F. DUDLEY trading as 'THE FURNITURE CLINIC'.
Vine House, Reach, **Cambridgeshire CB5 OJD**
TEL   0638 741989
FAX   0953 885800
OPEN   By Appointment.

Specialise in restoring antique and modern furniture, including French polishing, marquetry, carving, upholstery, re-leathering, gold tooling, re-silvering, caning and rushing.

PROVIDE Home Inspections. Free Estimates. Free Collection/Delivery Service.
SPEAK TO Mr A. Dudley.

Member of the Guild of Master Craftsmen and the Association of Master Upholsterers.
SEE Clocks, Collectors (Dolls, Toys, Mechanical Music).

FRANK GOODINGHAM
Studio 3, Hope Street Yard, Hope Street, Cambridge, **Cambridgeshire CB1 3NA**
TEL   0223 410702
OPEN   10–6 Mon–Fri.

Specialise in restoring 18th and 19th century gilded work, including composition or carved overmantels and pier glass frames.

PROVIDE Home Inspections. Refundable Estimates. Collection/Delivery by arrangement.
SPEAK TO Frank Goodingham.
SEE Picture Frames.

KENDAL FURNITURE RESTORATIONS
2 Clifton Road, Huntingdon, **Cambridgeshire PE18 7EJ**
TEL   0480 411811
FAX   0480 411444
OPEN   8–5 Mon–Fri.

Specialise in repairing, polishing and upholstering antique furniture as well as cane and rush seating, desk leather lining, manufacturing individually hand–made furniture.

PROVIDE Home Inspections. Free Collection/Delivery Service.
SPEAK TO Terence Brazier.
Member of LAPADA.

PAUL WALDMANN
41 Norfolk Street, Cambridge, **Cambridgeshire CB1 2LD**
TEL   0223 314001
OPEN   By Appointment.

Specialise in all aspects of furniture restoration plus fine cabinetmaking to commission.

PROVIDE Home Inspections. Free Estimates. Free Local Collection/Delivery Service. SPEAK TO Paul Waldmann. Member of BAFRA. This workshop is included on the register of conservators maintained by the Conservation Unit of the Museums and Galleries Commission.

ROBERT WILLIAMS

Osborn's Farm, 32 Church Street, Willingham, **Cambridgeshire CB4 5HT**
TEL   0954 260972
OPEN   9–6 Mon–Fri.

Specialise in all aspects of furniture restoration, including marquetry, carving and brass inlay, carefully cleaning and retaining old patinated surfaces.

PROVIDE Home Inspections. Free Estimates. Free Local Collection/Delivery Service. SPEAK TO Robert Williams. Member of BAFRA.

A. ALLEN ANTIQUE RESTORERS

Buxton Rd, Newtown, Newmills, Via Stockport, **Cheshire SK12 3JS**
TEL   0663 745274
OPEN   8–5 Mon–Fri; 9–12 Sat.

Specialise in restoring antique furniture, including 17th and 18th century oak and walnut pieces. Also restore Boulle work, inlay, gilding, upholstery and metalwork. Furniture can be designed or copied.

PROVIDE Home Inspections. Free/Chargeable Estimates. Collection/Delivery Service. SPEAK TO Tony Allen. SEE Clocks, Picture Frames, Silver.

ARROWSMITH ANTIQUES AND RESTORATIONS

Unit 1A, Bridge Street Mill, Macclesfield, **Cheshire**
TEL   0625 611880
OPEN   8.30–5.30 Mon–Sat.

Specialise in restoring 18th and 19th century furniture.

PROVIDE Home Inspections. Free Estimates. Free Collection/Delivery Service. SPEAK TO Paul Arrowsmith.

THE OLD BAKERY

21–23 Lower Fold, Marple Bridge, Via Stockport, **Cheshire SK6 5DU**
TEL   061 427 4699
OPEN   9–6 Mon–Fri.

Specialise in antique furniture restoration and the supply of feet, rockers, mouldings etc. No upholstery work carried out.

SPEAK TO Geoffrey Douglas.

ROGER G. TURNER

Hext Farm, Birch Vale, Stockport, **Cheshire SK12 5DH**
TEL   0663 742491
OPEN   By Appointment Only.

Specialise in restoring good quality period furniture, including all refinishing and structural work, but excluding major upholstery.

PROVIDE Home Inspections. Free Estimates. Free Local Collection/Delivery Service. SPEAK TO Roger G. Turner. Member of UKIC. This workshop is included on the register of conservators maintained by the Conservation Unit of the Museums and Galleries Commission.

ANN & DEREK MASON

11 Redmire Road, Grangefield, Stockton–on–Tees, **Cleveland TS18 4JR**
TEL   0642 614583
OPEN   9–7 Mon–Fri.

Specialise in restoring antique furniture.

PROVIDE Free estimates. SPEAK TO Derek Mason. Will do on–site work within a thirty–mile radius of Stockton.

JOANNE McKINLEY
118 High Street, Norton, Stockton–on–Tees, **Cleveland TS20 1DS**
TEL   0642 555033
OPEN   8.30–4.30 Mon–Fri; 9–12 Sat; closed Thur.

Specialise in restoring mirrors.

PROVIDE Chargeable Home Inspections. Free Estimates.
SPEAK TO Joanne McKinley.
Member of UKIC. This workshop is included on the register of conservators maintained by the Conservation Unit of the Museums and Galleries Commission.
SEE Porcelain

MALCOLM JOHNSON
"Dunmere", Tregrehan, St Austell, **Cornwall PL25 3TG**
TEL   072681 2537
OPEN   By Appointment.

Specialise in restoring by hand polished furniture, antique or modern; complete suites, grand pianos or table tops in situ. Also colour matching limed oak finishing if needed to blend with existing items. All work is hand stripped.

PROVIDE Home Inspections. Free Local Estimates. Free Local Collection/Delivery Service.
SPEAK TO Malcolm Johnson.
This is a three–generation family business. This workshop is included on the register of conservators maintained by the Conservation Unit of the Museums and Galleries Commission.

ST AUSTELL ANTIQUES CENTRE
(formerly The Furniture Store)
37/39 Truro Road, St Austell, **Cornwall PL25 5JE**
TEL   0726 63178 or 0288 81548
OPEN   10–5 Mon–Sat or By Appointment.

Specialise in furniture restoration.

PROVIDE Home Inspections. Free Estimates. Free Local Collection/Delivery Service.
SPEAK TO Roger Nosworthy.

PETER STANTON
12 The Crescent, Truro, **Cornwall TR1 3ES**
TEL   0872 70262
OPEN   9–5 Mon–Fri.

Specialise in restoring 17th and 18th century furniture and upholstery.

PROVIDE Home Inspections. Free Estimates. Chargeable Collection/Delivery Service.
SPEAK TO Peter Stanton.

TUDOR ROSE DEVELOPMENTS
Court Cottage, Higher Porthpean, St Austell, **Cornwall PL26 6AY**
TEL   0726 75653
OPEN   9–4 Mon–Fri.

Specialise in restoring and upholstering English and some Continental furniture. Copywork undertaken.

PROVIDE Home Inspections. Estimates. Collection/Delivery Service.
SPEAK TO Christopher Pascoe.
Restoration tuition and supplies available

PETER HALL & SON
Danes Road, Staveley, Kendal, **Cumbria LA8 9PL**
TEL   0539 821633
FAX   0539 821905
OPEN   9–5 Mon–Fri.

Specialise in restoring antique furniture, structural and inlay repair, repolishing, gilding, carving, marquetry, metalwork and traditional re–upholstery, recaning and rushing, repair of locks and brassware.

PROVIDE Local Home Inspections. Free

Estimates. Chargeable Collection/Delivery Service. SPEAK TO Jeremy Hall.
This workshop is included on the register of conservators maintained by the Conservation Unit of the Museums and Galleries Commission.

JOSEPH JAMES ANTIQUES
Corney Square, Penrith, **Cumbria CA11 7PX**
TEL 0768 62065
OPEN 9–5.30 Mon–Sat; closed Wed.

Specialise in repairing antique furniture, French polishing and re-upholstering.

PROVIDE Home Inspections. Free Estimates. Free Local Collection/Delivery Service. SPEAK TO Gordon Walker.
Also have soft furnishings workrooms.

SHIRE ANTIQUES
The Post House, High Newton, Newton–in–Cartmel, Nr. Grange–over–Sands, **Cumbria LA11 6JQ**
TEL 05395 31431
OPEN 9.30–5 Mon, Wed–Sat; 10–4 Sun; closed Tues.

Specialise in restoring 16th–18th century oak furniture.

PROVIDE Home Inspections. Free Estimates. Free Local Collection/Delivery Service. SPEAK TO Brian or Jean Shire.

CANE AND RUSH SEATING
50 Ashbourne Road, Derby, **Derbyshire DE22 3AD**
TEL 0332 344363
OPEN 10–4 Mon–Fri.

Specialise in replacing cane and rush in chairs, settees, bedheads. All patterns of cane can be reproduced, including single set, double set, sunset patterns, blind holes. Chairs which have been upholstered because nobody could be found to re–cane or rush them may be restored to their original appearance. Fine rush a speciality.

PROVIDE Home Inspections, Free Estimates. SPEAK TO Joan Gilbert.

MELBOURNE HALL FURNITURE RESTORERS
The Old Saw Mill, Melbourne Hall Craft Centre, Melbourne Hall, **Derbyshire DE7 1EN**
TEL 0332 864131
OPEN 9–5 Mon–Fri; 2–4.30 Sun By Appointment; Closed Sat.

Specialise in furniture repairs, including hand polishing.

PROVIDE Home Inspections. Free/Refundable Estimates. Collection/Delivery Service. SPEAK TO Neil Collumbell.

PENROSE AND RIETBERG
Broome's Barnes, Pilsey Lane, Pilsley Village, Nr. Bakewell, **Derbyshire DE4 1PF**
TEL 0246 583444
FAX 0246 583360
OPEN 9–5.30 Mon–Fri; 10–4 Sat.

Specialise in restoring traditionally upholstered fine quality antique chairs, sofas, settees. They also recover modern upholstered sofas and chairs, and offer a full interior design service.

PROVIDE Home Inspections. Free Local Estimates. Free Local Collection/Delivery Service. SPEAK TO Mark A. von Rietberg, Rory D. F. Penrose or Brian Rosen.

STEPHEN SIMMONS AND HELEN MILES
Broadstones, Main Road, Wensley,
Matlock, **Derbyshire DE4 2LH**
TEL   Workshop 0629 734826 Home
0629 732227
OPEN   10–4 Mon–Sat By Appointment.

Specialise in restoring antique furniture
and offer a range of services from light
cleaning to the challenge of re–building
and re–finishing pieces in very poor
condition. Also hand French polishing.

PROVIDE Home Inspections. Free
Estimates. Free Local
Collection/Delivery Service.
SPEAK TO Stephen Simmons or Helen
Miles.

NIGEL F. THOMPSON
Antiques Warehouse, 25 Lightwood
Road, Buxton, **Derbyshire**
TEL   0298 72967
OPEN   10–5 Mon–Sat.

Specialise in restoring brass and brass
and iron bedsteads and some furniture,
mainly Victorian mahogany and
Georgian oak, also re–upholstery, re–
caning and rushing.

PROVIDE Home Inspections.
Discretionary Estimates. Chargeable
Collection/Delivery Service.
SPEAK TO Nigel Thompson.

JAMES BELLCHAMBERS
Hayhill Coach House, Plymouth Road,
Totnes, **Devon TQ9 5LH**
TEL   0803 863465
OPEN   By Appointment.

Specialise in restoring quality wood
furniture of all periods.

PROVIDE Home Inspections. Free
Estimates. Chargeable
Collection/Delivery Service.
SPEAK TO James Bellchambers.
Member of UKIC. This workshop is

included on the register of conservators
maintained by the Conservation Unit of
the Museums and Galleries Commission.

D. J. BENT
Stonecourt, Membland, Newton Ferrers,
Plymouth, **Devon PL8 1HP**
TEL   0752 872 831
OPEN   By Appointment.

Specialise in restoring antique English
and Continental furniture, particularly
oak, walnut and mahogany.

PROVIDE Home Inspections. Free
Estimates. Chargeable
Collection/Delivery Service.
SPEAK TO Mr D. J. Bent.
Mr Bent teaches furniture restoration
and is a member of BAFRA and UKIC.
This workshop is included on the register
of conservators maintained by the
Conservation Unit of the Museums and
Galleries Commission.

RODERICK BUTLER
Marwood House, Honiton, **Devon
EX14 8PY**
TEL   0404 42169
OPEN   9.30–5.30 Mon–Sat.

Specialise in restoring antique furniture
and works of art.

PROVIDE Home Inspections. Free
Estimates. Free Collection/Delivery
Service.
SPEAK TO Roderick Butler.

CLIVE AND LESLEY COBB
Newhouse Farm, Bratton Fleming,
Barnstaple, **Devon EX31 4RT**
TEL   0598 710465
OPEN   9–5.30 Daily.

Specialise in restoring lacquer work,
chinoiserie and decorative painted
artefacts. Also create individual
decorative items to customers'
requirements.

PROVIDE Home Inspections. Free

Estimates. Chargeable Collection/Delivery Service. SPEAK TO Clive Cobb. Member of UKIC and the Guild of Master Craftsmen. This workshop is included on the register of conservators maintained by the Conservation Unit of the Museums and Galleries Commission. SEE Clocks.

J. COLLINS AND SON
63 High St, Bideford, **Devon** **EX39 2AN**
TEL   0237 473103
FAX   0237 475658
OPEN   9.30–5 Mon–Sat.

Specialise in restoring antique furniture.

PROVIDE Home Inspections. Free Estimates. Free Local Collection/Delivery Service. SPEAK TO Mr J. C. Biggs. Established 1953. Member of UKIC. This workshop is included on the register maintained by the Conservation Unit of the Museums and Galleries Commission.

MICHAEL HURST
326 Old Laira Road, Plymouth, **Devon** **PL3 6AQ**
TEL   0752 221161
ANS   0752 221161
OPEN   8.30–5 Mon–Fri; 9–12 Sat.

Specialise in restoring all antique and modern 1900 plus furniture, including, rush, sea–grass and cane work with a complete upholstery workshop using traditional methods and materials.

PROVIDE Home Inspections. Free Local Estimates. Free Collection/Delivery Service. SPEAK TO Michael Hurst or Elizabeth Powles.

LOVE'S FURNITURE RESTORATIONS
The Workshop, South Street, Axminster, **Devon EX13 5AD**
TEL   0297 35059
OPEN   8.30–5 Mon–Sat; closed Wed.

Specialise in restoring and repairing antique and grand furniture, French polishing.

PROVIDE Home Inspections. Free Estimates. Chargeable Collection/Delivery Service. SPEAK TO Jamie Love. Members of the Guild of Master Craftsmen; the family has been trading in Axminster since 1873.

PETER MOORE
The Workshop, 56 Sherwell Lane, Torquay, **Devon TQ2 6BE**
TEL   0803 605334
OPEN   8.30–5 Mon–Sat.

Specialise in restoring antique and solid timber furniture.

PROVIDE Home Inspections. Free Estimates. Chargeable Collection/Delivery Service. SPEAK TO Peter Moore. Member of the Guild of Master Craftsmen and Guild of Woodworkers.

TONY VERNON
15 Follett Road, Topsham, **Devon** **EX3 0JP**
TEL   0392 874635
OPEN   9–6 Mon–Fri.

Specialise in restoring and conserving antique English and Continental furniture, marquetry inlay, Boulle work, gilding, re-veneering and French polishing.

PROVIDE Home Inspections. Refundable Estimates. Chargeable Collection/Delivery Service. SPEAK TO Tony Vernon. Member of BAFRA, UKIC and IIC.

MICHAEL BARRINGTON
The Old Rectory, Warmwell, Dorchester, **Dorset DT2 8HQ**
TEL   0305 852104
OPEN   8.30–5.30 or By Appointment.

Specialise in restoring antique furniture and associated metalwork, gilding, painting, marquetry, organ casework and pipe gilding.

PROVIDE Free Local Estimates. Free/Chargeable Collection/Delivery Service.
SPEAK TO Michael Barrington.
Member of BAFRA.
SEE Clocks, Collectors (Toys).

BLACKWOODS
805 Christchurch Road, Boscombe, Bournemouth, **Dorset BH7 6AP**
TEL   0202 434800
OPEN   10–1, 2–4.30 Mon–Fri; 10–4 Sat.

Specialise in restoring antique English furniture, including marquetry, inlay, carving, turning and gilding; also upholstery and all types of polishing.

PROVIDE Home Inspections. Free/Refundable Estimates. Free Collection/Delivery Service.
SPEAK TO Richard Owen.
Member of BAFRA and UKIC. This workshop is included on the register maintained by the Conservation Unit of the Museums and Galleries Commission.

RICHARD BOLTON
Ash Tree Cottage, Whitecross, Netherbury, Bridport, **Dorset DT6 5NH**
TEL   030 888 474
OPEN   8.30–6 Mon–Fri.

Specialise in all aspects of sympathetic furniture restoration using traditional cabinetmaking and polishing techniques. Desk and table leathers supplied and fitted, upholstery, caning, rushing, brass casting and gilding services available.

PROVIDE Home Inspections. Free Estimates. Free Collection/Delivery Service.
SPEAK TO Richard Bolton.
Member of BAFRA.

PETER BRAZIER
Nash Court Farmhouse, Marnhull, Sturminster Newton, **Dorset DT10 1JZ**
TEL   0258 820255
OPEN   8.30–5.30 Mon–Fri or By Appointment.

Specialise in all aspects of furniture restoration and finishing, excluding gilding. Also run a non–ferrous foundry where missing mounts can be cast using the lost wax method.

PROVIDE Home Inspections. Free Estimates. Free Local Collection/Delivery Service.
SPEAK TO Peter Brazier.
Member of BAFRA.

THE CHETTLE GUILD
The Stables, Chettle House, Chettle, Blandford, **Dorset DT11 8DB**
TEL   0258 89576
OPEN   9–6 Mon–Sat.

Specialise in restoring furniture, including metalwork, fine gilding and oil and water gilding.

PROVIDE Home Inspections. Free Estimates. Free Local Collection/Delivery Service.
SPEAK TO Alastair or Andrew Arnold.
SEE Arms, Clocks, Collectors (Scientific Instruments).

CAROLE A. CURTIN
Brentry, Whitecliff Mill Street, Blandford, **Dorset DT11 7BQ**
TEL   0258 454273
         MOB 0831 312591
OPEN   By Appointment.

Specialise in conservation and restoration of giltwood, including frames and overmantles.

PROVIDE Home Inspections. Free Estimates. Chargeable Collection/Delivery Service.
SPEAK TO Carole Curtin.
Member of UKIC and IPCRA.

MRS CATHERINE MATHEW
Kiwi Cottage, Maperton Road, Charlton Horethorne, Sherborne, **Dorset DT9 4NT**
TEL 096 322 595
OPEN 9–6 Mon–Fri or By Appointment.

Specialise in repairing furniture, cleaning, regilding, cane seating.
PROVIDE Home Inspections. Free Estimates. Free Collection/Delivery Service.
SPEAK TO Catherine Mathew.
SEE Picture Frames.

G. A. MATTHEWS
The Cottage Workshop, 174 Christchurch Road, Parley Cross, Wimborne, **Dorset BH22 8SS**
TEL 0202 572665
OPEN 9–5 Mon–Fri.

Specialise in restoring antique furniture, all types of finishing and both modern and antique cabinetmaking.
PROVIDE Home Inspections. Free Estimates. Chargeable Collection/Delivery Service.
SPEAK TO G. A. Matthews.

CLAIRE TIMINGS GILDING
Unit 4, Westhill Barns, Evershot, Dorchester, **Dorset DT2 0LD**
TEL 0975 83267
FAX 0935 83574
OPEN 9.30–4 By Appointment.

Specialise in restoring gilded mirror frames and furniture.
PROVIDE Home Inspections. Free/Chargeable Estimates. Chargeable Collection/Delivery Service.
SPEAK TO Claire or Simon Timings.
Member of UKIC and SSCR. This workshop is included on the register of conservators maintained by the Conservation Unit of the Museums and Galleries Commission.
SEE Picture Frames.

TOLPUDDLE ANTIQUE RESTORERS
The Stables, Tolpuddle, Dorchester, **Dorset DT2 7HF**
TEL 0305 848739
OPEN 9–6 Mon–Fri; 12–5 Sat.

Specialise in restoring antique furniture.
PROVIDE Home Inspections. Free Estimates. Free Collection/Delivery Service.
Member of BAFRA.
SEE Clocks.

THE COLLECTOR
Douglas House, 23–25 The Bank, Barnard Castle, **Durham DL12 8PH**
TEL 0833 37783
OPEN By Appointment.

Specialise in restoring early oak and period furniture, including metalwork.
PROVIDE Home Inspections. Refundable Estimates. Chargeable Collection/Delivery Service.
SPEAK TO Robert Jordan or Paul Hunter. Also provide a full design service.
SEE Clocks

CLIVE BEARDALL
104B High Street, Maldon, **Essex CM9 7ET**
TEL 0621 857890
FAX 0621 857565
OPEN 8–6 Mon–Fri; 8–1 Sat.

Specialise in restoring period furniture, including marquetry, carving, gilding, leather desk lining, traditional hand French polishing and wax finishing. Does rush and cane seating.
PROVIDE Home Inspections. Free/Chargeable Estimates. Free/Chargeable Collection/Delivery Service.
SPEAK TO Clive Beardall.
Member of BAFRA and UKIC. This

workshop is included on the register of conservators maintained by the Conservation Unit of the Museums and Galleries Commission.

S. BOND & SON

14/15 North Hill, Colchester, **Essex CO1 1DZ**
TEL   0206 572925
OPEN   9–5 Mon–Sat.

Specialise in restoring antique and Victorian furniture.

PROVIDE Home Inspections. Free Estimates. Free Local Collection/Delivery Service.
SPEAK TO Robert Bond
This family firm has been established for over 140 years and is run by the fifth generation.
SEE Oil Paintings.

CHARLES COPE

The Forge, Church Road, Little Baddon, Nr. Chelmsford, **Essex CM3 4BN**
TEL   0245 222045
OPEN   By Appointment.

Specialise in restoring furniture and general woodwork, including polishing, veneers, etc.

PROVIDE Local Home Inspections. Free/Chargeable Estimates. Local Collection/Delivery Service.
SPEAK TO Charles Cope.
Member of UKIC.

DAVID, JEAN & JOHN ANTIQUES

587 London Road, Westcliff, **Essex SS0 9PQ**
TEL   0702 339106
FAX   0268 560563
OPEN   10–5 Mon–Sat; closed Wed.

Specialise in restoring Victorian and Edwardian furniture.

PROVIDE Home Inspections. Refundable Estimates. Free Collection/Delivery Service.

SPEAK TO David Howard.
SEE Clocks.

A. DUNN & SON

The White House, 8 Wharf Road, Chelmsford, **Essex CM3 4XL**
TEL   0245 354452
FAX   0245 494991
OPEN   7–5 Mon–Fri; By Appointment Sat.

Specialise in restoring antique furniture of all periods, especially marquetry and Boulle. Will also make new panels.

PROVIDE Home Inspections. Free Local Estimates. Collection/Delivery Service available.
SPEAK TO Bob Dunn.
This third–generation firm was started in 1896. They made the marquetry panels for the VSOE Orient Express and liners including the Queen Mary and Queen Elizabeth.

FORGE STUDIO WORKSHOPS

Stour Street, Manningtree, **Essex CO11 1BE**
TEL   0206 396222
OPEN   8.30–5 Mon–Fri; 9–12 Sat.

Specialise in restoring fine antique furniture, bespoke cabinetmaking, chair matching, church and heraldic carving.

PROVIDE Home Inspections. Free Estimates. Collection/Delivery Service.
SPEAK TO Dick Patterson.
Member of BAFRA.

TERRY HILLIARD

The Barn, Master Johns, Thoby Lane, Mountnessing, Brentwood, **Essex CM15 0JY**
TEL   0277 354717
OPEN   By Appointment.

Specialise in restoring gilded furniture, mirror frames and carving and gilding.

PROVIDE Home Inspections. Free

Estimates. Free Collection/Delivery
Service.
SPEAK TO Terry Hilliard.
Member of the Guild of Master
Craftsmen.
SEE Picture Frames.

LITTLEBURY ANTIQUES
58–60 Fairycroft Road, Saffron Walden,
Essex CB10 1LZ
TEL   0799 527961
FAX   0799 527961
OPEN   8.30–5.15 Mon–Fri; By
       Appointment Sat.

Specialise in restoring furniture of all
periods.

PROVIDE Home Inspections. Free
Estimates. Free/Chargeable
Collection/Delivery Service.
SPEAK TO N. H. D'Oyly.
SEE Clocks.

LOMAS PIGEON AND CO.
LTD
The Workshops, R/O 1 Beehive Lane,
Chelmsford, **Essex CM2 9SU**
TEL   0245 353708
FAX   0245 257706
OPEN   9–5 Mon–Fri; 9–12 Sat.

Specialise in restoring antique and
period furniture.

PROVIDE Home Inspections.
Free/Chargeable Estimates. Chargeable
Collection/Delivery Service.
SPEAK TO Bill Pigeon.
Member of BAFRA, AMU and UNIC.

MILLERS ANTIQUES
KELVEDON
46 High Street, Kelvedon, Colchester,
Essex CO5 9AG
TEL   0376 570098
FAX   0376 572186
OPEN   9–5.30 Mon–Fri; 10–4 Sat.

Specialise in restoring antique furniture,
French polishing, carving and gilding,

desk and table–top relining, upholstery
and bespoke furniture making.

PROVIDE Home Inspections. Free
Estimates. Chargeable
Collection/Delivery Service.
SPEAK TO Mr R. C. Miller.

SKILLCRAFTS
10 Park Street, Thaxted, Great Dunmow,
Essex CM6 2ND
TEL   0371 830162
OPEN   9–6 Mon–Sat.

Specialise in complete restoration of
antique and traditional furniture,
including an upholstery service.

PROVIDE Home Inspections. Free Local
Estimates. Free/Refundable
Collection/Delivery Service.
SPEAK TO Michael L. Rickwood.
Member of UKIC. This workshop is
included on the register of conservators
maintained by the Conservation Unit of
the Museums and Galleries Commission.

THOMAS STAFFORD
44 Marcos Road, Canvey Island, **Essex
SS8 7LE**
TEL   0268 680929
OPEN   8.30–6 Mon–Sat.

Specialise in all aspects of furniture
restoration and wood finishing
employing traditional and shellac waxed
finishes and modern spray techniques.
Other services include cabinet
manufacturing and joinery designed to
individual requirements.

PROVIDE Home Inspections. Free
Estimates. Free Collection/Delivery
Service.
SPEAK TO Thomas Stafford.
Member of the Guild of Master
Craftsmen.

TURPINS ANTIQUES
4 Stoney Lane, Thaxted, **Essex**
TEL   0371 830495 or 0860 883302
OPEN   10–5 Mon–Sat.

Specialise in restoring 18th century English furniture.

PROVIDE Home Inspections. Free Estimates. Chargeable Collection/Delivery Service.
SPEAK TO John Braund.

ANTIQUE FURNITURE RESTORATION
Gloucester Antique Centre, 1 Severn Road, Gloucester,
Gloucestershire GL1 2LE
TEL   0452 529716
FAX   0452 307161
OPEN   9.30–5 Mon–Sat; 1–5 Sun.

Specialise in restoring Georgian and Regency furniture as well as marquetry.

PROVIDE Home Inspections. Free Estimates. Free Collection/Delivery Service.
SPEAK TO Mr C. A. Cook.

KEITH BAWDEN
Mews Workshop, Montpellier Retreat, Cheltenham, **Gloucestershire GL50 2XG**
TEL   0242 230320
OPEN   7–4.30 Mon–Fri.

Specialise in conserving and restoring antique furniture and upholstery.

PROVIDE Free Estimates. Home Inspections. Local Collection/Delivery Service.
SPEAK TO Keith Bawden.
SEE Clocks, Oil Paintings, Porcelain, Silver.

FORUM ANTIQUES
20 West Way, Cirencester,
Gloucestershire GL7 1JA
TEL   0285 658406
OPEN   9–5.30 Mon–Sat.

Specialise in restoring 17th century oak furniture.

PROVIDE Home Inspections. Free

Estimates. Free Collection/Delivery Service.
SPEAK TO Weston Mitchell.

G. M. S. RESTORATIONS
The Workshops (rear of Bell Passage Antiques), High Street, Wickwar,
Gloucestershire GL12 8NP
TEL   0454 294251
FAX   0454 294251
OPEN   8–5 Mon–Fri.

Specialise in restoring furniture, polishing, carving, gilding and traditional upholstery.

PROVIDE Home Inspections. Refundable Estimates. Chargeable Collection/Delivery Service.
SPEAK TO Mr G. M. St George–Stacey. Member of LAPADA, Association of Master Upholsterers, Guild of Master Craftsmen, Guild of Woodcarvers, Guild of Antique Dealers and Restorers.
SEE Oil Paintings.

MRS JANET GIBBS
The Hope, Ampney St Peter, Cirencester, **Gloucestershire GL7 5SH**
TEL   0285 851227
OPEN   By Appointment.

Specialise in chair caning and rushing.

PROVIDE Home Inspections, Free Estimates.
SPEAK TO Janet Gibbs.

ALAN HESSEL
The Old Town Workshop, St George's Close, Moreton–in–Marsh,
Gloucestershire GL56 0LP
TEL   0608 50026
OPEN   8–5 Mon–Fri or By Appointment.

Specialise in restoring 17th–early 19th century English furniture, including marquetry, parquetry and oyster work with an emphasis on patina retention.

PROVIDE Home Inspections. Free

Estimates. Free/Chargeable
Collection/Delivery Service.
SPEAK TO Alan Hessel.
Member of BAFRA and UKIC.

STEPHEN HILL
No. 5 Cirencester Workshops, Brewery
Court, Cirencester, **Gloucestershire
GL7 2HA**
TEL   0285 658817
OPEN   9–5.30 Mon–Fri, Sat By
Appointment.

Specialise in all types of furniture
restoration, especially 18th century
walnut, oak and mahogany and pre-1900
furniture. Full traditional re-upholstery,
rush and cane seating.

PROVIDE Home Inspections. Free
Estimates. Free Local
Collection/Delivery Service.
SPEAK TO Stephen Hill.
Member of BAFRA.

HUNT AND LOMAS
Village Farm Workshops, Preston,
Cirencester, **Gloucestershire GL7 5PR**
TEL   0285 640111
OPEN   8.30–6. Mon–Fri or By
Appointment.

Specialise in all aspects of furniture
restoration, including carving and
gilding.

PROVIDE Home Inspections. Free
Estimates. Free Local
Collection/Delivery Service.
SPEAK TO Christian Macduff–Hunt.
Member of BAFRA and BADA Dip.

DONALD HUNTER
The Old School Room, Shipton Oliffe,
Cheltenham, **Gloucestershire GL54
4JQ**
TEL   0242 820755
OPEN   8–6 Mon–Fri.

Specialise in carving, gilding and
painted finishes to mirror frames, lacquer
work and antique furniture.

PROVIDE Home Inspections.
Free/Chargeable Estimates.
Collection/Delivery Service by
arrangement.
SPEAK TO Donald Hunter.
Member of BAFRA.

ANDREW LELLIOTT
6 Tetbury Hill, Avening, Tetbury,
Gloucestershire GL8 8LT
TEL   0453 835783 or 0453 832652
OPEN   By Appointment.

Specialise in restoring and conserving
18th and 19th century English furniture,
including oak, walnut, mahogany and
satinwood.

PROVIDE Home Inspections. Free
Estimates. Collection/Delivery Service.
Full Insurance Cover.
SPEAK TO Andrew Lelliott.
Member of BAFRA. This workshop is
included on the register of conservators
maintained by the Conservation Unit of
the Museums and Galleries Commission.
SEE Clocks.

A. J. PONSFORD ANTIQUES
51–53 Dollar Street, Cirencester,
Gloucestershire GL7 2AS
TEL   0285 652355
OPEN   8.30–5.30 Mon–Fri.

Specialise in restoring antique furniture
and upholstery.

PROVIDE Home Inspections. Free
Estimates. Free Collection/Delivery
Service.
SPEAK TO A. J. Ponsford.
SEE Oil Paintings, Picture Frames.

GODFREY ROBERTSON
Fourwinds, Ablington, Bibury,
Cirencester, **Gloucester GL7 5NX**
TEL   0258 740355
FAX   0285 740355 (On Demand
Only)
OPEN   By Appointment.

Specialise in restoring general antique furniture, including upholstery by appointment.

PROVIDE Home Inspections. Free/Chargeable Estimates. Chargeable Collection/Delivery Service. SPEAK TO Godfrey Robertson. Member of BAFRA and UKIC. SEE Clocks.

ANGUS STEWART
Sycamore Barn, Bourton Industrial Park, Bourton–on–the–Water, Cheltenham, **Gloucestershire GL54 2HQ**
TEL 0451 821611
OPEN 8–5.30 Mon–Fri.

Specialise in restoring antique furniture, works of art, gilded and lacquered furniture and mirrors.

PROVIDE Home Inspections. Free Estimates. Chargeable Collection/Delivery Service. SPEAK TO Angus Stewart. Member of BAFRA.

GUY BAGSHAW
Plain Farm, Old Dairy, East Tisted, Alton, **Hampshire GU34 3RT**
TEL 0420 58362
OPEN 8–6 Mon–Fri or By Appointment.

Specialise in 18th and early 19th century English furniture copy pieces.

PROVIDE Home Inspections. Free/Chargeable Estimates. Free Local Collection/Delivery Service. SPEAK TO Guy Bagshaw. Member of BAFRA. This workshop is included on the register of conservators maintained by the Conservation Unit of the Museums and Galleries Commission.

CORFIELD RESTORATIONS LTD
120 High Street, Lymington, **Hampshire SO41 9AQ**
TEL 0590 673532
OPEN 9.15–5.30 Mon–Sat.

Specialise in all furniture restoration, including gilding and upholstery.

PROVIDE Home Inspections. Free Estimates. Local Free Collection/Delivery Service. SPEAK TO Alan Bloomfield or Michael Corfield. Also at Setters Farm, Lymington. 0590 671977. SEE Oil Paintings, Picture Frames.

DYER AND FOLLETT LTD
Coward Road, Alverstoke, Gosport, **Hampshire PO12 2LD**
TEL 0705 582204
OPEN 9–12.45, 2.15–5.30 Mon–Fri; 9.15–12.45, 2.15–5 Sat.

Specialise in restoring of antique English and Continental furniture, French polishing, upholstery.

PROVIDE Local Home Inspections. Refundable Estimates, Free Local Collection/Delivery Service. SPEAK TO Mr E. A. Dyer.

GAYLORDS ANTIQUES
75 West Street, Titchfield, Fareham, **Hampshire PO14 4DG**
TEL 0329 843402
OPEN 10–4 Mon–Sat.

Specialise in restoring antique furniture, French polishing and upholstery.

PROVIDE Home Inspections. Free Estimates. Free Collection/Delivery Service. SPEAK TO Mr Hebbard.

JOHN HAYWARD
Cane and Woodcraft Centre, 57 High Street, Beaulieu, **Hampshire SO42 7YA**
TEL 0590 612211
OPEN 10–1,2–5 Wed–Sat; 12–5 Sun.

Specialise in restoring antique and modern cane, rush and seagrass seats.

Blind, double, fan, medallions, close and pre–woven canework undertaken.

PROVIDE Local Home Inspections. Free Estimates. Free Local Colection/Delivery Service.
SPEAK TO John Hayward.
Member of the Basketmakers' Association and trhe Guild of Master Craftsmen.
Mr Hayward gives talks and demonstrations.

DAVID C. E. LEWRY
'Wychelms', 66 Gorran Avenue, Rowner, Gosport, **Hampshire PO13 ONF**
TEL   0329 286901
OPEN   By Appointment.

Specialise in conserving and restoring 17th, 18th and early 19th century furniture.

PROVIDE Home Inspections. Refundable Estimates. Free/ Chargeable Collection/Delivery Service.
SPEAK TO David Lewry.
Member of BAFRA.

DOUGLAS J. LINCOLN
Athgarvan House, Shawford, Winchester, **Hampshire SO21 2AA**
TEL   0962 712662
OPEN   By Appointment.

Specialise in providing engraving services for decorated furniture, especially Boulle.

PROVIDE Local Home Inspections. Free Estimates. Chargeable Local Collection/Delivery Service.
SPEAK TO Douglas Lincoln.
Visiting tutor at West Dean. This workshop is included on the register of conservators maintained by the Conservation Unit of the Museums and Galleries Commission.
SEE Silver.

J. A. PRADO (PRADO CABINETMAKER AND RESTORER)
Great Weir House, The Great Weir, Alresford, **Hampshire SO24 9DB**
TEL   0962 732896
FAX   0962 734233
OPEN   By Appointment.

Specialise in restoring English furniture 1660 to 1815 with emphasis on marquetry and brass inlay.

PROVIDE Home Inspections. Free Estimates. Chargeable Collection/Delivery Service.
SPEAK TO Mr J. A. Prado.
This workshop is included on the register of conservators maintained by the Conservation Unit of the Museums and Galleries Commission.
SEE Clocks.

MR D. J. SMITH
34 Silchester Road, Pamber Heath, Nr. Basingstoke, **Hampshire RG26 6EF**
TEL   0734 700595
OPEN   8–6 Mon–Sat or By Appointment.

Specialise in restoration and reproduction of fine 18th century carved and giltwood furniture. Fine carving in wood and oil or water gilding and distressing.

PROVIDE Local Home Inspections. Free Estimates. Free Local Collection/Delivery Service.
SPEAK TO Douglas Smith.

THE TANKERDALE WORKSHOP
Tankerdale Farm, Steep Marsh, Petersfield, **Hampshire GU32 2BH**
TEL   0730 893839
FAX   0730 894523
OPEN   8 6 Mon–Fri.

Specialise in conserving and restoring furniture, including carving, gilding, lacquer work, japanning and cabinetmaking.

PROVIDE Home Inspections. Refundable Estimates. Chargeable Collection/Delivery Service.
SPEAK TO John Hartley.

THE BAROMETER SHOP
4 New Street, Leominster, **Hereford & Worcester HR6 8BT**
TEL   0568 613652
OPEN   9–5.30 Mon–Sat.

Specialise in restoring furniture, including hand French polishing, hand engraving, metalware. Mirrors re–silvered.

PROVIDE Home Inspections. Free Estimates. Free Collection/Delivery Service.
SPEAK TO Richard Cookson. CMBHI.
SEE Clocks, Collectors (Scientific Instruments).

I. AND J. L. BROWN LTD
58 Commercial Road, Hereford, **Hereford & Worcester HR1 2BP**
TEL   0432 358895
FAX   0432 275338
OPEN   9–5.30 Mon–Sat.

Specialise in restoring English country and French provincial furniture, chair rush work.

PROVIDE Free/Chargeable Estimates. Free/Chargeable Collection/Delivery Service.
SPEAK TO Ian Brown.
SEE **London SW6**.

B. R. HONEYBORNE
The Whyle Cottage, Pudleston, Leominster, **Hereford & Worcester HR6 0RE**
TEL   056887 250
OPEN   9–5 Mon–Sat.

Specialise in restoring antique furniture.

PROVIDE Home Inspections. Free Estimates. Chargeable Collection/Delivery Service.
SPEAK TO B. R. Honeyborne.

JENNINGS & JENNINGS
30 Bridge Street, Leominster, **Hereford & Worcester HR6 9JQ**
TEL   0568 512946
OPEN   10–5.30 Mon–Sat.

Specialise in conserving and restoring gilded items, including furniture and mirror frames.

PROVIDE Home Inspections. Free Estimates. Free/Chargeable Collection/Delivery Service.
SPEAK TO Sabina Jennings.
SEE Picture Frames.

H. W. KEIL LTD
Tudor House, Broadway, **Hereford & Worcester WR12 7DP**
TEL   0386 852408
OPEN   9.15–12.45, 2.15–5.30 Mon–Sat; closed Thur p.m.

Specialise in restoring 17th, 18th and 19th century furniture, mainly in oak, mahogany and walnut.

PROVIDE Refundable Estimates. Free Local Collection/Delivery Service.
SPEAK TO P. J. W. Keil.

KIMBER AND SON
6 Lower Howsell Road, Malvern Link, **Hereford & Worcester WR14 1EF**
TEL   0684 574339
OPEN   8.30–6 Mon–Fri; 9–12.30 Sat.

Specialise in restoring fine 18th and 19th century furniture.

PROVIDE Home Inspections. Free Estimates. Free Collection/Delivery Service.
SPEAK TO Mr E. M. Kimber.

MALVERN STUDIOS
56 Cowleigh Road, Malvern,
Hereford & Worcester WR14 1QD
TEL   0684 574913
OPEN   9–5 Mon–Thur. 9–4.45 Fri, Sat.

Specialise in restoring antique furniture, hand polishing, Boulle and gilt work.

PROVIDE Home Inspections. Refundable Estimates. Chargeable Collection/Delivery Service.
SPEAK TO Mr L. M. Hall.
Member of BAFRA and UKIC. This workshop is included on the register of conservators maintained by the Conservation Unit of the Museums and Galleries Commission.

NEIL POSTONS RESTORATIONS
29 South Street, Leominster,
Hereford & Worcester HR6 8JQ
TEL   0568 616677
FAX   0568 616677
OPEN   8.30–5.30 Mon–Fri.

Specialise in restoring period furniture , carving, tooling, carcase work, French polishing, re–leathering desk tops,

PROVIDE Home Inspections. Free Local Estimates. Chargeable Collection/Delivery Service.
SPEAK TO Neil Postons.

BRYAN WIGINGTON
Chapel Schoolroom, 1 Heolydwr, Hay on Wye, via Hereford, **Hereford & Worcester HR3 5AE**
Postal address via Hereford but located in Powys.
TEL   0497 820545
OPEN   By Appointment Only.

Specialise in a comprehensive range of techniques restoring 16th to 19th century furniture. They have a large stock of antique timber.

PROVIDE Home Inspections. Free Estimates. Free Local Collection/Delivery Service.

SPEAK TO Bryan Wigington.
Established in 1899, this is a third–generation family business.
Member of BAFRA.

BECKWITH & SON
St Nicholas Hall, St Andrew Street, Hertford, **Hertfordshire SG14 1HZ**
TEL   0992 582079
OPEN   9–1, 2–5.30 Mon–Sat.

Specialise in restoring antique English furniture, cabinetmaking and polishing.

PROVIDE Home Inspections. Chargeable Estimates. Free Local Collection/Delivery Service.
SPEAK TO G. Gray.

CENTRE OF RESTORATION AND ARTS
13–15 Victoria Street, St Albans,
Hertfordshire AL1 3JJ
TEL   0727 851508 FAX
OPEN   8.30–5.30 Mon–Fri.

Specialise in chair caning.

PROVIDE Local Home Inspections. Free/Chargeable Estimates. Chargeable Collection/Delivery Service.
SPEAK TO Paul Roe.

FARRELLY ANTIQUE RESTORATION
The Long Barn, 50 High Street, Tring,
Hertfordshire HP23 5AG
TEL   0442 891905
OPEN   9–4 Mon–Fri.

Specialise in restoring cabinets and chairs, carving, gilding, upholstery, polishing.

PROVIDE Home Inspections. Free Estimates. Chargeable Collection/Delivery Service.
SPEAK TO Paul Farrelly.

HERITAGE RESTORATIONS

24 Castle Street, Berkhamsted,
Hertfordshire HP4 2DW
TEL   0442 873819
OPEN   10–5 Daily.

Specialise in restoring furniture, caning and rushing and upholstery.

PROVIDE Free Estimates. Home Inspections.
SPEAK TO John Wilshire.
SEE Clocks, Porcelain.

HERTFORDSHIRE CONSERVATION SERVICE

Seed Warehouse, Maidenhead Yard, The Wash, Hertford, **Hertfordshire SG14 1PX**
TEL   0992 588966 or 504662
ANS   0992 588966
FAX   0992 503184
OPEN   9–6 Mon–Fri By Appointment.

Specialise in restoring furniture and other items of wood of any period.

PROVIDE Home Inspections.
Free/Chargeable Estimates. Chargeable Collection/Delivery Service.
SPEAK TO J. M. Macqueen.
This workshop is included on the register of conservators maintained by the Conservation Unit of the Museum and Galleries Commission.
SEE Carpets, Collectors (Dolls), Lighting, Porcelain, Oil Paintings, Picture Frames.

PHILLIPS OF HITCHIN

The Manor House, Hitchin,
Hertfordshire SG5 1JW
TEL   0462 432067
FAX   0462 441368
OPEN   9–5.30 Mon–Sat.

Specialise in restoring English and Continental furniture.

PROVIDE Home Inspections.
Free/Chargeable Estimates. Chargeable Collection/Delivery Service.
SPEAK TO Jerome Phillips.
SEE Specialist Booksellers.

CHARLES PERRY RESTORATIONS LTD

Praewood Farm, Hemel Hempstead Road, St Albans, **Hertfordshire AL3 6AA**
TEL   0727 853487
FAX   0727 846668
OPEN   Mon–Fri 8.30–6; By Appointment Sat.

Specialise in furniture restoration and allied trades including gilding, carving, polishing, marquetry, lacquerwork, marble, traditional upholstery, caning and rushing and expert advice and reports to clients intending to purchase at auction.

PROVIDE Home Inspections. Free Estimates. Chargeable Collection/Delivery Service.
SPEAK TO John Carr.
Mr Carr is a Member of BAFRA and the Guild of Master Craftsmen.
By Appointment to HM Queen Elizabeth II Antique Furniture Restorers.
This workshop is included on the list of conservators maintained by the Conservation Unit of the Museums and Galleries Commission.
SEE Clocks, Books, Collectors (Ship Models, Toys).

R. J. PERRY ANTIQUES

37–38 Bridge Street, Hitchin,
Hertfordshire SG5 2DF
TEL   0462 434525
FAX   0462 441811
OPEN   10–5.30 Mon–Sat.

Specialise in restoring furniture to a very high standard, re–veneering, re–polishing, replacement where required of applied metal beading. Brass, copper and spelter repaired and re–polished where appropriate.

PROVIDE Home Inspections. Free Estimates. Free Local

Collection/Delivery Service.
SPEAK TO Ronald Perry.
Member of LAPADA.

JOHN RUSH
39 Christchurch Road, Tring,
Hertfordshire HP23 4EH
TEL 044282 5387
OPEN 10.30–1 Mon–Sat or By Appointment.

Specialise in restoring all types of upholstered furniture, re–upholstery and frame restoration.

PROVIDE Home Inspections. Free Estimates. Free/Chargeable Collection/Delivery Service.
SPEAK TO John Rush.
Fellow of the Association of Master Upholsterers. This workshop is included on the register of conservators maintained by the Conservation Unit of the Museums and Galleries Commission.

ST OUEN ANTIQUES LTD
Vintage Corner, Old Cambridge Road,
Puckeridge, **Hertfordshire SG11 1SA**
TEL 0920 821336
FAX 0920 822877
OPEN 10–5 Mon–Sat.

Specialise in restoring 18th and 19th century English, Continental and gilded furniture and 19th century paintings.

PROVIDE Home Inspections. Refundable Estimates. Chargeable Collection/Delivery Service.
SPEAK TO Tim or John Blake.
SEE Oil Paintings.

LOUISE SEYMOUR UPHOLSTERY
Binghams Park, Water End, Hemel Hempstead, **Hertfordshire HP1 3BN**
TEL 0442 252652
ANS 0442 252652
OPEN 8–6 Mon–Fri.

Specialise in traditionally upholstering all furniture, including repairs to frames

and period waxing of show wood.

PROVIDE Home Inspections. Free Estimates. Chargeable Collection/Delivery Service.
SPEAK TO Louise Seymour.

TRACY'S FRENCH POLISHING AND FURNITURE RESTORERS
55 Great North Road, Brookmans Park,
Hertfordshire AL9 6LA
TEL 0707 652144
FAX 0707 645153
OPEN 8–5 Mon–Fri.

Specialise in all aspects of original hand French polishing and wood-finishing.

PROVIDE Home Inspections. Free Estimates. Free Collection/Delivery Service.
SPEAK TO E J Tracy or Irene.
They prefer to carry out their work in situ.

VICTOR WHINES
29 River Close, Waltham Cross,
Hertfordshire EN8 7QR
TEL 0992 712246
OPEN 9–5.30 Mon–Fri.

Specialise in restoring antique painted furniture and Chinese lacquer. Also do graining, marbling and gilding.

PROVIDE Home Inspections. Free Estimates.
SPEAK TO Victor Whines.

OLD ROPERY ANTIQUES
East Street, Kilham, Nr. Driffield, **North Humberside YO25 0ST**
TEL 026282 233
OPEN 9.30–5 Mon–Sat.

Specialise in restoring furniture.

PROVIDE Home Inspections. Chargeable Estimate. Free Collection/Delivery Service.
SPEAK TO John Butterfield.

SEE Clocks, Collectors (Scientific Instruments).

ADRIAN J. BLACK
36A Freeman Street, Grimsby, **South Humberside DN32 7AG**
TEL   0472 824823 and 355668
OPEN   By Appointment.

Specialise in restoring English antique furniture and cabinetmaking.

PROVIDE Home Inspections. Free Estimates. Chargeable Collection/Delivery Service.
SPEAK TO Adrian Black.

T. M. AKERS PERIOD FURNITURE RESTORATIONS
39 Chancery Lane, Beckenham, **Kent BR3 2NR**
TEL   081 650 9179
OPEN   9–6 Mon–Fri.

Specialise in restoring English period furniture up to 1900.

PROVIDE Home Inspections. Free Estimates. Free Collection/Delivery Service.
SPEAK TO Tim Akers.
Member of BAFRA, LAPADA and UKIC. This workshop is included on the register of conservators maintained by the Conservation Unit of the Museums and Galleries Commission.

ANTIQUE RESTORATIONS
The Old Wheelwright's Shop, Brasted Forge, Brasted, Westerham, **Kent TN16 1JL**
TEL   0959 563863
FAX   0959 561262
OPEN   9–5 Mon–Fri; 10–1 Sat.

Specialise in restoring furniture, including traditional upholstery, polishing.

PROVIDE Refundable Estimates. Free Collection/Delivery Service.
SPEAK TO Raymond Konyn.
Member of BAFRA and the Antique and Fine Art Disasters Emergency Mobile Unit.
SEE Clocks, Lighting.

WILLIAM ANTHONY BIRCH
Tenterden Rushcraft, Station Road, Tenterden, **Kent TN30 6JB**
TEL   0580 763326
OPEN   9.15–5 Mon–Sat, 9.15–1 Wed.

Specialise in restoring cane and rush furniture and repairing all woodwork.

PROVIDE Local Home Inspections. Free Estimates in workshop. Chargeable Collection/Delivery Service.
SPEAK TO W. A. Birch.
This workshop is included on the register of conservators maintained by the Conservation Unit of the Museums and Galleries Commission.

BENEDICT CLEGG
Rear of 20 Camden Road, Tunbridge Wells, **Kent TN1 2PT**
TEL   0392 548095
OPEN   8.30–5.30 Mon–Fri or By Appointment.

Specialise in restoring furniture, including Boulle work and marquetry.

PROVIDE Home Inspections. Free Estimates. Chargeable Collection/Delivery Service.
SPEAK TO Benedict Clegg.
SEE Clocks.
Member of BAFRA.

ROBERT COLEMAN
The Oasthouse, Three Chimneys, Biddenden, **Kent TN27 8LW**
TEL   0580 291520
OPEN   By Appointment.

Specialise in restoring mahogany and walnut English furniture.

PROVIDE Home Inspections. Free Estimates. Free Collection/Delivery Service.

SPEAK TO Robert Coleman.
Member of BAFRA and the Guild of Master Craftsmen.

FORGE ANTIQUES AND RESTORATION
Rye Road, Sandhurst, Cranbrook, **Kent TN18 5JG**
TEL   0580 850308 and 850665
OPEN   9–5 Daily.

Specialise in repairing and polishing furniture, wood turning, carving, veneering.

PROVIDE Home Inspections. Free Estimates. Chargeable Collection/Delivery Service.
SPEAK TO James Nesfield.

GILTWOOD RESTORATION
71 Bower Mount Road, Maidstone, **Kent ME16 8AS**
TEL   0622 752273
OPEN   9–6 Mon–Fri.

Specialise in restoring fine gilded furniture, frames and architectural ornament, water–gilded or oil–gilded.

PROVIDE Home Inspections. Free Estimates. Free Collection/Delivery Service.
SPEAK TO Martin Body.

ANTHONY HARRINGTON
Squerryes Court Workshops, Squerryes Court, Westerham, **Kent TN16 ISJ**
TEL   0959 64936
FAX   0959 64936
OPEN   9–5 Mon–Fri.

Specialise in restoring antique wood carving and gilding.

PROVIDE Home Inspections. Free Estimates. Free Collection/Delivery Service.
SPEAK TO Anthony Harrington.

RICKY HOLDSTOCK
Hillside Cottage, The Forstal, Hernhill, Faversham, **Kent ME13 9JQ**
TEL   0227 751204
FAX   0227 751204
OPEN   By Appointment.

Specialise in weaving chair seats and panels in cane, rush and Danish cord.

PROVIDE Home Inspections. Free Estimates.
SPEAK TO Ricky Holdstock.

LANGOLD ANTIQUES
Oxon Hoath, Tonbridge, **Kent**
TEL   0732 810577
OPEN   9–5 Mon, Thur, Fri.

Specialise in restoring furniture.

PROVIDE Free Collection/Delivery Service.
SPEAK TO Mr Bayne–Powell.

TIMOTHY LONG RESTORATION
26 High Street, Seal, Nr. Sevenoaks, **Kent TN15 OAP**
TEL   0732 762606
OPEN   By Appointment.

Specialise in restoring 18th and 19th century English and Continental furniture.

PROVIDE Home Inspections. Free Local Estimates. Free Local Collection/Delivery Service.
SPEAK TO Tim Long.
Member of BAFRA. This workshop is included on the register of conservators maintained by the Conservation Unit of the Museums and Galleries Commission.

BRUCE LUCKHURST
Little Surrenden WSorkshops,
Bethersden, **Kent TN26 3BG**
TEL   0233 829589
OPEN   9–5 Mon–Fri.

Specialise in furniture of all kinds.

PROVIDE Home Inspections. Chargeable
Estimates. Chargeable
Collection/Delivery Service.
SPEAK TO Bruce Luckhurst.
Member of BAFRA and UKIC. This
workshop is included on the register
maintained by the Conservation Unit of
the Museums and Galleries Commission.
SEE Clocks, Musical Instruments.

R. M. RESTORATIONS
Chaddesden Barn, Morants Court Road,
Dunton Green, **Kent TN13 2TR**
TEL   0732 741604
OPEN   7.30–5.30 Mon–Sat.

Specialise in restoring English furniture
from 1700–1830.

PROVIDE Home Inspections. Free
Estimates. Chargeable
Collection/Delivery Service.
SPEAK TO Richard Marson.
Member of BAFRA.

J. T. RUTHERFORD & SON
55 Sandgate High Street, Folkestone,
Kent CT20 3AH
TEL   0303 249515
OPEN   8.30–6 Mon–Sat or By
        Appointment.

Specialise in restoring period furniture.

PROVIDE Home Inspections. Refundable
Estimates. Free/Chargeable
Collection/Delivery Service.
SPEAK TO John Rutherford.

R. G. SCOTT
Furniture Mart, Bath Place and Grotto
Hill, Margate, **Kent CT9 2BU**
TEL   0843 220653
OPEN   9.30–1, 2–5 Mon–Sat; closed
        Wed.

Specialise in restoring furniture,
veneering, cabinet work, marquetry.

PROVIDE Home Inspections. Free
Estimates. Free Local
Collection/Delivery Service.
SPEAK TO Ron Scott.

ALAN GRICE ANTIQUES
106 Aughton Street, Ormskirk,
Lancashire L39 3BS
TEL   0695 572007
OPEN   10–6 Mon–Sat.

Specialise in restoring English and
Continental antique furniture.

PROVIDE Home Inspections.
Free/Chargeable Estimates. Chargeable
Collection/Delivery Service.
SPEAK TO Alan Grice.

ERIC SMITH ANTIQUE RESTORATIONS
Park Road Church, Park Road, Darwen,
Lancashire BB3 2LD
TEL   0254 776222
OPEN   9–6 Mon–Fri or By
        Appointment.

Specialise in a complete service covering
the sympathetic restoration of all periods
of English furniture, particularly
vernacular.

PROVIDE Home Inspections. Free
Estimates. Chargeable
Collection/Delivery Service.
SPEAK TO Eric Smith
Member of UKIC.
SEE Clocks.

RICHARD ZAHLER
Lane House, Fowgill, Bentham,
Lancaster, **Lancashire LA2 7AH**
TEL   05242 61998
OPEN   9–6 Mon–Fri or By
        Appointment.

Specialise in restoring mirror frames, water and oil gilding.

SPEAK TO Richard Zahler.

Member of UKIC and the Guild of Master Craftsmen. This workshop is included on the egister maintained by the Conservation Unit of the Museums and Galleries Commission.

SEE Books, Oil Paintings, Picture Frames.

ROBERT BINGLEY ANTIQUES

Church Street, Wing, Oakham, **Leicestershire LE15 8RS**

TEL   057 285 725 or 314

OPEN   9–5 Mon–Sat; 11–4 Sun.

Specialise in restoring antique furniture, including walnut, oak, mahogany and rosewood.

PROVIDE Home Inspections. Free Estimates. Free Collection/ Delivery Service.

SPEAK TO Robert Bingley.

JOHN GARNER

51–53 High Street East, Uppingham, **Leicestershire LE15 9PY.**

TEL   0572 823607

FAX   0572 821654

OPEN   9–5.30 Mon–Sat; By Appointment Sun.

Specialise in restoring antique furniture, mainly 18th and 19th century.

PROVIDE Home Inspections. Free Collection/Delivery Service.

SPEAK TO John or Paul Garner.

SEE Oil Paintings.

E. & C. ROYALL

10 Waterfall Way, Medbourne, Nr. Market Harborough, **Leicestershire LE15 8EE**

TEL   0858 83744

OPEN   8.30–5 Mon–Fri.

Specialise in restoring antique English, Continental and Oriental furniture, including lacquer, Boulle and inlay work, carving, veneering, French polishing and mouldings.

PROVIDE Home Inspections. Free Estimates. Chargeable Collection/Delivery Service.

SPEAK TO C. Royall.

SEE Porcelain.

TATTERSALL'S

14 Orange Street and 2 Bear Yard, Orange Street, Uppingham, **Leicestershire LE15 9SQ**

TEL   0572 821171

OPEN   9.30–5 Tues–Sat; closed Mon & Thur.

Specialise in restoring of upholstered furniture and mirrors. Specialist restorers of rush and cane furniture.

PROVIDE Home Inspections. Free Estimates. Chargeable Collection/Delivery Service.

SPEAK TO Janice Tattersall.

SEE Carpets.

BURGHLEY FINE ART CONSERVATION LTD

Burghley House, Stamford, **Lincolnshire PE9 3JY**

TEL   0780 62155

OPEN   By Appointment.

Specialise in conserving and restoring painted furniture, European lacquer, mirror frames and gilding.

PROVIDE Home Inspections. Free Estimates. Chargeable Collection/Delivery Service.

SPEAK TO Michael Cowell.

Any work undertaken is fully documented.

SEE Oil Paintings, Picture Frames.

E. CZAJKOWSKI & SON

96 Tor–O–Moor Road, Woodhall Spa, **Lincolnshire LN10 6SB**

TEL   0526 352895

OPEN   9–5 Mon–Fri.

Specialise in restoring antique furniture, including marquetry, lacquerwork, carving, gilding and upholstery. Also copy furniture.

PROVIDE Home Inspections. Free Estimates. Free Local Collection/Delivery Service.
SPEAK TO Mr M. J. Czajkowski.
Member of COSIRA and UKIC. This workshop is on the register of conservators maintained by the Conservation Unit of the Museums and Galleries Commission.
SEE Clocks.

***

LINCOLNSHIRE CONSERVATION STUDIO
c/o Museum of Lincolnshire Life, Burton Road, Lincoln, **Lincolnshire LN1 3LY**
TEL   0522 533207
OPEN   9–5 Mon–Fri.

Specialise in restoring gilding and frames to museum conservation standards.

PROVIDE Home Inspections. Free/Chargeable Estimates. Chargeable Collection/Delivery Service.
SPEAK TO Stephanie Margrett or David Fisher.
Member of UKIC. This workshop is included on the register of conservators maintained by the Conservation Unit of the Museums and Galleries Commission.
SEE Arms, Porcelain, Lighting.

***

JOHN SMITH FINE FURNITURE RESTORATION
69 High Street, Blyton, Gainsborough, **Lincolnshire DN21 3JX**
TEL   0427 628443
OPEN   9–5 Mon–Fri By Appointment,

Specialise in restoring 18th and 19th century furniture.

PROVIDE Home Inspections. Free Estimates. Free/Chargeable Collection Delivery Service.

SPEAK TO John Smith.
Member of UKIC and BADA. This workshop is included on the register of conservators maintained by the Conservation Unit of the Museums and Galleries Commission.

***

I. & P. PRITCHARD
17 Heathcote Grove, **London E4 6RZ**
TEL   081 529 2884
OPEN   By Appointment.

Specialise in restoring chairs, re–caning, rushing, Danish cord, some Victorian garden furniture.

PROVIDE Home Inspections. Free Estimates. Free/Chargeable Collection/Delivery Service.
SPEAK TO Iorwerth or Phyllis Pritchard.
Member of Basketmakers Association. This workshop is included on the register of conservators maintained by the Conservation Unit of the Museums and Galleries Commission.

***

R. D. ROBINS UPHOLSTERY LTD
50A Bignold Road, **London E7 0EX**
TEL   081 503 1153
FAX   081 503 1153
OPEN   7.30–5 Mon–Fri.

Specialise in a full upholstery service, including walling, tenting, re–covering sofas and chairs, headboards etc.

PROVIDE Home Inspections. Free Estimates. Chargeable Collection/Delivery Service.
SPEAK TO Mr B. S. Ansell.
Member of Association of Master Upholsterers.
SEE **London SW19**
SEE Carpets.

***

ELMER–MENAGE
78A Cecilia Road, **London E8 2ET**
TEL   071 923 1338
OPEN   9–6 Mon–Fri.

Specialise in restoring 18th–19th century rosewood furniture. Will also undertake marquetry restoration including Boulle.

PROVIDE Refundable Home Inspections. Chargeable Collection/Delivery Service.
SPEAK TO Chris Elmer.

DAVID TURNER
4 Atlas Mews, Ramsgate Street, **London E8 2NA**
TEL   071 249 2379
OPEN   10–6 Mon–Fri.

Specialise in restoring small pieces of furniture and leather screens.

PROVIDE Home Inspections. Free Estimates. Free Collection/Delivery Service.
SEE Porcelain, Silver.

YOUNG'S FRENCH POLISHING
570–572–574 Commercial Road, **London E14 7JD**
TEL   071 790 4474 and 790 4691
FAX   071 265 9476
OPEN   9.30–6 Mon–Sat; closed Thur.

Specialise in polishing, renovating, repairing, French polishing door-barring and glazing. Leather–lining tables and desk–tops, upholstery repairs and coverings.

PROVIDE Home Inspections. Free Estimates. Chargeable Collection/Delivery Service.
SPEAK TO Mr S. R. Young.

HOMEGUARD LIMITED
80–84 St Mary Road, **London E17 9RE**
TEL   081 520 4464
FAX   081 520 8335
OPEN   9–12.15, 1.30–5 Mon–Fri.

Specialise in refurbishment and manufacture of locks and keys dating back to the 15th century. All types of keys cut and locks repaired

PROVIDE Free/Chargeable Home Inspections. Chargeable Estimates.
SPEAK TO A. J. Camfield or P. M. Camfield.
Established 1948. This workshop is included on the register of conservators maintained by the Conservation Unit of the Museums and Galleries Commission.

MICHAEL PARFETT
Unit 407, Clerkenwell Workshops, 31 Clerkenwell Close, **London EC1R 0AT**
TEL   071 490 8768
OPEN   By Appointment.

Specialise in all aspects of restoration to furniture and mirror frames inclusive of on–site architectural carving and gilding. No upholstery work.

PROVIDE Home Inspections. Free Estimates. Local Free Collection/Delivery Service.
SPEAK TO Michael Parfett.
Licenciate of the City and Guilds of London, Member of UKIC. This workshop is included on the register of conservators maintained by the Conservation Unit of the Museums and Galleries Commission.
SEE Collectors (Musical Instruments), Picture Frames.

BOSWELL AND DAVIS
The Holywell Centre, 1 Phipp Street, **London EC2A 4PS**
TEL   071 739 5738
FAX   071 729 9882
OPEN   9–6 Mon–Fri.

Specialise in restoring English and Continental furniture, including cabinetmaking, French polishing, turning, marquetry work, leather desk lining, gilding, upholstery, painted furniture. Locks repaired and keys made. Lost wax casting.

PROVIDE Home Inspections. Free Estimates. Free Collection/Delivery Service.
SPEAK TO David Boswell.
SEE Clocks

PETER CHAPMAN ANTIQUES Incorporating CHAPMAN RESTORATIONS

10 Theberton Street, **London N1 0QX**
TEL   071 226 5565
FAX   081 348 4846
OPEN   9.30–6 Mon–Sat.

Specialise in restoring Georgian, Regency and Victorian furniture, including Arts and Crafts, Gothic Revival and Aesthetic Movement. Also provide a transport damage and repair service.

PROVIDE Home Inspections. Refundable Estimates. Chargeable Collection/Delivery Service.
SPEAK TO Peter Chapman or Tony Holohan.
Member of LAPADA.
SEE Oil Paintings, Picture Frames, Porcelain, Silver.

MATTHEW CRAWFORD FURNITURE RESTORATION

Basement, 74–77 White Lion Street, **London N1 1QP**
TEL   071 278 7146
OPEN   9–5 Mon–Fri.

Specialise in restoring 16th–early 20th century English furniture, including inlay, recarving, leather, cane and upholstery.
Can also copy existing pieces.

PROVIDE Home Inspections. Free Estimates. Free Collection/Delivery Service.
SPEAK TO Matthew Crawford.

JULIAN KELLY

26A Gopsall Street, **London N1**
TEL   071 739 2949
FAX   071 739 2949
OPEN   9–5 Mon–Fri.

Specialise in wood carving, making chairs to match existing ones and general restoration work.

PROVIDE Free Estimates.
SPEAK TO Julian Kelly.

BARBARA SEBTI

34–36 Cross Street **London N1 2BQ**
TEL   071 226 3374
FAX   071 226 3374
OPEN   9.30–6 Mon–Sat; By Appointment Sun.

Specialise in carving and gilding decorative furniture, but will take on all furniture restoration.

PROVIDE Home Inspections. Refundable Estimates. Chargeable Collection/Delivery Service.
SPEAK TO Barbara Sebti.

VICTORIA ILLINGWORTH

Petherton Antiques, 124 Petherton Road, **London N5 2RT**
TEL   071 226 6597
OPEN   10–6 Tues–Sat.

Specialise in restoring furniture, especially marquetry and veneered pieces, but excluding gilding and lacquer work.

PROVIDE Free Estimates. Free Local Collection/Delivery Service.
SPEAK TO Victoria Illingworth.

ALEXANDER LEY & SON

13 Brecknock Rd, **London N7 0BL**
TEL   071 267 3645
FAX   071 267 4462
OPEN   8–6 Mon–Fri.

Specialise in restoring antique frames, gilt furniture and mirrors. Also reproduction carving and gilding.

PROVIDE Home Inspections. Free Estimates. Free Collection/Delivery Service.
SPEAK TO Alexander or Anthony Ley.
SEE Picture Frames.

B S H RESTORERS LTD
7A Tynemouth Terrace, Tynemouth Road, **London N15 4AP**
TEL   081 808 7965
FAX   081 801 5313
OPEN   7–3.30 Mon–Fri.

Specialise in restoring antique English and Continental furniture.

PROVIDE Home Inspections. Free/Chargeable Estimates. Free Collection/Delivery Service.
SPEAK TO Barry Howells.

CLIFFORD J. TRACY
6–40 Durnford Street, **London N15 5NQ**
TEL   081 800 4773 or 4774
FAX   081 800 4351
OPEN   7.30–5 Mon–Thur; 7.30–4 Fri.

Specialise in restoring furniture, including carving, marquetry, Boulle, leather–lining and re–upholstery.

PROVIDE Home Inspections. Free Estimates. Free Collection/Delivery Service.
SPEAK TO Clifford Tracy.
Member of BAFRA and UKIC. Will do minor repairs on site.
SEE Clocks.

A. J. BRETT & CO. LTD
Blenheim Works, 168C Marlborough Rd, **London N19 4NP**
TEL   071 272 8462
FAX   071 272 5102
OPEN   7–4.30 Mon–Fri.

Specialise in restoring antique furniture, including upholstery, metalwork, gilding and decorating, French polishing, table–lining.

PROVIDE Home Inspections. Free Estimates. Free Collection/Delivery Service.
SPEAK TO Emma Whitley.

Members of the Guild of Master Craftsmen. Successfully restored the furniture damaged in the fire at Hampton Court.

MAX E. OTT LTD
1A Southcote Road, **London N19 5BJ**
TEL   071 607 1384
FAX   071 607 3506
OPEN   6.30–8.30 Mon–Fri.

Specialise in restoring antique furniture of all periods. Also copies of period furniture.

PROVIDE Home Inspections. Free Estimates. Free Collection/Delivery Service.
SPEAK TO Max Ott.

PHILIP J. WOLFF
4 Esther Close, **London N21 1AW**
TEL   081 364 0024
OPEN   By Appointment.

Specialise in restoring carved and gilded antiques and fine furniture, decorative and architectural gilding, specialising in matt and burnish water gilding, powder gilding (water base) and oil gilding.

PROVIDE Home Inspections by arrangement. Estimates by agreement.
SPEAK TO Philip J. Wolff.
Mr Wolff has had forty-six years' experience. He is an Hon. Member of the Guild of Master Craftsmen

K. RESTORATIONS
2A Ferdinand Place, **London NW1 8EE**
TEL   071 482 402
FAX   071 267 6712
OPEN   8–6 Mon–Fri.

Specialise in restoring all antique furniture including French polishing and renovation of leather upholstery and the supply of desk leathers.

PROVIDE Home Inspections. Free Estimates. Chargeable Collection/Delivery Service.
SPEAK TO David Peston.
Member of the Guild of Antique Dealers and Restorers.

THE MORLEY UPHOLSTERY WORKS LTD

82–86 Troutbeck, Albany St, **London NW1 4EJ**

TEL   071 387 3846 and 388 0651
OPEN   8–4.30 Mon–Fri.

Specialise in renovating antique and modern upholstery.

PROVIDE Home Inspections. Chargeable Estimates. Free Collection/Delivery Service.
SPEAK TO Mr E. G. Vidler.

MURGA CANDLER LTD

57 Bayham Place, **London NW1 0ET**

TEL   071 387 7830
OPEN   8–5 Mon–Fri.

Specialise in leather–lining of desk and table–tops, loose leathers, upholstery in suede and leather.

PROVIDE Free Estimates.
SPEAK TO John Murga.

JOHN SZAKALY

2 Chartley Avenue, **London NW2 7RA**

TEL   081 450 5882
OPEN   9–6 Mon–Fri.

Specialise in restoration of antique furniture and polishing.

PROVIDE Home Inspections. Free Estimates. Free Collection/Delivery Service.
SPEAK TO John Szakaly.

ANTIQUE LEATHERS

4 Park End, South Hill Park, **London NW3 2SE**

TEL   071 435 8582
FAX   071 435 7799
OPEN   8–5 Mon–Fri.

Specialise in restoring leather work of all kinds, upholstery, bellows, desk–tops with gold tooling, screens, backgammons.

PROVIDE Free Estimates.
Free/Chargeable Collection/Delivery Service.
SPEAK TO Jackie Crisp or Roy Holliday.

J. CRISP

48 Roderick Road, **London NW3 2NL**

TEL   081 340 0668
FAX   071 485 8566
OPEN   10–6 Mon–Fri.

Specialise in restoring antique and modern and office furniture, leather work, staining, polishing, reviving bookshelf leather, loose leathers.

PROVIDE Home Inspections. Refundable Estimates. Free Chargeable Collection/Delivery Service.
SPEAK TO Mr J. Crisp.

ROSS ANTHONY FULLER

23 Rosecroft Avenue, **London NW3 7QA**

TEL   071 435 4562
OPEN   Mon–Sat By Appointment.

Specialise in restoration and conservation of antique furniture particularly wood carving and finishing.

PROVIDE Home Inspections. Free/Chargeable Estimates. Free Local Collection/Delivery Service.
SPEAK TO Ross Anthony Fuller.
This workshop is included on the register of conservators maintained by the Conservation Unit of the Museum and Galleries Commission.
SEE Porcelain.

GREVILLE MARCHANT

157 Audley Road, **London NW4 3EN**

TEL   081 202 1844
ANS   081 202 1844
OPEN   8.30–6 Mon to Fri; 10–5.30 Sun.

Specialise in restoring all types of furniture, especially chairs. Copies made to match existing pieces; also architectural joinery.

PROVIDE Home Inspections. Free Estimates. Free Collection/Delivery Service.
SPEAK TO Greville Marchant.
Mr Marchant holds a Licentiateship to the City & Guilds.

RODERIC COWING

Unit 12, Liddell Road, **London NW6 2EW**
TEL   071 328 6025
OPEN   10–6 Mon–Fri.

Specialise in upholstery restoration.

PROVIDE Home Inspections. Chargeable/Refundable Estimates. Chargeable Collection/Delivery Service.
SPEAK TO Roderic Cowing.

JOHN CHAMBERS

4 Nugent Terrace, **London NW8 9QB**
TEL   071 289 1393
OPEN   9–5 Mon–Fri.

Specialise in restoring and repairing English 17th and 18th century oak, walnut and mahogany furniture.

PROVIDE Home Inspections.Free Estimates in Central London only. Chargeable Collection/Delivery Service.
SPEAK TO John Chambers.

WELLINGTON GALLERY

1 St. John's Wood High Street, **London NW8 7NG**
TEL   071 586 2620
OPEN   10–5.30 Mon–Sat.

Specialise in restoring furniture.

PROVIDE Home Inspections. Free Estimates. Chargeable Collection/Delivery Service.
SPEAK TO Mrs Maureen Barclay or Mr K. J. Barclay.
Member of LAPADA.
SEE Oil Paintings, Porcelain, Silver.

BALLANTYNE BOOTH LTD

Cadogan House, Hythe Road, **London NW10 6RS**
TEL   081 960 3255
FAX   081 960 4567
OPEN   8–6 Mon–Fri.

Specialise in restoring all antique furniture and related items, including cabinetmaking, veneering, turning, leatherwork, carving, gilding, polishing and metalwork.

PROVIDE Home Inspections. Free Estimates. Chargeable Collection/Delivery Service.
SPEAK TO Helen Mark or Scott Bowran.
Member of UKIC. This workshop is included on the register of conservators maintained by the Conservation Unit of the Museum and Galleries Commission.

RICHARD MARK–WARDLAW

Unit BO2, Acton Business Centre, School Road, **London NW10 6TD**
TEL   081 961 7066
FAX   081 965 0829
OPEN   10–6 Mon–Fri.

Specialise in restoring all cabinetwork, including veneers, polishing, gilding.

PROVIDE Home Inspections. Free Estimates. Free Collection/Delivery Service.
SPEAK TO Richard Mark–Wardlaw.
Member of UKIC.

ADAMS & SHERIDAN

7 Ashbourne Parade, Finchley Road, **London NW11 0AD**
TEL   081 455 6970
OPEN   9–5.30 Mon–Sat.

Specialise in repairing antique and modern furniture, French polishing and re–covering.

PROVIDE Home Inspections. Free/Refundable Estimates. Collection/Delivery Service.

SPEAK TO Mrs Healy.
Member of the Association of Master
Upholsterers.

JEREMY CZERKAS
103 Wentworth Road, **London NW11
ORH**
TEL   081 458 5140
OPEN   By Appointment.

Specialise in restoring antique furniture,
including traditional upholstery and
caning.

PROVIDE Home Inspections. Free
Estimates. Free/Chargeable
Collection/Delivery Service.
SPEAK TO Jeremy Czerkas.

ELIZABETH LAWRENCE
107 Wentworth Road, **London NW11
ORH**
TEL   081 455 1691
OPEN   By Appointment.

Specialise in traditional upholstery and
re-upholstery, refurbishment and
restoration.

PROVIDE Home Inspections.
Free/Chargeable Collection/Delivery
Service.
SPEAK TO Elizabeth Lawrence.

PHOENIX ANTIQUE FURNITURE RESTORATION LIMITED
96 Webber Street, **London SE1 0QN**
TEL   071 928 3624
OPEN   By Appointment.

Specialise in restoring and conserving
furniture, including cabinetmaking,
polishing, upholstery, metalwork, desk
lining. Specialist chair doctors and can
make furniture to order.

PROVIDE Home Inspections. Free
Estimates. Chargeable
Collection/Delivery Service.
SPEAK TO David Battle.

PARAGON FURNITURE
Unit 2C, Ashleigh Commercial Estate,
Westmoor Street, **London SE7 8NQ**
TEL   081 305 2332
OPEN   8–5 Mon–Fri.

Specialise in restoring antique furniture
and conversions.

PROVIDE Home Inspections. Free
Estimates. Free Collection/Delivery
Service.
SPEAK TO G. Matthews or J. Watson.

GREENWICH CONSERVATION WORKSHOPS
Spread Eagle Antiques of Greenwich, 8–
9 Nevada Street, **London SE10 9JL**
TEL   081 305 1666
OPEN   10–5.30 Mon–Sat.

Specialise in restoring furniture.

PROVIDE Home Inspections. Refundable
Estimates. Free/Chargeable
Collection/Delivery Service.
SPEAK TO Richard Moy.
SEE Oil Paintings.

RELCY ANTIQUES
9 Nelson Road, **London SE10 9JB**
TEL   081 858 2812
FAX   081 293 4135
OPEN   10–6 Mon–Sat.

Specialise in restoring 18th and 19th
century English and Continental
furniture.

PROVIDE Home Inspections.
Free/Chargeable Estimates.
Collection/Delivery Service by
arrangement.
SPEAK TO Robin Challis.
SEE Collectors (Scientific Instruments),
Oil Paintings, Silver.

A. FAGIANI
30 Wagner Street, **London SE15 1NN**
TEL   071 732 7188
OPEN   8–5.30 Mon–Fri.

Specialise in repairing and restoring antique English and Continental furniture and polishing.

PROVIDE Home Inspections. Free Estimates. Free Collection/Delivery Service.
SPEAK TO Mr A. Fagiani.

SOPHIE LEVENE GILDING AND RESTORATION
63A Cheltenham Road, **London SE15 3AF**
TEL   071 639 5735
FAX   081 299 0923
OPEN   10–6 Mon–Fri.

Specialise in restoring all styles of gilded decoration to period furniture, frames, architectural features, objets d'art etc. They also provide a range of services including repair and reproduction of composition mouldings, carving and paint finishes carried out on site or in their London studio.

PROVIDE Home Inspections. Free Estimates. Chargeable Collection/Delivery Service.
SPEAK TO Sophie Levene. Member of UKIC. This workshop is included on the register of conservators maintained by the Conservation Unit of the Museums and Galleries Commission.
SEE Picture Frames.

J. T. GROSSE LTD
12 Verney Road, **London SE16 3DH**
TEL   071 231 7969
OPEN   7.30–5.30 Mon–Fri; Sat By Appointment.

Specialise in restoration of antique and other fine furniture, including repair, polishing and re-upholstering.

PROVIDE Home Inspections. Free Estimates. Free Collection/Delivery Service.
SPEAK TO A. F. Grosse.
This family business has been established since 1911.

CRAWLEY STUDIOS
39 Wood Vale, **London SE23 3DS**
TEL   081 299 4121
FAX   081 299 0756
OPEN   9–6.15 Mon–Fri.

Specialise in restoring painted furniture, lacquer, gilding, papier mâché and polishing.

PROVIDE Home Inspections. Free Estimates. Chargeable Collection/Delivery Service.
SPEAK TO Marie Louise Crawley.
Member of BAFRA, UKIC and the Guild of Master Craftsmen.
SEE Silver

OSSWOSKI WORKSHOP
83 Pimlico Road, **London SW1W 8PH and at 595 Kings Road,** London SW6 2EL
TEL   071 730 3256 and 731 0334
OPEN   10–6 Mon–Fri; 10–1 Sat.

Specialise in restoring and gilding 18th century giltwood mirrors, furniture and carvings.

PROVIDE Free Estimates.
SPEAK TO Mark or Matthew Ossowski.

SPINK AND SON LTD
Furniture Restoration Department, c/o 5–7 King Street, **London SW1Y 6QS**
TEL   071 735 2224
FAX   071 735 2224
OPEN   8–5.30 Mon–Fri.

Specialise in restoring antique and Fine English furniture, including cabinetwork, metalwork, Boulle, ivory, marquetry, caning and traditional hand-finishing.

PROVIDE Home Inspections. Free Estimates. Chargeable Collection/Delivery Service.
SPEAK TO Peter Holmes.

ARNOLD WIGGINS AND SONS LTD
4 Bury Street, **London SW1Y 6AB**
TEL   071 925 0195
FAX   071 839 6928
OPEN   9.30–5.30 Mon–Fri.

Specialise in conserving and restoring period furniture.

PROVIDE Home Inspections. Free Estimates. Chargeable Collection/Delivery Service.
SPEAK TO Michael Gregory.
Members of BADA, the Master Woodcarvers Association and the Society of Gilders.
SEE Picture Frames.

PETER DUDGEON LTD
Brompton Place, **London SW3 1QE**
TEL   071 589 0322
FAX   071 589 1910
OPEN   9–5.30 Mon–Fri; 10–5 Sat.

Specialise in restoring upholstered furniture, French chairs etc.

PROVIDE Home Inspections. Free Estimates. Collection/Delivery Service.
SPEAK TO Hugh Garforth–Bles or William Dudgeon.
They have been established for over forty years.

M. P. GERVAL & ASSOCIATES
28 Cheyne Walk, **London SW3 5HH**
TEL   071 351 2840
FAX   071 351 5374
OPEN   9.30–6 By Appointment.

Specialise in restoring carved, composition and other types of frames and mirrors, gilt or otherwise finished.

PROVIDE Home Inspections. Free Estimates. Free Local Collection/Delivery Service.
SPEAK TO Marie–Pierre Gerval.
Member of UKIC. This workshop is included on the register of conservators

maintained by the Conservation Unit of the Museums and Galleries Commission.
SEE Picture Frames.

JOANNA PIOTROWSKA
A. & J. Antique Restoration, Chenil Galleries F3–J4, 181–183 Kings Road, **London SW3 5EB**
TEL   071 352 2704 or 081 578 9688
OPEN   11–5 Thur, Fri, Sat.

Specialise in restoring gilt mirrors and furniture, gilding, lacquering and painting.

PROVIDE Home Inspections. Free Estimates. Collection/Delivery Service.
SPEAK TO Joanna or Andrew Piotrowska.

JOHN HEAP
No.1 The Polygon, **London SW4 0JG**
TEL   071 627 4498
OPEN   By Appointment.

Specialise in restoring painted antique furniture, gesso work and gilding.

PROVIDE Home Inspections. Free Estimates. Free Collection/Delivery Service.
SPEAK TO John Heap.
SEE Porcelain, Silver.

DAVID ALEXANDER ANTIQUES & KATE THURLOW
102 Waterford Road, **London SW6 2HA**
TEL   071 731 4644
OPEN   By Appointment.

Specialise in restoring 16th–17th century European furniture.

PROVIDE Home Inspections. Chargeable Collection/Delivery Service.
SPEAK TO Kate Thurlow or Rodney Robertson.

I. AND J. L. BROWN LTD
636 Kings Road, **London SW6 2DU**
TEL   071 736 4141
OPEN   9–5.30 Mon–Sat.

Specialise in restoring English country and French Provincial furniture. Also undertake chair rush work.

PROVIDE Free/Chargeable Estimates. Free/Chargeable Collection/Delivery Service.
SPEAK TO Peter Place.
SEE Furniture **Hereford & Worcester**.

PETER L. JAMES
681 Fulham Road, **London SW6 5PZ**
TEL   071 736 0183
OPEN   7.30–5.30 Mon–Fri.

Specialise in restoring lacquer, painted and gilded furniture and mirror frames.

PROVIDE Home Inspections. Refundable Estimates. Chargeable Collection/Delivery Service.
SPEAK TO Peter L. James.
SEE Picture Frames.

MICHAEL MARRIOTT LTD
588 Fulham Road, **London SW6 5NT**
TEL   071 736 3110
FAX   071 731 2632
OPEN   9.30–5.30 Mon–Fri.

Specialise in restoring furniture, including traditional upholstery.

PROVIDE Home Inspections in London, outside London for major restorations only. Free Estimates. Collection/Delivery Service.
SPEAK TO Michael Marriott.
SEE Picture Frames.

AUBREY BROCKLEHURST
124 Cromwell Road, **London SW7 4ET**
TEL   071 373 0319
OPEN   9–1, 2–5.30 Mon–Fri; 10–1 Sat.

Specialise in restoring and repairing antique furniture.

PROVIDE Home Inspections. Free Estimates. Chargeable Collection/Delivery Service.
SPEAK TO Aubrey Brocklehurst, Ms Gill or Mrs Leonard.
Mr Brocklehurst is a member of BADA and he, Ms Gill and Mrs Leonard are all FBHIs.
SEE Clocks.

CAMILLA REDFERN
32 Abbey Business Centre, Ingate Place, **London SW8 3NS**
TEL   071 627 0935
FAX   071 498 0144
OPEN   8.30–6 Mon–Fri or By Appointment.

Specialise in restoring all antiques of a gilded parcel, including mirror frames. Provides a frame search service.

PROVIDE Home Inspections. Free Estimates. Chargeable Collection/Delivery Service.
SPEAK TO Camilla Redfern.
Member of UKIC and IIC. This workshop is included on the register of conservators maintained by the Conservation Unit of the Museums and Galleries Commission.
SEE Picture Frames.

P & F BINNINGTON
Re-locating in S.W. London.
TEL   081 977 2570
ANS   081 977 2570
OPEN   By Appointment.

Specialise in restoring all kinds of antique furniture, including surfaces decorated in marquetry, paint, carving and gilding.

PROVIDE Home Inspections. Free Local Estimates. Chargeable Collection/Delivery Service.
SPEAK TO Jane Bishop.
Member of BAFRA.
SEE Porcelain.

CHAIR REPAIRS
FRENCH POLISHING
FURNITURE RESTORATION
AND TRADITIONAL UPHOLSTERY

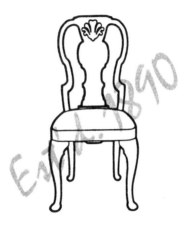

Antique or Modern
R. HORNSBY
071-225 2888

33 Thurloe Place, South Kensington
London SW7 2HQ

Specialise in restoring furniture, including French polishing, chair repairs, cabinet work and repairs, traditional upholstery.

PROVIDE Home Inspections. Free Estimates. Collection/Delivery Service Available.

SPEAK TO Mr R. Gough.
Established 1890

CALLANAN LTD
Unit 7, Parkfields Industrial Estate,
Culvert Place, Culvert Road, **London
SW11 5BA**
TEL 071 828 7577
OPEN 9–6.30 Mon–Fri.

Specialise in restoring mirror frames.

PROVIDE Home Inspections. Free
Estimates. Chargeable
Collection/Delivery Service.
SPEAK TO David Callanan.
SEE Picture Frames.

W. J. COOK AND SONS
167 Battersea High Street, **London
SW11 3JS**
TEL 071 736 5329
OPEN 8–7 Mon–Fri.

Specialise in restoring all types of
furniture, late 17th century to present
day, including gilding, carving,
leathering, upholstery and marquetry.

PROVIDE Home Inspections. Free
Estimates. Free Local
Collection/Delivery Service.
SPEAK TO Mr Cook.
This is a family business established over
thirty years.
SEE **Wiltshire.**

DELIA BRAIN
136 Putney Bridge Road, **London
SW15 2NQ**
TEL 081 874 1678
OPEN 9–5 Mon–Fri.

Specialise in restoring 18th and 19th
century painted furniture and specialist
paint techniques such as marbling and
graining.

PROVIDE Home Inspections.
Free/Refundable Estimates. Chargeable
Collection/Delivery Service.
SPEAK TO Delia Brain.
Ms Brain also restores and retouches
scenic wallpaper on site.

ALAN S. STONE
3 Wadham Road, **London SW15**
TEL 081 870 1606
OPEN 9–4.30 Mon–Fri; 9–2.30 Sat.

Specialise in restoring 18th and 19th
century furniture.

PROVIDE Home Inspections. Free
Estimates. Free Collection/Delivery
Service.
SPEAK TO Alan S. Stone.

WEAVER NEAVE & DAUGHTER
17 Lifford Street, **London SW15 1NY**
TEL 081 785 2464
OPEN 9–6 Mon–Fri.

Specialise in all cane and rush work for
antique furniture.

PROVIDE Home Inspections. Free
Estimates. Collection/Delivery Service
by arrangement.
SPEAK TO Rosslyn Neave.

E. & A. WATES LTD
82–84 Mitcham Lane, **London
SW16 6NR**
TEL 081 769 2205
FAX 081 677 4766
OPEN 9–6 Mon–Sat; 9–7 Thur.

Specialise in repairing fine furniture
including re–upholstery, French
polishing, caning and carving.

PROVIDE Home Inspections.
Free/Refundable Estimates.
SPEAK TO Mr R. D. Wates.
Established 1900.

GRAEME PHILLIPS RESTORATION
Broadway Studios, 28 Tooting High
Street, **London SW17 0RG**
TEL 081 672 4465
FAX 081 767 3247
OPEN 9.30–6 Mon–Fri.

Specialise in restoring furniture from

1685 to 1840, especially early walnut and high Regency, special concern given to good colour and surface.

PROVIDE Home Inspections. Chargeable Estimates. Chargeable Collection/Delivery Service.
SPEAK TO Graeme Phillips.
Member of UKIC, BADA Dip.

ATHELDENE RESTORATION
1A Atheldene Road, **London SW18 3BN**
TEL   081 874 0157
FAX   071 731 7018
OPEN   8.30–5.30 Mon–Fri.

Specialise in restoring antique furniture, especially 18th century.

PROVIDE Home Inspections. Free Estimates. Chargeable Collection/Delivery Service.
SPEAK TO Paul McNaney.
Member of UKIC.

SERENA CHAPLIN
32 Elsynge Road, **London SW18 2HN**
TEL   081 870 9455
FAX   081 877 0943
OPEN   By Appointment.

Specialise in restoring mirror frames and other gilded objects as well as restoring and conserving antique lacquer such as screens, cabinets and trays.

PROVIDE Free Estimates.
SPEAK TO Serena Chaplin.
Ms Chaplin also runs five day introductory courses in gilding and lacquer.
SEE Picture Frames.

COMPTON HALL RESTORATION
Unit A, 133 Riverside Business Centre, Haldane Place, **London SW18 4UQ**
TEL   081 874 0762
OPEN   9–5 Mon–Fri.

Specialise in restoring painted furniture,

lacquer, gilding, papier mâché, penwork, Tole.

PROVIDE Home Inspections. Free Estimates. Collection/Delivery Service by arrangement.
SPEAK TO Lucinda Compton, Jane Hall or Henrietta Hohler.
Member of BAFRA and UKIC. This workshop is included on the register maintained by the Conservation Unit of the Museums and Galleries Commission.
SEE Silver.

PLOWDEN AND SMITH LTD
190 St Ann's Hill, **London SW18 2RT**
TEL   081 874 4005
FAX   081 874 7248
OPEN   9–5.30 Mon–Fri.

Specialise in restoring and conserving fine furniture and upholstery.

PROVIDE Home Inspections. Free Estimates. Free Collection/Delivery Service.
SPEAK TO Bob Butler.
SEE Oil Paintings, Silver, Porcelain, Display.

CONNOLLY LEATHER LTD
Wandle Bank, **London SW19 1DW**
TEL   081 542 5251 and 543 4611
FAX   081 543 7455
OPEN   9–12.45, 1.30–4 Mon–Fri.

Specialise in restoring leather chairs, screens, wallpanelling. Also carry out gold embossing.

PROVIDE Home Inspections. Free Estimates. Free Collection/Delivery Service.
SPEAK TO Mr C. Carron.
SEE Lighting.

R. D. ROBINS UPHOLSTERY LTD
1–9 Tennyson Road, **London SW19 8SH**
TEL   081 540 0711
FAX   081 503 1153
OPEN   7.30–5 Mon–Fri.

Specialise in a full upholstery service, including walling, tenting, re–covering sofas and chairs, headboards etc.

PROVIDE Home Inspections. Free Estimates. Chargeable Collection/Delivery Service.
SPEAK TO Mr B. S. Ansell.
Member of Association of Master Upholsterers.
SEE **London E7**
SEE Carpets.

TONY GUEST FRAMING
10 Ogle Street, **London W1P 7LQ**
TEL   071 580 8786
OPEN   8–5 Mon–Fri.

Specialise in restoring antique mirror frames and gilded furniture.

PROVIDE Home Inspections. Free Estimates. Collection/Delivery Service by arrangement.
SPEAK TO Tony Guest or David Duncan.
SEE Picture Frames.

W. R. HARVEY & CO. (ANTIQUES) LTD
5 Old Bond Street, **London W1X 3TA**
TEL   071 499 8385
FAX   071 495 0209
OPEN   10–5.30 Mon–Sat.

Specialise in restoring fine English period (1650–1830) furniture and works of art.

PROVIDE Home Inspections. Free Estimates. Free Collection/Delivery Service.
SPEAK TO Mr K. Shakespeare or Mr A. D. Harvey.
Member of BADA and the Guild of Master Craftsmen. This workshop is included on the register of conservators maintained by the Conservation Unit of the Museums and Galleries Commission.

RICHARD KERLEY
6 York Mansions, 84 Chiltern Street, **London W1M 1PT**
TEL   071 486 6483
OPEN   By Appointment.

Specialise in restoring furniture; Boulle work and carving, English water gilding. Also copy chairs and mirror frames to match clients' own pieces.

PROVIDE Home Inspections. Chargeable Estimates. Chargeable Collection/Delivery Service.
SPEAK TO Richard Kerley.

TELESHIELD LIMITED
152 New Cavendish Street, **London W1M 7FJ**
TEL   071 631 3605
FAX   071 580 5787

Specialise in refurbishment and manufacture of locks and keys dating back to 15th century, all types of keys cut and locks repaired.

PROVIDE Free/Chargeable Home Inspections.
SPEAK TO B. D. Camfield.

G. D. WARDER AND SONS LTD
14 Hanway Place, **London W1P 9DG**
TEL   071 636 1867
OPEN   9–4.30 Mon–Fri.

Specialise in water gilding and carving, gilding and restoration of period mirrors, antique furniture, frames and bijoutiers. Reproduction Regency mirrors made to order.

PROVIDE Free Estimates. Chargeable Collection/Delivery Service.
SPEAK TO David or Robert Warder.

BOURLET
32 Connaught Street, **London W2 2AY**
TEL   071 724 4837
OPEN   11–5.30 Mon–Fri; By Appointment Sat.

Specialise in restoring furniture.

PROVIDE Home Inspections. Free Estimates. Collection/Delivery Service.
SPEAK TO Gabrielle Rendell.
SEE Oil Paintings, Picture Frames.

H. J. HATFIELD & SON
42 St Michael's Street, **London**
W2 1QP
TEL   071 723 8265
FAX   071 706 4562
OPEN   9–1, 2–5 Mon–Fri.

Specialise in restoring English and French 17th–19th century furniture.

PROVIDE Home Inspections. Free Estimates.
SPEAK TO Philip Astley–Jones.
SEE Silver.

LESLEY WILSON
14 Dordrecht Road, **London W3 7TE**
TEL   081 743 0909
OPEN   By Appointment.

Specialise in the restoration of upholstered furniture, working closely with wood and textile conservators.

PROVIDE Home Inspections. Free Estimates. Free/Chargeable Collection/Delivery Service.
SPEAK TO Lesley Wilson.
Member of UKIC. This workshop is included on the register of conservators maintained by the Conservation Unit of the Museums and Galleries Commission.

THE OLD CINEMA
160 Chiswick High Road, **London**
W4 1PR
TEL   081 995 4166
OPEN   10–6 Daily.

Specialise in comprehensive restoration and upholstery service for antique and Victorian furniture.

PROVIDE Free Estimates. Free Collection/Delivery Service.
SPEAK TO Martin Hanness.

PETER JAMES AVERSON–MAUNDER
73 Queen Anne's Grove, **London**
W5 3XP
TEL   081 567 6586
OPEN   9–5.30 Mon–Fri By
        Appointment Only.

Specialise in restoring rush and cane in antique and modern furniture, excluding settees. Minor repairs to framework and re–seating in Danish cord and pre–woven cane.

PROVIDE Local Home Inspections. Free Estimates. Chargeable Collection/Delivery Service.
SPEAK TO Peter James Averson–Maunder.
Member of the Guild of Master Craftsmen.

BADGER ANTIQUES
12 St Mary's Road, **London W5 5ES**
TEL   081 567 5601
OPEN   10–6 Mon–Sat.

Specialise in restoring furniture.

PROVIDE Home Inspections. Free Estimates. Free Collection/Delivery Service.
SPEAK TO Michael Allders.
SEE Clocks.

C. J. G. GILDERS & CARVERS
Unit 10, Sandringham Mews, **London**
W5 5DF
TEL   081 579 2341
OPEN   10–5 Mon–Sat.

Specialise in restoring antique mirrors and gilt furniture.

PROVIDE Home Inspections. Free Estimates. Free Collection/Delivery Service within London.
SPEAK TO Chris Gostomski.
SEE Picture Frames.

ROBERT H. CRAWLEY
Aberedeen House, 75 St Mary's Road, (Side entrance on St Mary's Square),
London W5 5RH
TEL   081 566 5074
OPEN   9–5 Mon–Fri.

Specialise in restoring antique furniture.

PROVIDE Home Inspections. Free

Estimates. Chargeable
Collection/Delivery Service.
SPEAK TO Robert Crawley.
Member of BAFRA.

BARNET ANTIQUES
79 Kensington Church Street, **London
W8 4BG**
TEL   071 376 2817
OPEN   10–5.30 Mon–Sat.

Specialise in all aspects of furniture
restoration, including cabinet repairs,
carving, gilding, turning, decoration,
metalwork, keys and locks, straightening
warped items, polishing, fretwork, Boulle
and brass inlay.

PROVIDE Home Inspections. Free
Estimates. Chargeable
Collection/Delivery Service.
SPEAK TO Richard Gerry.

DON HOLMES ANTIQUES
47C Earls Court Road (in Abingdon
Villas), **London W8 6EE**
TEL   071 937 6961 or 020 888 0254
OPEN   2–7 Fri; 9.30–5.30 Sat or By
         Appointment.

Specialise in restoring and repairing
18th and 19th century furniture, mainly
mahogany.

PROVIDE Home Inspections. Refundable
Estimates. Chargeable
Collection/Delivery Service.
SPEAK TO Don or Sarah Holmes.

ARTHUR SEAGER
25A Holland Street, **London W8 4NA**
TEL   071 937 3262
FAX   071 937 3262
OPEN   10–5.30 Mon–Sat.

Specialise in restoring 17th and 18th
century oak furniture.

PROVIDE Home Inspections. Free
Estimates. Free/Chargeable
Collection/Delivery Service.
SPEAK TO Arthur Seager.

A. SPIGARD
77 Kensington Church Street, **London
W8 4BG**
TEL   071 937 2461
OPEN   9–6 Mon–Sat.

Specialise in restoring antique furniture.

PROVIDE Refundable Estimates.
Chargeable Collection/Delivery
Service.
SPEAK TO A. Spigard.

LAWRENCE BRASS AND SON
154 Sutherland Avenue, **London W9**
TEL   071 636 3401
OPEN   8–5 Mon–Fri.

Specialise in restoring fine furniture,
including metalwork, gilding,
upholstery. They cast furniture mounts
in all metals and do fire gilding and
specialise in difficult or impossible
commissions.

PROVIDE Home Inspections.
Free/Chargeable Estimates. Free
Collection/Delivery Service.
SPEAK TO Mr Murray.
Member of BAFRA, UKIC. This
workshop is included on the register of
conservators maintained by the
Conservation Unit of the Museums and
Galleries Commission.
SEE **Avon.**

TITIAN STUDIO
Unit H, 326 Kensal Road, **London W10
5BN**
TEL   081 960 6247 and 969 6126
OPEN   9–6 Mon–Fri.

Specialise in carving, gilding, lacquer,
painted furniture and French polishing.

PROVIDE Home Inspections.
Free/Chargeable Estimates. Chargeable
Collection/Delivery Service.
SPEAK TO Rodrigo Titian or Rosario
Titian.
Member of BAFRA.

DAVID HORDERN RESTORATIONS LIMITED
1A Codrington Mews, Blenheim Crescent, **London W11 2EH**
TEL   071 727 8855
FAX   071 792 9164
OPEN   9–6 Mon–Fri.

Specialise in restoring quality antique furniture, including Boulle, cabinetwork, carving, gilding, ivory, lacquer, leather, marble, marquetry, metalwork, ormolu, polishing and upholstery.

PROVIDE Home Inspections. Free Estimates. Chargeable Collection/Delivery Service.
SPEAK TO David Hordern.
Member of UKIC and BAFRA. This workshop is included on the register of conservators maintained by the Conservation Unit of the Museums and Galleries Commission.

ROSEMARY COOK RESTORATION
78 Stanlake Road, **London W12 7HJ**
TEL   081 749 7977
OPEN   By Appointment.

Specialise in restoring painted surfaces, including furniture and rush seating.

PROVIDE Home Inspections. Free Estimates. Free Collection/Delivery Service in London.
SPEAK TO Rosemary Cook.
SEE Porcelain, Silver.

COUTTS GALLERIES
75 Blythe Road, **London W14 OHD**
TEL   071–602–3980
OPEN   10–5 Mon–Fri; By Appointment Sat.

Specialise in restoration of decorative antique furniture, including gilding, carving, modelling, lacquerwork, cabinetwork, French polishing.

PROVIDE Home Inspections, Free Estimates, Free Collection/Delivery Service.
SPEAK TO Seabury Burdett–Coutts.
SEE Oil Paintings, Picture Frames.

FELLOWES AND SAUNDERSON
116 Blythe Road, **London W14 0UH**
TEL   071 603 7475
OPEN   9.30–5.30 Tues–Fri, 10–4 Sat.

Specialise in restoration of antique mirrors. They have their own range of gilded and hand–finished frames.

PROVIDE Home Inspections. Free Estimates. Free Collection/Delivery Service.
SPEAK TO Joan Saunderson.
SEE Picture Frames.

PHOEBE MASON
17 Russell Road, **London W14 8HU**
TEL   071 602 5694
OPEN   By Appointment Only.

Specialise in restoring mirror frames, including gilding, ornamentation and plasterwork.

PROVIDE Home Inspections. Free/Chargeable Estimates. Free/Chargeable Collection/Delivery Service.
SPEAK TO Phoebe Mason.
SEE Picture Frames, Silver.

PAUL FERGUSON
Unit 20, 21 Wren Street, **London WC1X OHF**
TEL   071 278 8759
FAX   071 278 8759
OPEN   9–5.30 Mon–Fri.

Specialise in restoring carved and gilded furniture, girandoles, torchères.

PROVIDE Home Inspections. Free Estimates. Collection/Delivery Service by arrangement.
SPEAK TO Paul Ferguson.
SEE Picture Frames.

S. H. JEWELL
26 Parker Street, **London WC2B 5PH**
TEL   071 405 8520
OPEN   9–5.30 Mon–Fri; By
Appointment Sat.

Specialises in 19th and 20th century
English furniture repairs and polishing,
table-lining and upholstery.

PROVIDE Home Inspections. Free
Estimates. Chargeable
Collection/Delivery Service.
SPEAK TO S. H. Jewell

TREEN ANTIQUES
Treen House, 72 Park Road,
Prestwich, Greater Manchester
M25 8FA
TEL   061 740 1063
FAX   061 720 7244
OPEN   by appointment.

Specialise in conserving and
restoring antique English
furniture, particularly regional
furniture with an emphasis on
finish and coating preservation.

PROVIDE Home Inspections.
Free/Refundable Estimates. Free
Local Collection/Delivery.
Services include environmental
monitoring, housekeeping advice,
furniture analysis/research, cane
and rushwork.
SPEAK TO Simon Feingold.
Member of FHS, GADAR, UKIC
and RFS

CASEMENTS THE CABINETMAKERS
Slack Lane Works, Pendlebury, Salford,
Greater Manchester M27 2QT
TEL   061 794 1610
OPEN   8–6 Mon–Fri; 8–1 Sat.

Specialise in antique restoration,
including veneering, French polishing
and turning. One–off copy pieces.

PROVIDE Home Inspections Refundable
Estimates. Chargeable
Collection/Delivery Service.
SPEAK TO D. Casement.

MICHAEL BENNETT
100 Market Street, Hoylake, Wirral,
Merseyside L47 3BE
TEL   051 632 4331
FAX   051 632 6220
OPEN   By Appointment.

Specialise in invisible repairs of late
17th–early 18th century furniture with
emphasis on blending in both colour and
patina of repairs. Also Boulle and
marquetry work.

PROVIDE. Home Inspections. Mostly Free
Estimates. Collection/ Delivery Service
by arrangement.
SPEAK TO Michael Bennett.

PILGRIMS PROGRESS
1A–3A Bridgewater Street, Liverpool,
Merseyside L1 OAR
TEL   051 708 7515
FAX   051 709 1465
OPEN   9–5 Mon–Fri; 1–4 Sat.

Specialise in restoring antique furniture,
including cabinet-work, French
polishing, re-upholstery.

PROVIDE Home Inspections. Free
Estimates. Free/Chargeable
Collection/Delivery Service.
SPEAK TO Selwyn Hyams.

WELLINGTON CRAFTS (1980)
123St John's Road, Waterloo, Liverpool,
Merseyside L22 9QE
TEL   051 920 5511
OPEN   9.30–5 Mon, Tues; 9.30–2 Wed;
9.30–5.30 Thur–Sat.

Specialise in cane, rush and bèrgère
restoration.

PROVIDE Home Inspections. Refundable Estimates. Chargeable Collection/Delivery Service.
SPEAK TO Neville Hymus.
SEE Picture Frames.

H. AKSERALIAN
79 Mollison Way, Edgware, **Middlesex HA8 5QU**
TEL   081 952 6432 evenings.
OPEN   By Appointment.

Specialise in chair caning, repairs to cane work, reseating, staining cane work and sea–grass seating, including bèrgère suites.
PROVIDE Home Inspections. Free Estimates. Chargeable Collection/Delivery Service.
SPEAK TO Harry Akseralian.

ANTIQUE RESTORATIONS
45 Windmill Road, Brentford, **Middlesex TW8 0QQ**
TEL   081 568 5249
OPEN   8–5 Mon–Fri.

Specialise in restoring and conserving painted and gilded furniture, Oriental lacquer and japanning.
PROVIDE Home Inspections. Free/Chargeable Estimates. Free Local Collection/Delivery Service.
SPEAK TO Reginald Dudman.

R. BECKFORD
6 Elms Lane, Wembley, **Middlesex HA0 2NH**
TEL   081 904 4735
OPEN   9.30–6 Mon–Fri.

Specialise in repairing and restoring all types of furniture, polishing and refinishing.
PROVIDE Home Inspections. Free Estimates. Chargeable Collection/Delivery Service.
SPEAK TO R. Beckford.

CHURCH LANE RESTORATIONS
1 Church Lane, Teddington, **Middlesex TW11 8PA**
TEL   081 977 2526
OPEN   7.30–5 Mon–Thur; 7.30–4 Fri.

Specialise in restoring period furniture and French polishing.
PROVIDE Home Inspections. Free Estimates. Free Collection/Delivery Service.
SPEAK TO Mr Vincent.
Member of LAPADA.

MARIA J. LESIAK
Leliwa, 71 St Anne's Avenue, Stanwell, Staines, **Middlesex TW19 7RL**
TEL   0784 257401
FAX   0784 257401
OPEN   By Appointment.

Specialise in restoring decorative objects, including lacquerwork.
PROVIDE Home Inspections. Free Estimates. Free Local Collection/Delivery Service.
SPEAK TO Maria J. Lesiak.
Member of UKIC and an Associate Member of ABPR. This workshop is included on the register of conservators maintained by the Conservation Unit of the Museums and Galleries Commission.
SEE Picture Frames, Oil Paintings.

R. V. MORGAN & CO.
Unit 41, 26–28 The Queensway, Ponders End, Enfield, **Middlesex EN3 5UU**
TEL   081 805 0353
OPEN   8–5.30 Mon–Fri; 8–3 Sat.

Specialise in all aspects of furniture restoration, specialist cabinetmaking and French polishing.
PROVIDE Home Inspections. Free/Chargeable Estimates. Chargeable Collection/Delivery Service.
SPEAK TO Mr R. V. Morgan.

PHELPS LTD
133–135 St Margarets Road,
Twickenham, **Middlesex TW1 1RG**
TEL   081 892 1778
FAX   081 892 3661
OPEN   9–5.30 Mon–Sat.

Specialise in restoring 19th and early
20th century furniture.

PROVIDE Home Inspections. Free
Estimates. Chargeable
Collection/Delivery Service.
SPEAK TO R. Phelps.

BARNT GREEN ANTIQUES
93 Hewell Road, Barnt Green,
Birmingham, **West Midlands B45 8NL**
TEL   021 445 4942
OPEN   9–5 30 Mon–Fri; 9–1 Sat.

Specialise in restoring and conserving
antique furniture, gilding.

PROVIDE Home Inspections. Free
Estimates. Chargeable
Collection/Delivery Service.
SPEAK TO Mr P. Slater. Member of
BAFRA.
SEE Clocks.

HAMPTON UTILITIES (B'HAM) LTD
15 Pitsford Street, Hockley,
Birmingham, **West Midlands B18 6LJ**
TEL   021 554 1766
OPEN   8–4 Mon–Fri.

Specialise in restoring and repairing
mirror frames, including gilding.

PROVIDE Free Estimates. Chargeable
Collection/Delivery Service.
SPEAK TO C. Harrison.
SEE Picture Frames, Silver.

GEOFFREY HASSALL ANTIQUES
20 New Road, Solihull, **West Midlands
B91 3DP**
TEL   021 705 0068
OPEN   9.30–1, 2–5.30 Tues–Sat.

Specialise in restoring all periods of
furniture.

PROVIDE Home Inspections. Free
Estimates. Free/Chargeable
Collection/Delivery Service.
SPEAK TO Geoffrey Hassall.

PHIL HILL (ROCKING HORSES)
188 Alcester Road South, Kings Heath,
Birmingham, **West Midlands B14 6DE**
TEL   021 444 0102
OPEN   9.30–6 Mon–Fri or By
        Appointment.

Specialise in restoring furniture,
including all aspects of wood carving,
gesso, painting, wax/oil finish.

PROVIDE Home Inspections. Free
Estimates. Free Collection/Delivery
Service.
SPEAK TO Phil Hill.
SEE Collectors (Toys).

JOHN HUBBARD ANTIQUES AND FINE ART
224–226 Court Oak Road, Harborne,
Birmingham, **West Midlands B32 2EG**
TEL   021 426 1694
FAX   021 428 1214
OPEN   9–6 Mon–Sat.

Specialise in restoring 18th and 19th
century fine furniture and decorative
items, including carving, veneering,
polishing and leather lining.

PROVIDE Home Inspections. Refundable
Estimates. Collection/Delivery Service.
SPEAK TO John Hubbard or David Taplin.

DAVID BARTRAM FURNITURE
The Raveningham Centre, Castell Farm,
Beccles Road, Raveningham, Nr.
Norwich, **Norfolk NR14 6NU**
TEL   050 846 721
OPEN   10–5.30 Daily.

Specialise in comprehensive antique restoration service in their own workshops covering furniture, gilding, upholstery.

PROVIDE Home Inspections. Free Estimates. Collection/Delivery Service.
SPEAK TO David Bartram.
Member of BAFRA and UKIC. This workshop is included on the register of conservators maintained by the Conservation Unit of the Museums and Galleries Commission.
SEE Silver, Clocks.

ERIC BATES & SONS

Melbourne House, Bacton Road, North Walsham, **Norfolk NR28 0RA**
TEL   0692 403221
FAX   0692 404388
OPEN   8.30–4.30 Mon–Fri.

Specialise in restoring antique furniture and upholstery. They also hand make period style oak furniture.

PROVIDE Home Inspections. Refundable Estimates. Collection/Delivery Service by arrangement.
SPEAK TO Eric Bates.

DAVID BOHN

The Old Rectory, Bradenham, **Norfolk IP25 7QL**
TEL   0362 820918
FAX   0362 820918
OPEN   9–5.30 Mon–Fri or by Appointment.

Specialise in all aspects of the conservation and restoration of giltwood furniture.

PROVIDE Home Inspections. Chargeable Estimates. Chargeable Collection/Delivery Service.
SPEAK TO David Bohn.
They have had over thirty years experience. This workshop is included on the register of conservators maintained by the Conservation Unit of the Museum and Galleries Commission.

BROCKDISH ANTIQUES (M. & L. E. PALFREY)

Commerce House, Brockdish, Diss, **Norfolk IP21 4JL**
TEL   037 975 498
OPEN   9–5.30 Mon–Sat; closed Wed.

Specialise in sympathetic restoration of antique furniture, including antique upholstery, using only traditional methods.

PROVIDE Home Inspections. Free Estimates. Free Collection/Delivery Service.
SPEAK TO Michael Palfrey.
This is a three-generation family business.

DISS ANTIQUES RESTORATION SERVICES

2–3 Market Place, Diss, **Norfolk IP22 3JT**
TEL   0379 642213
FAX   0379 642213
OPEN   8–5 Mon–Sat.

Specialise in all antique furniture restoration, as well as copper and brass. They undertake to finish with care by hand every individual piece to retain its age and patina.

PROVIDE Home Inspections. Free Estimates. Collection/Delivery Service.
SPEAK TO Brian Wimshurst.
Member of the Guild of Master Craftsmen and LAPADA.

PETER HOWKINS

39–40 King Street, Great Yarmouth, **Norfolk NR30 2PQ**
TEL   0493 851180
OPEN   9–5.30 Mon–Sat or By Appointment.

Specialise in restoring antique furniture.

PROVIDE Home Inspections.
SPEAK TO Valerie Howkins or Frank Hume.
Member of NAG.
SEE Silver (different address).

RODERICK LARWOOD
The Oaks, Station Road, Larling,
Norwich, **Norfolk NR16 2QS**
TEL   0953 717937
OPEN   8–6 Mon–Fri.

Specialise in restoring 18th century
furniture, brass inlay.

PROVIDE Home Inspections. Free Local
Estimates. Free Collection/Delivery
Service.
SPEAK TO Roderick Larwood.
Member of BAFRA.

PENNY LAWRENCE
Fairhurst Gallery, Bedford Street,
Norwich, **Norfolk NR1AS**
TEL   0603 632064
OPEN   9–5 Mon–Fri.

Specialise in restoring and conserving
painted furniture.

PROVIDE Home Inspections. Free
Estimates. Free/Chargeable
Collection/Delivery Service.
SPEAK TO Penny Lawrence.
This workshop is included on the register
of conservators maintained by the
Conservation Unit of the Museums and
Galleries Commission.
SEE Oil Paintings, Picture Frames, Silver.

RICHARD J. McPHEE CABINETMAKER
20 Muspole Street, Norwich, **Norfolk
NR3 1DJ**
TEL   0603 667701
OPEN   8–1, 2–6 Mon–Fri; 8–1 Sat.

Specialise in all aspects of restoration of
antique furniture, including polishing,
upholstery, cabinetwork and brass.

PROVIDE Home Inspections.
Free/Chargeable Estimates. Chargeable
Collection/Delivery Service.
SPEAK TO Richard McPhee.
Member of UKIC and the Guild of
Master Craftsmen. This workshop is
included on the register of conservators
maintained by the Conservation Unit of

the Museums and Galleries Commission.
SEE Clocks

CLASSIC UPHOLSTERY
Estate Yard, Upper Harlestone,
Northampton, **Northamptonshire
NN7 4EH**
TEL   0604 584556
OPEN   8.30–5 Mon–Fri.

Specialise in traditionally restoring and
renovating upholstered furniture.

PROVIDE Home Inspections. Free
Estimates. Free Collection/Delivery
Service.
SPEAK TO Mark Austin.
Member of the Association of Master
Upholsterers.

THE LEATHER CONSERVATION CENTRE
34 Guildhall Road, Northampton,
Northamptonshire NN1 1EW
TEL   0604 232723
FAX   0604 602070
OPEN   9–6 Mon–Fri.

Specialise in conservation of all types of
leather objects, especially decorated
screens and wall hangings and furniture
upholstery. Advice given on sources of
appropriate specialist leather and
conservation materials.

PROVIDE Home Inspections. Chargeable
Estimates. Chargeable Collection/
Delivery Service.
SPEAK TO Roy Thomson.
SEE Carpets, Lighting.

DOMENICO LUCISANO 'THE WOODCARVER'
The Grange Farm, Sywell,
Northamptonshire NN6 0BE
TEL   0604 713982
OPEN   8–5 Mon–Fri.

Specialise in any woodcarving.

PROVIDE Home Inspections. Free Estimates. Chargeable Collection/Delivery Service. SPEAK TO Domenico Lucisano.

BRYAN PERKINS ANTIQUES

52 Cannon Street, Wellingborough, **Northamptonshire NN8 4DT**
TEL   0933 228812
OPEN   9–5.30 Mon–Fri; 10–12.30 Sat.

Specialise in restoring antique furniture and French polishing, especially chests of drawers and mahogany dining tables.

PROVIDE Home Inspections. Free Estimates. Chargeable Collection/Delivery Service. SPEAK TO B. or J. Perkins.

J. A. & T. HEDLEY

3 St Mary's Chare, Hexham, **Northumberland NE46 1NQ**
TEL   0434 602317
OPEN   9–5 Mon–Sat; 9–12 Thur.

Specialise in restoring antique furniture and French polishing.

PROVIDE Free Estimates. Chargeable Collection/Delivery Service. SPEAK TO D. Hall or W. H. Jewitt. SEE Picture Frames.

JOHN SMITH OF ALNWICK LTD

West Cawledge Park, Alnwick, **Northumberland NE66 2HJ**
TEL   0665 604363
OPEN   10–5 Daily (Gallery).

Specialise in restoring antique English and Continental furniture.

PROVIDE Home Inspections. Chargeable Estimates. Chargeable Collection/Delivery Service. SPEAK TO Mr P. J. Smith

T. S. BARROWS & SON

Hamlyn Lodge, Station Road, Ollerton, Nr. Newark, **Nottinghamshire NG22 9BN**
TEL   0623 823600
OPEN   8.30–5 Mon–Fri.

Specialise in restoring furniture, French polishing, cabinetmaking.

PROVIDE Home Inspections. Chargeable Collection/Delivery Service. SPEAK TO Norman Barrows. A three–generation family business.

FLORENCE CONSERVATION & RESTORATION

102 Nottingham Road, Long Eaton, Nottingham, **Nottinghamshire NG10 2BZ**
TEL   0602 733625
OPEN   8–5 Mon–Fri; 9–12 Sat.

Specialise in restoring gesso frames, gilding and gold leafing. They also repair and restore marquetry, painted and inlaid furniture.

PROVIDE Home Inspections. Refundable Estimates. Chargeable Collection/Delivery Service. SPEAK TO Ron Florence. SEE Oil Paintings, Porcelain.

THE KEYHOLE

Dragonwyck, Far Back Lane, Farnsfield, Newark, **Nottinghamshire NG22 8JX**
TEL   0623 882590
OPEN   By Appointment.

Specialise in restoring locks and keys, anything from a jewel box to a church door key. They also supply period locks and keys, duplicate keys, composite keys and lock servicing.

PROVIDE Home Inspections. Estimates by negotiation. Chargeable Collection/Delivery Service. SPEAK TO George or Valerie Olifent.

Member of the Master Locksmiths Association. This workshop is included on the register of conservators maintained by the Conservation Unit of the Museums and Galleries Commission.

BARBARA BIBB
149 Kingston Road, Oxford,
Oxfordshire OX2 6RP
TEL   0865 56444
OPEN   9–5 Mon–Sat.

Specialise in restoring gilded frames and mirrors, lacquer tables and screens etc.

PROVIDE Home Inspections. Free Estimates. Free Local Collection/Delivery Service.
SPEAK TO Barbara Bibb.
Member of ABPR. This workshop is included on the register of conservators maintained by the Conservation Unit of the Museums and Galleries Commission.
SEE Oil Paintings, Picture Frames.

COUNTRY CHAIRMEN
Home Farm, Ardington, Wantage,
Oxfordshire OX12 8PY
TEL   0235 833614
OPEN   8.30–5.30 Mon–Fri; 10–1 Sat.

Specialise in restoring and repairing antique furniture, rush and cane seating of chairs.

PROVIDE Home Inspections. Estimates. Collection/Delivery Service.
SPEAK TO Tony Handley or Gareth Hudson.

ALISTAIR FRAYLING– CORK
2 Mill Lane, Wallingford, **Oxfordshire OX10 ODH**
TEL   0491 826221
OPEN   10–6 Mon–Fri; By Appointment Sat.

Specialise in restoring fine antique furniture and brass fittings.

PROVIDE Home Inspections. Free

Estimates. Chargeable Collection/Delivery Service.
SPEAK TO Alistair Frayling–Cork.
Member of BAFRA.
SEE Clocks, Collectors (Musical Instruments).

MARK GRIFFIN FURNITURE
Byrebrook Studio, Lower Farm, Northmoor, **Oxford OX8 1AU**
TEL   0865 300171
OPEN   8.30–5.30 Mon–Sat.

Specialise in restoring fine period furniture, including veneering, traditional finishes.

PROVIDE Home Inspections. Chargeable Estimates. Free Collection/Delivery Service.
SPEAK TO Mark Griffin.
Memner of BAFRA.

LA CHAISE ANTIQUE
30 London Street, Faringdon,
Oxfordshire SN7 7AA
TEL   0367 241001
OPEN   9.30–5.30 Mon–Sat.

Specialise in restoring and re–upholstering 18th and 19th century furniture using traditional materials, deep buttoning, leather table–liners.

PROVIDE Home Inspections. Free Estimates. Free Collection/Delivery Service.
SPEAK TO Roger Clark.
Member of the Guild of Master Craftsmen.

MANOR FARM RESTORATIONS
Nettlebed, **Oxfordshire OX14 4QX**
TEL   0491 641186
OPEN   By Appointment.

Specialise in the proper restoration of fine furniture, including Boulle and marquetry, gilding and decorated work.

PROVIDE Home Inspection. Free

Estimates. Chargeable
Collection/Delivery Service.
SPEAK TO Nicola Shreeve and Anne
Kelaart.

COLIN PIPER
RESTORATION
Highfield House, The Greens, Leafield,
Witney, **Oxfordshire OX8 5NP**
TEL   0993 87593
OPEN   8–6 Mon–Sat.

Specialise in restoring all 17th to 19th
century furniture.

PROVIDE Home Inspections.
Free/Chargeable Estimates.
Free/Chargeable Collection/Delivery
Service.
SPEAK TO Colin Piper.
SEE Clocks.

ROY D. STRATTON
Wayside, Great Coxwell, Faringdon,
Oxfordshire SN7 7NB
TEL   0367 240030
OPEN   8–8 Daily.

Specialise in restoring all types of
antique furniture except Boulle work
and gilded furniture.

PROVIDE Home Inspections. Free
Estimates. Free Collection/Delivery
Service.
SPEAK TO Roy Stratton.
Member of BAFRA.

TERENCE C. J. WALSH
Park Farmhouse, Hook Norton,
Banbury, **Oxfordshire OX15 5LR**
TEL   0608 730293
OPEN   Mon–Sat By Appointment.

Specialise in restoring 17th–19th
century furniture, including Boulle and
marquetry. They also do upholstery,
including four–poster beds and
headboards.

PROVIDE Home Inspections. Chargeable
Collection/Delivery Service.
SPEAK TO Terence Walsh.

WEAVES AND WAXES
53 Church Street, Bloxham, Banbury,
Oxfordshire OX15 4ET
TEL   0295 721535
FAX   0295 271867
OPEN   9–1, 2–5.30 Tues–Fri; 9–1,2–4
         Sat.

Specialise in restoring antique furniture,
including polishing, veneering, general
repairs, gilding, rush and cane seating,
brass facsimilies, upholstery, leather
skivers fitted.

PROVIDE Home Inspections.
Free/Chargeable Estimates. Chargeable
Collection/Delivery Service.
SPEAK TO Laurie Grayer.
SEE Clocks.

WITNEY RESTORATIONS
Workshop: Unit 17, Hanborough
Business Park, Main Road, Long
Hanborough, **Oxfordshire OX7 2LH**
Accounts and Enquiries: 96–100 Corn
Street, Witney, **Oxfordshire OX8 7BU**
TEL   0993 703902 accounts and
         enquiries
         0993 883336 workshop
FAX   0993 779852
OPEN   9.30–5 Mon–Fri.

Specialise in restoring and conserving
fine antique furniture as well as
decorative furniture and objects.

PROVIDE Home Inspections. Free
Estimates. Chargeable
Collection/Delivery Service.
SPEAK TO Mr R. Woollen or Mrs J. Jarrett.
SEE Clocks.

RICHARD HIGGINS
The Old School, Longnor, Nr.
Shrewsbury, **Shropshire SY5 7PP**
TEL   0743 718162
OPEN   8–6 Mon–Fri.

Specialise in restoring fine antique and
country furniture, including Boulle,

marquetry, rosewood, mahogany, oak, walnut.

PROVIDE Home Inspections. Free/Chargeable Estimates. Collection/Delivery Service by arrangement. SPEAK TO Richard Higgins. Member of BAFRA and UKIC. This workshop is included on the register of conservators maintained by the Conservation Unit of the Museums and Galleries Commission. SEE Clocks, Collectors (Mechanical Music).

C. J. PRITCHARD

143A Belle Vue Road, Shrewsbury, **Shropshire SY3 7NN**
TEL   0743 362854
OPEN 8.15–1, 2.15–4 Mon–Fri.

Specialise in restoring and conserving antique furniture.

PROVIDE Home Inspections. Refundable Estimates. Chargeable Collection/Delivery Service. SPEAK TO Mr A. W. Jones.

ST MARY'S ANTIQUES AND CABINETMAKERS

2 Lower Bar, Newport, **Shropshire TF10 1BQ**
TEL   0952 811549
OPEN 9–6 Mon–Fri; 9–12 Sat.

Specialise in restoring antique furniture and will supply bespoke furniture.

PROVIDE Home Inspections. Free Estimates. Free/Chargeable Collection/Delivery Service. SPEAK TO Ray Edwards

T. R. BAILEY

11 St Andrew's Road, Stogursey, Bridgwater, **Somerset TA5 1TE**
TEL   0278 732887
OPEN By Appointment.

Specialise in restoring English furniture.

PROVIDE Free Estimates. Collection/Delivery Service by arrangement. SPEAK TO Tim Bailey. SEE Silver.

BOXWOOD ANTIQUE RESTORERS

67 High Street, Wincanton, **Somerset BA9 9JZ**
TEL   0963 33988
OPEN 8.30–6 Mon–Sat.

Specialise in restoring fine furniture, French polishing, wax polishing, carving, metalwork and tortoiseshell.

PROVIDE Home Inspections. Free Estimates. Free Collection/Delivery Service. SPEAK TO Alan Stacey. Member of BAFRA. Delivers regularly to London.

NICHOLAS BRIDGES

68 Lower Street, Merriott, **Somerset TA16 5NW**
TEL   0460 74672
OPEN By Appointment.

Specialise in all aspects of furniture restoration and finishing, including marquetry, carving, French polishing, turning, gilding, brass casting, caning and rushing, upholstery, desk and table leathers.

PROVIDE Home Inspections. Free Estimates. Free Local Collection/Delivery Service. SPEAK TO Nicholas Bridges. Member of BAFRA.

J. BURRELL

Westerfield House, Seavington St Mary, Ilminster, **Somerset TA19 OQR**
TEL   0460 240610
OPEN By Appointment.

Specialise in restoring antique furniture,

including structural repairs, veneering, marquetry, lacquer work, carving, wax polishing.

PROVIDE Home Inspections. Refundable Estimates. Chargeable Collection/Delivery Service.
SPEAK TO J. Burrell.
Member of BAFRA. This workshop is included on the register of conservators maintained by the Conservation Unit of the Museums and Galleries Commission.

CASTLE HOUSE
Bennetts Field Estate, Wincanton, **Somerset BA9 9DT**
TEL   0963 33884
OPEN   8.30–5.30 Mon–Fri.

Specialise in complete service for restoration and conservation of period antique furniture, including Boulle, marquetry and all period finishes.

PROVIDE Home Inspections.
SPEAK TO Michael Durkee.
Member of BAFRA. This workshop is included on the register maintained by the Conservation Unit of the Museums and Galleries Commission.

G. J. DICK–READ
Duxhams, Dulverton, **Somerset TA22 9EJ**
TEL   0398 23460
OPEN   By Appointment.

Specialise in restoring furniture of any period, including painted and gilded furniture, Tunbridge ware, wood turning. They do not include Boulle work.

PROVIDE Home Inspections. Free Local Estimates. Chargeable Collection/Delivery Service.
SPEAK TO John Dick–Read.
This workshop is included on the register of conservators maintained by the Conservation Unit of the Museums and Galleries Commission.
SEE Porcelain.

JENNIFER M. JOHN
Myrtle Cottage, Merryfield Lane, Ilton, Ilminster, **Somerset TA19 9EZ**
TEL   0460 53963
OPEN   9–5 Mon–Sat or By Appointment.

Specialise in cane seating, including medallions, blind and close caning as well as seating in sea–grass rush and string.

PROVIDE Home Inspections. Free Estimates. Free Local Collection/ Delivery Service.
SPEAK TO Jennifer John.
Member of the Basketmakers Association.

RECTORY RESTORATIONS
Raddington, Nr. Wiveliscombe, Taunton, **Somerset TA4 2QW**
TEL   03986 271
OPEN   By Appointment.

Specialise in restoring all types of antique furniture.

PROVIDE Home Inspections. Free Estimates. Free Local Collection/Delivery Service.
SPEAK TO Simon Coates.

EDWARD VENN ANTIQUE RESTORATIONS
52 Long Street, Williton, Taunton, **Somerset TA4 4QU**
TEL   0984 32631
OPEN   8.30–5.30 Mon–Fri.

Specialise in restoring antique furniture up to 1900.

PROVIDE Chargeable Estimates. Chargeable Collection/Delivery Service
SPEAK TO Mr Venn.
SEE Clocks.

THE ANTIQUE RESTORATION STUDIO

The Old Post Office, Haughton, **Staffordshire ST18 9JH**
TEL   0785 780424
FAX   0785 780157
OPEN   9–5 Mon–Fri.

Specialise in restoring antique and modern furniture.

PROVIDE Home Inspections. Free Estimates. Free Collection/Delivery Service.
SPEAK TO D. P. Albright.
SEE Porcelain, Oil Paintings, Carpets.

ANTIQUES WORKSHOP

43–45 Hope Stret, Hanley, Stoke–on–Trent, **Staffordshire ST1 5BT**
TEL   0782 273645
OPEN   9–5 Mon–Fri; 10–4 Sat.

Specialise in repairing and restoring oak and mahogany and French polishing of the latter.

PROVIDE Home Inspections. Free Estimates. Chargeable Collection/Delivery Service.
SPEAK TO Howard Oakes.

JALNA ANTIQUES

'Jalna', Coley Lane, Little Haywood, Nr. Stafford, **Staffordshire ST18 OUP**
TEL   0889 881381
OPEN   9–5 Daily.

Specialise in restoring upholstery, carving, veneering and French polishing.

PROVIDE Home Inspections. Free Estimates. Free Collection/Delivery Service.
SPEAK TO Geoff Hancox.

A. C. PRALL RESTORATIONS

Highfield Farm, Uttoxeter Road, Draycott, **Staffordshire ST11 9AE**
TEL   0782 399022
OPEN   9–7 Mon–Fri.

Specialise in restoring Georgian furniture.

PROVIDE Free Estimates. Free/Chargeable Collection/Delivery Service.
SPEAK TO Mr Prall.
SEE Clocks.

ROGER & SYLVIA ALLAN

The Old Red Lion, Bedingfield, Eye, **Suffolk IP23 7LQ**
TEL   0728 628491
OPEN   By Appointment.

Specialise in restoring antique furniture, carved objects and treen.

PROVIDE Home Inspections. Free Estimates.
SPEAK TO Roger Allan.
SEE Oil Paintings, Silver.

ANTIQUE RESTORATION

Unit 3, Bench Barn Farm, Clare, **Suffolk**
TEL   0787 277635
OPEN   8–5 Mon–Fri; 8–12 Sat.

Specialise in restoring furniture. Will also design and manufacture furniture to commission.

PROVIDE Home Inspections. Free Estimates. Free Local Collection/Delivery Service.
SPEAK TO Terry Wheeler.

BALLYBEG RESTORATIONS AND HARCOURT ANTIQUES

101 Kingsway, Mildenhall, **Suffolk IP28 7HS**
TEL   0638 712378
OPEN   By Appointment.

Specialise in restoring antique furniture including, upholstery, gilding, painted furniture, marquetry, veneering, French polishing.

PROVIDE Home Inspections. Free

Estimates. Free Collection/Delivery
Service.
SPEAK TO Mr P. B. Bailey.

JOHN GAZELEY
ASSOCIATES FINE ART
17 Fonnereau Road, Ipswich, **Suffolk**
IP1 3JR
TEL   0473 252420
OPEN   By Appointment.

Specialise in gilding and repairing
mirror frames as well as making
reproduction frames.

PROVIDE Free Estimates.
SPEAK TO Dr. John Gazeley.
SEE Oil Paintings, Picture Frames.

MICHAEL D. LOCKWOOD
BADA Dip.
Whitegates Bungalow, The Common,
Mellis, Nr. Eye, **Suffolk IP23 8DY**
TEL   0379 788126
OPEN   9–6 Mon–Sat or By
       Appointment.

Specialise in restoring mainly high
quality Georgian furniture, including
satinwood, walnut, rosewood, ebony,
oak, cherry, fruitwood, marquetry, inlay,
bandings, wood carvings, upholstery,
leather, button work, traditional
rollstitch edge work.

PROVIDE Refundable Home Inspections.
Free/Chargeable Estimates. Chargeable
Collection Delivery Service.
SPEAK TO Michael Lockwood.
Member of UKIC. This workshop is
included on the register of conservators
maintained by the Conservation Unit of
the Museums and Galleries Commission.

NETTLE HALL
RESTORATION
Unit 1, Corner Farm, Sibton,
Saxmundham, **Suffolk IP17 2NE**
TEL   Workshop 0728 79550 or Home
       0728 724466.
OPEN   9–5 Mon–Sat.

Specialise in restoring and conserving
antique furniture, inlay work, marquetry,
cabinetmaking, French polishing,
gilding.

PROVIDE Home Inspections. Free
Estimates. Chargeable
Collection/Delivery Service.
SPEAK TO Thomas Mark Spirling.

JULIA PARK,
CONSERVATION
SERVICES
9 Cardigan Street, Ipswich, **Suffolk**
IP1 3PF
TEL   0473 216862
OPEN   9–5 Mon–Fri.

Specialise in restoring lacquer and
Chinoiserie furniture and objects.

PROVIDE Home Inspections.
Free/Chargeable Estimates. Chargeable
Collection/Delivery Service.
SPEAK TO Julia Park.
Member of IIC. This workshop is
included on the register of conservators
maintained by the Conservation Unit of
the Museum and Galleries Commission.
Professionally trained restorer of 14 years
experience.

PEASENHALL ART &
ANTIQUES GALLERY
Peasenhall, Nr. Saxmundham, **Suffolk**
IP17 2HJ
TEL   072 879 224
OPEN   9–6 Daily.

Specialise in restoring antique furniture.
They also make and repair walking sticks.

PROVIDE Local Home Inspections. Free
Estimates. Free Local
Collection/Delivery Service.
SPEAK TO Mike Wickins.
SEE Oil Paintings.

PEPPERS PERIOD
PIECES
23 Churchgate Street, Bury St Edmunds,
Suffolk IP33 1RG
TEL   0284 768786
OPEN   10–5 Mon–Sat.

Specialise in restoring furniture.

PROVIDE Home Inspections. Refundable Estimates.
Free/Chargeable Collection/Delivery Service.
SPEAK TO M. E. Pepper.
SEE Clocks.

MARK PETERS ANTIQUES
Green Farm Cottage, Thurston, Bury St. Edmunds, **Suffolk IP31 3SN**
TEL   0359 30888
OPEN   8.30–6 Mon–Fri, 8.30–1 Sat.

Specialise in all aspects of period furniture restoration.

PROVIDE Home Inspections. Chargeable Estimates. Chargeable Collection/Delivery Service.
SPEAK TO Mark Peters.
Member of UKIC. This workshop is included on the register of conservators maintained by the Conservation Unit of the Museum and Galleries Commission.

MICHAEL ADDISON ANTIQUES
28–30 Godstone Road, Kenley, **Surrey CR8 5JE**
TEL   081 668 6714
OPEN   10–5 Mon–Sat.

Specialise in restoring antique furniture and upholstery.

PROVIDE Home Inspections. Free Estimates. Free Collection/Delivery Service.
SPEAK TO M. Addison.

A. E. BOOTH & SON
9 High Street, Ewell, Epsom, **Surrey KT17 1SG**
TEL   081 393 5245
OPEN   9–5 Mon–Fri.

Specialise in repairs to chairs, antique and reproduction furniture, including

polishing, gilding and upholstery.

PROVIDE Home Inspections. Free/Refundable Estimates. Free Collection/Delivery Service.
SPEAK TO D. J. Booth.
Member of BAFRA.
SEE Clocks.

IAN CALDWELL
9A The Green, Dorking Road, Tadworth, **Surrey KT20 5SQ**
TEL   0737 813969
OPEN   10–5.30 Mon–Sat; closed Wed.

Specialise in restoring furniture, including gilding, lacquer work and upholstery.

PROVIDE Home Inspections. Free Collection/Delivery Service.
SPEAK TO Ian Caldwell.
Member of LAPADA.

COURTLANDS RESTORATION
Courtlands, Park Road, Banstead, **Surrey SM7 3EF**
TEL   0737 352429
FAX   0737 373255
OPEN   8–6 Mon–Sat.

Specialise in restoring antique furniture, including traditional and French polishing, simulation effects, cabinetmaking, turning and carving, veneer repairs, gilding, metal repairs.

PROVIDE Home Inspections. Free Estimates. Free Collection/Delivery Service.
SPEAK TO David Sayer.
Member of BAFRA.

G. & R. FRASER SINCLAIR
11 Orchard Works, Streeters Lane, Beddington, **Surrey SM6 7ND**
TEL   081 669 5343
OPEN   8–5.30 Mon–Fri.

Specialise in restoring 18th century English furniture.

PROVIDE Home Inspections. Free Estimates. Free Collection/Delivery Service.
SPEAK TO Glen Sinclair.
Member of BAFRA.

HEARN–COOPER LTD
46 Park Hill Road, Wallington, **Surrey SM6 0SB**
TEL 081 395 5498
OPEN 8.30–5.30 Mon–Fri; By Appointment Sat.

Specialise in restoring Oriental lacquer and European lacquered furniture.

PROVIDE Home Inspections. Estimates.
SPEAK TO Richard Hearn–Cooper.

HEATH–BULLOCK
8 Meadrow, Godalming, **Surrey GU7 3HN**
TEL 0483 422562
FAX 0483 426077
OPEN 10–1, 2–4 Mon–Sat.

Specialise in restoring and upholstering antique furniture. They have a long tradition in leather upholstery.

PROVIDE Home Inspections. Free Estimates. Chargeable Collection/Delivery Service.
SPEAK TO Roger Heath-Bullock.

MICHAEL HEDGECOE
Rowan House, 21 Burrow Hill Green, Chobham, Woking, **Surrey GU24 8QS**
TEL 0276 858206
OPEN 8–5 Mon–Fri.

Specialise in restoring top quality English and French 18th and 19th century furniture, as well as best quality upholstery.

PROVIDE Home Inspections. Free

Estimates. Chargeable Collection/Delivery Service.
SPEAK TO Michael Hedgecoe.
Member of LAPADA and BAFRA.

JOHN KENDALL
156 High Street, Old Woking, **Surrey GU21 9JH**
TEL 0483 771310
OPEN 9–5 Mon–Fri.

Specialise in restoration of fine furniture.

PROVIDE Home Inspections. Free Estimates. Chargeable Collection/Delivery Service.
SPEAK TO John Kendall.
SEE Clocks.

RICHARD LAWMAN–WARWICK ANTIQUE RESTORATIONS
32 Beddington Lane, Croydon, **Surrey CR0 4TB**
TEL 081 688 4511
OPEN 9–6 Tues–Sat.

Specialise in restoring fine furniture, leathering, caning, rushing, upholstery.

PROVIDE Home Inspections. Free Estimates. Free Collection/Delivery Service.
SPEAK TO Richard Lawman.
Member of the Guild of Master Craftsmen. This workshop is included on the register of conservators maintained by the Conservation Unit of the Museums and Galleries Commission.
SEE Clocks.

TREVOR LAWRENCE FURNITURE
Rectory Barn, High Street, Limpsfield, Oxted, **Surrey RH8 0DG**
TEL 0883 730300 or 730301
FAX 0883 730300
OPEN 8–5 Mon–Fri; 9–1 Sat.

Specialise in all aspects of furniture

MICHAEL HEDGECOE

Antique Furniture Restoration
and
Reupholstery

Restorers to some of the finest dealers and houses in the country.

**Weekly London collection
Carriage countrywide**

21, Burrow Hill Green, Chobham, Woking, Surrey
Telephone: (0276) 858 206

---

restoration and finishing. Traditional upholstery and re–upholstery.

PROVIDE Home Inspections. Free Estimates. Chargeable Collection/Delivery Service.
SPEAK TO Trevor Lawrence.

MANOR ANTIQUES AND RESTORATIONS
2 New Shops, High Street, Old Woking, **Surrey GU22 9JW**
TEL   0483 724666
MOB   0860 851956
FAX   0483 750366
OPEN   10–5 Mon–Fri; 10–4.30 Sat.

Specialise in restoring furniture, including French polishing, inlay work, chair–caning and rush work.

PROVIDE Home Inspections. Free Estimates. Collection/Delivery Service.
SPEAK TO Alan Wellstead.

Member of the Guild of Master Craftsmen.
SEE Clocks, Picture Frames.

SIMON MARSH RESTORATIONS
The Old Butchers Shop, High St, Bletchingley, **Surrey RH1 4PA**
TEL   0883 743350
OPEN   By Appointment.

Specialise in restoring fine furniture.

PROVIDE Home Inspections. Free/Refundable Estimates. Chargeable Collection/Delivery Service.
SPEAK TO Mrs Marsh.
Member of BAFRA.

TIMOTHY NAYLOR ASSOCIATES
26B Dunstable Road, Richmond, **Surrey TW9 1UH**
TEL   081 332 0444
OPEN   8–5.30 Mon–Fri.

Specialise in restoring 18th century English furniture, including marquetry and carving.

PROVIDE Home Inspections. Free Estimates. Collection/Delivery Service by arrangement.
SPEAK TO Timothy Naylor.

N. J. NEWMAN
22 Eastcroft Road, West Ewell, **Surrey KT19 9TX**
TEL   081 393 0538
OPEN   By Appointment.

Specialise in restoring English and Continental furniture.

PROVIDE Home Inspections. Free/Chargeable Estimates. Chargeable Collection/Delivery Service.
SPEAK TO Nick Newman.
Member of BAFRA. This workshop is included on the register of conservators maintained by the Conservation Unit of the Museums and Galleries Commission.

CHARLES OWEN RESTORATIONS (GILDER)
The Studio, 1 Hillrise, Shere Road, West Horsley, **Surrey KT24 6EF**
TEL   0483 285271
OPEN   By Appointment.

Specialise in restoring gilt furniture and overmantels.

PROVIDE Home Inspections. Free Estimates.
SPEAK TO Charles Owen.
SEE Picture Frames.

PRECISION PARTS COMPANY
Keystone House, Plaistow Road, Dunsfold, **Surrey GU8 4PF**
TEL   0483 200445
OPEN   By Appointment.

Specialise in making metal parts to replace missing items on furniture.

PROVIDE Home Inspections. Free Estimates.
SPEAK TO Vincent Lee–Brown.
Member of UKIC and Fellow of RGS. This workshop is included on the register of conservators maintained by the Conservation Unit of the Museums and Galleries Commission.
SEE Silver.

SAGE ANTIQUES & INTERIORS
High Street, Ripley, **Surrey GU23 6BB**
TEL   0483 224396
FAX   0483 211996
OPEN   9.30–5.30 Mon–Sat.

Specialise in restoring furniture 1600–1840, including oak, walnut, mahogany and fruitwood.

PROVIDE Free Estimates. Collection/Delivery Service.
SPEAK TO Howard or Chrissie Sage.
Member of LAPADA and the Guild of Master Craftsmen.
SEE Oil Paintings, Porcelain.

R. SAUNDERS
71 Queens Road, Weybridge, **Surrey KT13 9UQ**
TEL   0932 842601
OPEN   9.15–5 Mon–Sat; closed Wed.

Specialise in repairing goood quality English furniture pre–1830 and later.

PROVIDE Home Inspections. Free Estimates. Free Collection/Delivery Service.
SPEAK TO J. B. Tonkinson.
SEE Oil Paintings, Porcelain, Silver.

MICHAEL SCHRYVER ANTIQUES
The Granary, 10 North Street, Dorking, **Surrey RH4 1DN**
TEL   0306 881110
FAX   0306 876168
OPEN   8.30–5.30 Mon–Fri; 8.30–12.30 Sat.

Specialise in restoring fine quality period furniture, including metalwork, period and contemporary upholstery.

PROVIDE Home Inspections. Free Estimates. Free Collection/Delivery Service.
SPEAK TO Michael Schryver.

SHAUN VICKERS
Foxgloves, Clock Barn Lane, Busbridge, Godalming, **Surrey GU8 4AZ**
TEL　　0483 429964
FAX　　0483 424360
OPEN　　9–6 Mon–Fri.

Specialise in restoring furniture, including gilding, marquetry and Boulle work.

PROVIDE Home Inspections. Free Estimates. Free Local Collection/Delivery Service.
SPEAK TO Shaun Vickers.
SEE Picture Frames, Clocks.

JUDITH WETHERALL trading as J.B. SYMES
28 Silverlea Gardens, Horley, **Surrey RH6 9BB**
TEL　　0293 775024
OPEN　　8.30–5.30 By Appointment Only.

Specialise in restoring painted and gilded furniture and japanned and lacquered boxes, mirror frames and carving.

PROVIDE Free Local Home Inspections. Free Estimates. Chargeable Collection/Delivery Service.
SPEAK TO Judith Wetherall.
Member of UKIC and IIC. This workshop is included on the register of conservators maintained by the Conservation Unit of the Museums and Galleries Commission.
SEE Clocks, Picture Frames, Porcelain.

JOHN COWDEROY ANTIQUES
42 South Street, Eastbourne, **East Sussex BN21 4XB**
TEL　　0323 720058
FAX　　0323 410163
OPEN　　9.30–1, 2.30–5 Mon–Fri; 9.30–1 Wed, Sat.

Specialise in restoring furniture and French polishing.

PROVIDE Home Inspections. Free Estimates. Chargeable Collection/Delivery Service.
SPEAK TO David or Richard Cowderoy. Member of LAPADA.
SEE Clocks, Collectors (Mechanical Music).

FIRELEAD LTD
Banff Farm, Upper Clayhill, Uckfield Rd, Ringmer, Lewes, **East Sussex BN8 5RR**
TEL　　0273 890918
FAX　　0273 890691
OPEN　　8–5.30 Mon–Fri By Appointment.

Specialise in full antique restoration, including re-leathering writing surfaces, upholstery, re-silvering mirrors, keys made for old locks, marquetry repairs, water-gilding. Also duplicate items to match other pieces.

PROVIDE Local Home Inspections. Local Free Estimates. Chargeable Collection/Delivery Service.
SPEAK TO David Gilbert.
SEE Oil Paintings.

JOHN HARTNETT & SON
2 Victoria Street, Brighton, **East Sussex BN1 3FP**
TEL　　0273 328793
FAX　　0273 749860
OPEN　　9–6 Mon–Fri.

Specialise in restoring fine furniture, including French polishing, upholstery, leather insets, lacquer and japanning marquetry and inlay, caning and rushing, carving, gilding.

PROVIDE Home Inspections. Free Estimates. Collection/Delivery Service.
SPEAK TO John Hartnett.

D. J. MATTHEWS
20-21 Newark Place, Brighton, **East Sussex BN2 2NT**
TEL   0273 602427
OPEN   7.30–5 Mon–Fri.

Specialise in restoring antique furniture, particularly that which has a painted finish, including trays, small boxes, screens and papier mâché items.

PROVIDE Local Home Inspections. Free Estimates.
SPEAK TO D. J. Matthews.
Member of the Guild of Master Craftsmen.

THE OLD BAKERY FURNISHING COMPANY
Punnetts Town, Nr. Heathfield, **East Sussex TN21 9DS**
TEL   0323 487167
FAX   0323 487167
OPEN   9–5 Mon–Fri; 9–1 Sat.

Specialise in restoring antique furniture, including tapestry work and traditional upholstery.

PROVIDE Free/Chargeable Home Inspections. Estimates. Chargeable Collection/Delivery Service.
SPEAK TO Ann Spencer.

GRAHAM PRICE ANTIQUES LTD
Unit 4, Chaucer Industrial Estate, Polegate, **East Sussex BN26 6JD**
TEL   0323 487167 and 485301
FAX   0323 483904
OPEN   8–6 Mon–Fri.

Specialise in restoring antique furniture, especially 17th–19th century English and Continental furniture.

PROVIDE Home Inspections. Free Estimates. Collection/Delivery Service.
SPEAK TO G. J. Price or C. M. Springett.

PETER SEMUS CRAFTING ANTIQUES
The Warehouse, Gladstone Land, Portslade, **East Sussex BN41 1LJ**
TEL   0273 420154
FAX   0273 430355
OPEN   8–6 Mon–Fri.

Specialise in restoring antique furniture, making bespoke furniture and reproduction furniture.

PROVIDE Home Inspections. Refundable Estimates. Free Collection/Delivery Service.
SPEAK TO Peter Semus.

YELLOW LANTERN ANTIQUES LTD
34 & 34B Holland Road, Hove, **East Sussex BN3 1JL**
TEL   0273 771572
OPEN   9.30–1, 2.15–5.30 Mon–Fri; 9–1, 2.15–4.30. Sat.

Specialise in cleaning of ormolu and bronze and restoring furniture.

PROVIDE Home Inspections. Free Estimates. Free Collection/Delivery Service.
SPEAK TO Mr or Mrs B. R. Higgins.
Member of LAPADA.
SEE Silver

CAROL BANKS AND SON
September Cottage, 88 Victoria Road, Shoreham–by–Sea, **West Sussex BN4 5WS**
TEL   0273 461647.
OPEN   By Appointment

Specialise in conservation and restoration of carved and gilded finished mirror frames, columns, brackets, console tables.

PROVIDE Local Home Inspections. Free
Estimates.
SPEAK TO Carol Banks.
SEE Picture Frames, Porcelain.
Member of UKIC.

RICHARD BEALE CONSERVATION
West Chiltington, **West Sussex**
TEL   0798 813380
OPEN   9.30–5 Mon–Fri.

Specialise in conserving and restoring
antique furniture, including English
japanned, Oriental lacquer, French vernis
Martin, gilded and painted furniture,
frames and related objets d'art.

PROVIDE Home Inspections. Free
Estimates. Chargeable
Collection/Delivery Service.
SPEAK TO Richard Beale.

P. G. CASEBOW
Pilgrims, Mill Lane, Worthing, **West
Sussex BN13 3DE**
TEL   0903 264045
OPEN   By Appointment.

Specialise in restoring period furniture,
turning, fretwork, inlay and marquetry.

PROVIDE Home Inspections. Free
Estimates. Chargeable
Collection/Delivery Service.
SPEAK TO Peter Casebow.
Member of BAFRA.

SONIA DEMETRIOU
The Studio, Tillington Cottage,
Tillington, Petworth, **West Sussex
GU28 0RA**
TEL   0798 44113
OPEN   9.30–6 Mon–Fri.

Specialise in cleaning and restoring all
types of decorated furniture and objets
d'art, including japanned work and Tôle
ware.

PROVIDE Local Home Inspections. Free
Local Estimates.
SPEAK TO Sonia Demetriou.

DOWNLAND RESTORATION
Wepham Farm Yard, Wepham, Arundel,
West Sussex BN18 9RQ
TEL   0903 883387
OPEN   8.30–5 Mon–Fri.

Specialise in restoring all aspects of 18th
and 19th century furniture, including
gilding, polishing, veneering.

PROVIDE Home Inspections.
Free/Chargeable Estimates. Chargeable
Collection/Delivery Service.
SPEAK TO Simon MacIntyre.
Member of UKIC. This workshop is
included on the register of conservators
maintained by the Conservation Unit of
the Museums and Galleries Commission.

GARNER & CO.
Stable Cottage, Steyning Road, Wiston,
West Sussex BN44 3DD
TEL   0903 814565
OPEN   By Appointment (Tel Mon–Fri
9–5.30).

Specialise in conserving fine period
(1600–1850) English and Continental
furniture and works of art, including
painted furniture and gilded frames.

PROVIDE Home Inspections. Estimates.
SPEAK TO Sid Garner.
SEE Clocks, Porcelain, Silver.

JOHN HART
'Tawgarney', First Avenue, Batchmere,
Birdham, **West Sussex PO20 7LQ**
TEL   0243 513235
FAX   0243 513235
OPEN   8–5 Mon–Fri.

Specialise in restoring antique furniture
and wooden objects. Also provide an
advisory service.

PROVIDE Home Inspections. Free

Estimates. Chargeable
Collection/Delivery Service.
SPEAK TO John Hart.
Member of UKIC. This workshop is
included on the register of conservators
maintained by the Conservation Unit of
the Museums and Galleries Commission.

NOEL & EVA-LOUISE PEPPERALL

Dairy Lane Cottage, Walberton,
Arundel, **West Sussex BN18 0PT**
TEL   0243 551282
OPEN   By Appointment.

Specialise in restoring antique furniture,
including painted furniture and gilding.

PROVIDE Home Inspections. Free
Estimates. Chargeable
Collection/Delivery Service.
SPEAK TO Noel or Eva–Louise Pepperall.
Mr Pepperall is a member of BAFRA.
This workshop is included on the register
of conservators maintained by the
Conservation Unit of the Museums and
Galleries Commission.

ALBERT PLUMB

31 Whyke Lane, Chichester, **West
Sussex PO19 2JS**
TEL   0243 788468
OPEN   9.30–5 Mon–Sat.

Specialise in antique furniture
restoration.

PROVIDE Home Inspections. Free
Estimates. Collection/Delivery Service.
SPEAK TO Albert Plumb.
SEE Lighting.

THAKEHAM FURNITURE

Rock Road, Storrington, **West Sussex
RH20 3AE**
TEL   0903 745464
OPEN   8.30–5 Mon–Fri.

Specialise in restoring 18th and 19th
century furniture, including marquetry,
veneering, cabinetwork and French
polishing.

PROVIDE Home Inspections.
Free/Chargeable Estimates.
Free/Chargeable Collection/Delivery
Service.
SPEAK TO Mr Chavasse.
Member of BAFRA.

WEST DEAN COLLEGE

West Dean, Chichester, **West Sussex
PO18 00Z**
TEL   0243 63 301
FAX   0243 63 342
OPEN   9–5 Mon–Fri.

Specialise in training conservators and
restorers in the fields of antique
furniture. They will also undertake
restoration work.

PROVIDE Local Home Inspections. Free
Estimates.
SPEAK TO Peter Sarginson.
SEE Books, Clocks, Porcelain, Silver.

DAVID WESTON

East Lodge, Woldringfold, Lower
Beeding, Horsham, **West Sussex
RH13 6NJ**
TEL   0403 891617
OPEN   By Appointment.

Specialise in restoring composition
frames and gilding.

PROVIDE Free Estimates.
SPEAK TO David Weston.
Also make reproduction composition
frames.
SEE Picture Frames.

WILSON ANTIQUES

57–59 Broadwater Road, Worthing,
West Sussex BN14 8AH
TEL   0903 202059
OPEN   9–5 Mon–Sat.

Specialise in restoring antique furniture.

PROVIDE Home Inspections. Free
Estimates. Free Collection/Delivery
Service.
SPEAK TO Frank Wilson.
Member of LAPADA.

ABERCROMBIES
142 Manor House Road, Jesmond,
Newcastle–upon–Tyne, **Tyne & Wear
NE2 2NA**
TEL   091 281 7182
FAX   091 281 7183
OPEN   10–6 Tues–Fri; 10–4 Sat.

Specialise in traditional re–upholstery
and furniture restoration.

PROVIDE Home Inspections. Free
Estimates. Collection/Delivery Service.
SPEAK TO Mr C. N. Stell.
The showroom has an extensive
collection of archive wallpaper and
fabrics.

SUSAN B. AIRY
The Old Barn, Radway, **Warwickshire
CV 35 0UF**
TEL   0295 87392
OPEN   8–8 Daily.

Specialise in restoring painted furniture
and mirrors.

PROVIDE Home Inspections. Free
Estimates. Chargeable
Collection/Delivery Service.
SPEAK TO Susan Airy.
Member of UKIC. This workshop is
included on the register of conservators
maintained by the Conservation Unit of
the Museums and Galleries Commission.
SEE Oil Paintings, Picture Frames.

TAYLOR & BROOK RE–UPHOLSTERY LTD
5 Greenhill Street, Stratford upon Avon,
Warwickshire CV37 6LF
TEL   0789 269604
OPEN   9–5 Mon–Sat.

Specialise in re–upholstering antique
and quality traditional furniture, re–
caning and supply of all upholstery
sundries and materials for DIY.

PROVIDE Home Inspections, Free

Estimates, Free Collection/Delivery
Service all within a ten–mile radius.
SPEAK TO Collin Brook.

THE ODD CHAIR
19 Castle Road, Kenilworth,
Warwickshire CV8 1NG
TEL   0926 511978
OPEN   By Appointment.

Specialise in restoring rush, cane and
seagrass seating, including cleaning,
polishing and repairing, carried out in
situ if necessary.

PROVIDE Home Inspections. Free
Estimates. Chargeable
Collection/Delivery Service.
SPEAK TO Richard Cook.

CHAIRPERSONS OF MARSHFIELD
40 High Street, Marshfield, Nr.
Chippenham, **Wiltshire SN14 8LP**
TEL   0225 891431
OPEN   By Appointment.

Specialise in cane and rush seating. Also
repair wicker, rattan, bamboo and willow
chairs and can arrange for chair frames to
be repaired.

PROVIDE Home Inspections. Free
Estimates. Free Collection/Delivery
Service to Bath/Bristol/London and
M4 corridor.
SPEAK TO Michael Pitts.

W. J. COOK AND SONS LTD
High Trees House, Savernake Forest,
Marlborough, **Wiltshire SN8 4NE**
TEL   0672 513017
FAX   0672 514455
OPEN   8–7 Mon–Fri.

Specialise in restoring all types of
furniture, late 17th century to present
day, including gilding, carving,
leathering, upholstery and marquetry.

PROVIDE Home Inspections. Free Estimates. Free Local Collection/Delivery Service.
SPEAK TO Mr Cook.
This is a family business established over thirty years.
SEE London SW11.

PHILIP NOBES FURNITURE RESTORATION

80 Norman Road, Gorse Hill, Swindon, **Wiltshire SN2 1AX**
TEL   0793 617528
FAX   0793 615483
OPEN   8–6 Mon–Sat.

Specialise in complete restoration to all aspects of furniture. Repair, hand polishing, colouring, waxing. Commission work undertaken. High standard of workmanship.
PROVIDE Home Inspections. Free Estimates. Collection/Delivery Service.
SPEAK TO Philip Nobes.

PHILIP HAWKINS

The Old School Workshop, High Street, Maiden Bradley, Warminster, **Wiltshire BA12 7JG**
TEL   0985 844752
OPEN   By Appointment.

Specialise in restoring early oak, country and period furniture.
PROVIDE Home Inspections. Free Estimates. Free Collection/Delivery Service.
SPEAK TO Philip Hawkins.
Member of BAFRA.

ROD NAYLOR

208 Devizes Road, Hilperton, Trowbridge, **Wiltshire BA14 7QP**
TEL   0225 754497
OPEN   By Appointment.

Specialise in restoring fine quality wood–carving and cabinetwork, including gilding, marquetry etc. Also supply hard–to–find items for restorers such as three–dimensional copying machines, embossed lining paper and small replica knobs suitable for tea caddies, boxes and secrétaires.

PROVIDE Home Inspections. Free Estimates. Free Collection/Delivery Service.
SPEAK TO Rod Naylor.
SEE Lighting, Porcelain.

MARCO PITT

Staple House, High Street, Tisbury, **Wiltshire SP3 6LD**
TEL   0747 870420
OPEN   9–6 Mon–Sat.

Specialise in restoring carving, gilding, Boulle work, all types of finishes, furniture metalwork, locks, painted furniture. They are cabinetmakers and can restore any type and style of antique furniture.

PROVIDE Home Inspections. Free Estimates. Free Collection/Delivery Service.
SPEAK TO Marco Pitt.
Member of BAFRA.

RESTORATIONS UNLIMITED

Pinkney Park, Malmesbury, **Wiltshire SN16 0NX**
TEL   0666 840888
OPEN   8.30–5 Mon–Fri; By Appointment Sat, Sun.

Specialise in restoring antique furniture, veneering, inlay, rush and cane seating and will also make furniture to match existing pieces.

PROVIDE Home Inspections. Free Estimates. Free Collection/Delivery Service.
SPEAK TO Richard Pinchis.
SEE Oil Paintings, Porcelain, Clocks.

SHENSTONE RESTORATIONS
23 Lansdown Road, Swindon, **Wiltshire SN1 3NE**
TEL   0793 644980
OPEN   By Appointment.

Specialise in restoring smaller decorative items, including marquetry, inlay and veneering. They work in bone, mother-of– pearl, ebony and ivory and its substitutes. They also do Boulle marquetry and marble restoration.

PROVIDE Local Home Inspections. Chargeable Estimates. Chargeable Collection/Delivery Service.
SPEAK TO Blair Shenstone.
SEE Silver.

JOHN TIGHE
One Oak, Lights Lane, Alderbury, Salisbury, **Wiltshire SP5 3AL**
TEL   0722 710231
OPEN   By Appointment.

Specialise in restoring 18th and 19th century furniture and gilding.

PROVIDE Home Inspections. Free Estimates.
SPEAK TO John Tighe.
Member of BAFRA.

PHOEBE CLEMENTS
19 Middlethorpe Drive, York, **North Yorkshire YO2 2NG**
TEL   0904 708279
OPEN   By Appointment.

Specialise in restoring ormolu and furniture mounts.

PROVIDE Home Inspections. Free/Chargeable Estimates. Free Collection/Delivery Service.
SPEAK TO Phoebe Clements.
This workshop is included on the register of conservators maintained by the Conservation Unit of the Museums and Galleries Commission.
SEE Silver, Arms.

NIDD HOUSE ANTIQUES
Nidd House, Bogs Lane, Harrogate, **North Yorkshire HG1 4DY**
TEL   0423 884739
OPEN   9–5 Mon–Fri or By Appointment.

Specialise in restoring furniture and upholstery, cane and rush seats, leaf and powder gilding, gesso work, inlay.

PROVIDE Home Inspections. Free Local Estimates. Chargeable Collection/Delivery Service.
SPEAK TO Mr D. Preston.
Member of the Guild of Master Craftsmen and UKIC. This workshop is included on the register of conservators maintained by the Conservation Unit of the Museums and Galleries Commission.
SEE Collectors (Scientific Instruments), Porcelain, Silver.

T. L. PHELPS
8 Mornington Terrace, Harrogate, **North Yorkshire HG1 5DH**
TEL   0423 524604
OPEN   8.30–6 Mon–Fri or By Appointment.

Specialise in restoring fine English and Continental furniture.

PROVIDE Home Inspections. Free Estimates. Chargeable Collection/Delivery Service.
SPEAK TO Timothy Phelps.
Member of BAFRA.

ANDREW G. PODMORE & SON
49A East Mount Road, York, **North Yorkshire YO2 2BD**
TEL   0904 627717
OPEN   8.30–5 Mon–Fri.

Specialise in restoring antique furniture, French polishing and upholstery.

PROVIDE Home Inspections. Free Estimates. Free/Chargeable Collection/Delivery Service.
SPEAK TO David Podmore.

G. SHAW RESTORATIONS

Jansville, Quarry Lane, New Park,
Harrogate, **North Yorkshire**
HG1 3HR
TEL   0423 503590
OPEN   7–6 Mon–Fri or By
      Appointment.

Specialise in restoring antique furniture
and copying furniture to customers'
requirements.

PROVIDE Home Inspections. Free
Estimates.
SPEAK TO G. or M. G. S. Shaw.

DOVETAIL RESTORATIONS

112–114 London Road, Sheffield,
South Yorkshire S2 4LR
TEL   0742 700273
OPEN   9–4.30 Mon–Sat.

Specialise in restoring furniture,
including French polishing and stripping
by hand.

PROVIDE Home Inspections. Free
Estimates. Free Collection/Delivery
Service.
SPEAK TO Darren Beedle.

NEIL TRINDER

Burrowlee House, Broughton Road,
Sheffield, **South Yorkshire S6 2AS**
TEL   0742 852428
OPEN   9–5 Mon–Fri.

Specialise in restoring furniture,
woodwork, Boulle work, marquetry,
carving and gilding.

PROVIDE Home Inspections. Free
Estimates. Chargeable
Collection/Delivery Service.
SPEAK TO Neil Trinder.
Member of UKIC and BAFRA. This
workshop is included on the register of
conservators maintained by the
Conservation Unit of the Museums and
Galleries Commission.

GEARY ANTIQUES

114 Richardshaw Lane, Pudsey, Leeds,
West Yorkshire LS28 6BN
TEL   0532 564122
OPEN   10–5.30 Mon–Sat; closed Wed.

Specialise in conserving and restoring
furniture and upholstery and allied skills.

PROVIDE Home Inspections. Free
Estimates. Free Collection/Delivery
Service.
SPEAK TO J. A. Geary.

RODNEY FARMER KEMBLE

16 Crag Vale Terrace, Glusburn, Nr.
Keighley,
West Yorkshire BD20 8QU
TEL   0535 636954 or 633702
OPEN   8.30–5.30 Mon–Fri; 8.30–12
      Sat or By Appointment.

Specialise in all aspects of furniture
restoration and finishing, including
upholstery and cabinet repairs.

PROVIDE Home Inspections. Free
Estimates. Free Collection/Delivery
Service.
SPEAK TO Rodney Kemble.
Member of BAFRA.

THE SCAGLIOLA COMPANY

Chapeltown Business Centre, 231
Chapeltown Road, Leeds,
West Yorkshire LS7 3DX
TEL   0532 626811
FAX   0532 625448
OPEN   9–5 Mon–Fri.

Specialise in restoring scagliola
(traditional marble-finish based on a
plaster recipe) on table surfaces, columns,
pedestals, panels, floors and inlays.

PROVIDE Home Inspections. Free
Estimates. Chargeable
Collection/Delivery Service.
SPEAK TO Michael Koumbouzis.

This workshop is included on the register of conservators maintained by the Conservation Unit of the Museums and Galleries Commission.

FRANK WOODS T/A ABBOTSWOOD

22 Littlethorpe Hill, Hartshead, Liversedge,
West Yorkshire WF15 8AZ
TEL   0274 876314
FAX   0274 861529
OPEN   By Appointment.

Specialise in restoring furniture, especially 16th and 17th century oakwork, matching, copy carving and furniture copies.

PROVIDE Home Inspections. Free Estimates. Free/Chargeable Collection Delivery Service.
SPEAK TO Frank Wood.
Member of UKIC.

THOMAS H. KEARNEY AND SONS

Treasure House Antiques, 123 University Street, Belfast,
Co. Antrim BT7 1HP.
TEL   0232 231055
OPEN   8–6 Mon–Fri.

Specialise in restoring antique furniture of all types, upholstery, polishing.

PROVIDE Home Inspections. Free Estimates.
SPEAK TO Thomas Kearney.

PATRICK CABOURNE-BASSETT

The Farm House, Sarsfield's Court, Glanmire, **Co. Cork**
TEL   021 821076
OPEN   By Appointment.

Specialise in restoring Georgian and Victorian furniture and some Boulle repairs.

PROVIDE Home Inspections. Free Estimates.
SPEAK TO Patrick Cabourne–Bassett.
Member of IPCRA.

T. J. MITCHELL LTD

4 Lower Pembroke Street, Dublin 2, **Co. Dublin**
TEL   01 766881
OPEN   9–12.45, 2–5.30 Mon–Fri.

Specialise in restoring English and Irish furniture.

PROVIDE Home Inspections. Refundable Estimates. Collection/Delivery Service by arrangement.
SPEAK TO Tommy Mitchell or Maura Mitchell.

JENNY SLEVIN

9 Innisboffin, Bailey View, Harbour Road, Dalkey, **Co. Dublin**
TEL   01 280 3429
OPEN   By Appointment.

Specialise in restoring lacquerwork on screens, furniture, boxes. Will also clean and repair mirror frames.

PROVIDE Home Inspections. Free/Chargeable Estimates. Collection/Delivery Service by arrangement.
SPEAK TO Jenny Slevin.
Member of IPCRA.
SEE Carpets, Porcelain, Picture Frames, Collectors (Wax).

SUSAN MULHALL

Blackwood, Robertstown, Naas, **Co. Kildare**
TEL   045 60336
OPEN   By Appointment.

Specialise in restoring furniture and mirror frames, including gilding and gessowork.

PROVIDE Home Inspections. Free/Chargeable Estimates.

Collection/Delivery Service by arrangement.
SPEAK TO Susan Mulhall.
Member of IPCRA.
SEE Picture Frames.

WLODEK SZUSTKIEWICZ
Stacumny House, Celbridge, **Co. Kildare**
TEL   01 628 8345 ex.10
OPEN   By Appointment.

Specialise in restoring brown wood furniture and mirror frames, including carving and gilding, gesso work.

PROVIDE Home Inspections. Free Estimates. Free Collection/Delivery Service.
SPEAK TO Wlodek Szustkiewicz.
Member of IPCRA.
SEE Picture Frames.

KARL AND CLAIRE DAVENPORT
Kilbrook, Enfield, **Co. Meath**
TEL   0405 41214
OPEN   By Appointment.

Specialise in restoring good antique furniture, including marquetry, inlay, wood-carving, French polishing and upholstery.

PROVIDE Home Inspections.
Free/Chargeable Estimates. Chargeable Collection/Delivery Service.
SPEAK TO Karl or Claire Davenport.
Member of IPCRA.

EMILY NAPER
Loughcrew, Oldcastle, **Co. Meath**
TEL   049 41356
FAX   049 41722
OPEN   By Appointment.

Specialise in restoring water- and oil-gilded mirror frames and gilt furniture, gesso painted finishes and marbling.

PROVIDE Home Inspections. Free

Estimates. Chargeable Local Collection/Delivery Service.
SPEAK TO Emily Naper.
Member of IPCRA.
SEE Picture Frames.

VALERIE McCOY
Fan–na–Greine, Glendalough, **Co. Wicklow**
TEL   0404 45125
OPEN   By Appointment.

Specialise in restoring and gilding mirror frames.

PROVIDE Home Inspections. Free Estimates. Free Collection/Delivery Service.
SPEAK TO Valerie McCoy.
Member of IPCRA.
SEE Porcelain, Picture Frames

ST JAMES'S GALLERY LTD
Smith Street, St Peter Port, **Guernsey, Channel Islands**
TEL   0481 720070
OPEN   9–5 Mon–Fri, 9–1 Sat or By Appointment.

Specialise in restoring 18th and 19th century English and Continental furniture, Edwardian furniture.

PROVIDE Home Inspections. Chargeable Estimates. Collection/Delivery Service by arrangement.
SPEAK TO Mrs Whittam.
SEE Clocks, Porcelain.

JAMES FLAVELL BOOKBINDER AND RESTORER
26 Foreland Road, Bembridge, **Isle of Wight PO35 5XW**
TEL   0983 872856
OPEN   9–5.30 Mon–Fri, 9–12.30 Sat.

Specialise in inlaying and replacement of leather–covered tables and desk tops.

PROVIDE Home Inspections. Free Estimates. Free Collection/Delivery Service.
SPEAK TO James Flavell.
Mr Flavell is City and Guilds qualified, Member of the Society of Bookbinders, Associate Member of Designer Bookbinders. This workshop is included on the register of conservators maintained by the Conservation Unit of the Museums and Galleries Commission.
SEE Oil Paintings, Books

CHISHOLME ANTIQUES
5 Orrock Place, Hawick, **Borders TD9 0HQ**
TEL   0450 76928
OPEN   9–6 Mon–Fri.

Specialise in restoring antique furniture, including veneering, tortoiseshell, ivory, gilding and composition work, rush seating, caning and upholstery.

PROVIDE Home Inspections. Free Estimates. Chargeable Collection/Delivery Service.
SPEAK TO Mr Roberts.
SEE Carpets.

GRANT LEES
98 Gala Park, Galashiels, Selkirkshire, **Borders TD1 1EZ**
TEL   0896 3721
OPEN   9–6 Mon–Sat; closed Wed & Sat a.m.

Specialise in restoring old and antique locks.

PROVIDE Home Inspections. Free Estimates. Chargeable Collection/Delivery Service.
SPEAK TO Grant Lees.
SEE Clocks, Collectors (Mechanical Music).
This workshop is in the Scottish Conservation Directory.

LYNWOOD REPRODUCTIONS
Lynwood, Eskdalemuir, Langholm, Dumfriesshire, **Dumfries & Galloway DG13 0QH**
TEL   03873 73211
OPEN   9–6 Mon–Fri.

Specialise in restoring carved and gilded wood furniture and frames. They also have the facility to make copies of most wood–carvings and can undertake gilding of any sort.

PROVIDE Home Inspections. Free Estimates. Chargeable Collection/Delivery Service.
SPEAK TO John or Nancy Chinnery.
Member of SSCR and the Guild of Master Craftsmen.
SEE Picture Frames.

JUDITH A. LIVINGSTON
Willowbrae, 3 Pittenweem Road, Anstruther, **Fife KY10 3DS**
TEL   0333 310 425
OPEN   By Appointment.

Specialise in restoring antique furniture, veneering, French polishing, carving and mouldings.

PROVIDE Home Inspections. Free/Chargeable Estimates.
SPEAK TO Judith Livingston.
Member of SSCR. This workshop is in the Scottish Conservation Directory.

JOHN McWILLIAM BEATON
16 Fingal Place, Portree, Isle of Skye, **Highland IV51 9ND**
TEL   0478 3290
OPEN   By appointment.

Specialise in restoring furniture, including wood–carving such as making replica pieces and pieces from photographs.

PROVIDE Home Inspections. Free

Estimates. Chargeable
Collection/Delivery Service.
SPEAK TO Ian Beaton.
Member of SSCR. This workshop is in
the Scottish Conservation Directory.

PETER DAVIS
Unit 5, Glen Nevis Place, Fort William,
Highland PH33 6DA
TEL   0397 704039
OPEN   8–5 Mon–Fri.

Specialise in handmade furniture and
furniture repair and restoration, wood–
turning.

PROVIDE Home Inspections. Free
Estimates. Chargeable
Collection/Delivery Service.
SPEAK TO Peter Davis.

GILES PEARSON
Brightmony House, Auldern, **Highland
IV12 5PP**
TEL   0667 55550
OPEN   9–6 Daily.

Specialise in rush and cane work for
chairs, stools and bèrgère suites.

PROVIDE Home Inspections. Free
Estimates. Collection/Delivery Service
by arrangement.
SPEAK TO Giles Pearson.
This workshop is in the Scottish
Conservation Directory.
SEE Silver.

LUIGI M. VILLANI
Traditional Antique Restoration and
Consultancy Service, The Stable, Altyre,
Forres, **Highland IV36 OSH**
TEL   0309 672572
OPEN   8 a.m.–10 p.m. Mon–Fri.

Specialise in repair and restoration of
antique furniture, frames and fittings,
including marquetry (structural, inlay
and finish), marble (furniture and
fittings), gilding.

PROVIDE Home Inspections. Estimates.

SPEAK TO Luigi M. Villani or Rosalie
Stuart.
Run a consultancy and training service
on restoration, wood stains and finishes
and also give lectures.
SEE Porcelain.

CAROL CARSTAIRS
67 George Street, Edinburgh, **Lothian
EH2 2JG**
TEL   031 220 3931
OPEN   9.30–6 Mon–Fri or By
Appointment.

Specialise in conservation and
restoration of gilding on furniture and
architectural projects plus carving and
lacquer work.

PROVIDE Home Inspections. Free Local
Estimates. Chargeable
Collection/Delivery Service.
SPEAK TO Carol Carstairs.
Member of SSCR. This workshop is in
the Scottish Conservation Directory.

ANSELM FRASER
The Carthouse, Crauchie, East Linton,
Lothian EH40 3EB
TEL   0620 860067
OPEN   9–4.30 Mon–Fri.

Specialise in restoring antique furniture,
including veneer repairs, wood–carving
and turning, Boulle and marquetry work,
inlays, gilding, gesso mouldings, grain
simulation, metal repairs, French
polishing, simple upholstery, carcase
repairs.

PROVIDE Home Inspections. Free
Estimates. Free/Chargeable
Collection/Delivery Service.
SPEAK TO Anselm Fraser.
This workshop is in the Scottish
Conservation Directory.

J. & J. HARDIE
ANTIQUES LTD
222–224 Newhaven Road, Edinburgh,
Lothian EH6 4JY
TEL   031 552 7080
OPEN   8.30–5.30 Mon–Fri; 9–4.30 Sat.

Specialise in restoring all periods of fine furniture up to 1930s, including Continental pieces.

PROVIDE Home Inspections. Free Estimates. Chargeable Collection/Delivery Service. This workshop is in the Scottish Conservation Directory.

BARBARA HOPE
18 Buckstone Wood, Edinburgh, **Lothian EH10 6QW**
TEL   031 445 3606
FAX   031 445 3606
OPEN   By Appointment.

Specialise in restoring giltwood furnishing with especial interest in verre eglomisé and simulated finishes.

PROVIDE Home Inspections. Free/Chargeable Estimates. SPEAK TO Barbara Hope. Member of UKIC and SSCR. This workshop is in the Scottish Conservation Directory.

HOUNDWOOD ANTIQUES RESTORATION
7 West Preston Street, Edinburgh, **Lothian EH8 9PX**
TEL   031 667 3253
OPEN   By Appointment.

Specialise in restoring antique furniture.

PROVIDE Home Inspections. Free Estimates. Chargeable Collection/Delivery Service. SPEAK TO Mr A Gourlay. SEE Porcelain, Silver.

W. R. MARTIN
Bowden Springs Fishery, Linlithgow, **Lothian EH49 6QE**
TEL   0506 847269
OPEN   9–5 Daily or By Appointment.

Specialise in restoring solid wood furniture and objects. They also make

copies and specialise in designs by Charles Rennie Mackintosh.

PROVIDE Home Inspections. Free Estimates. Chargeable Collection/Delivery Service. SPEAK TO Wil Martin. This workshop is in the Scottish Conservation Directory.

TRIST & McBAIN
9 Cannongate Venture, New Street, Edinburgh, **Lothian EH8 8VH**
TEL   031 557 3828
OPEN   8.30–5.30 Mon–Fri; By Appointment Sat.

Specialise in conserving and restoring period furniture, including Boulle, marquetry, wood–turning, French polishing. They also do cane and rush seating and desk leathers.

PROVIDE Home Inspections. Free Estimates. Free Collection/Delivery Service. SPEAK TO William Trist or Andrew McBain. This workshop is in the Scottish Conservation Directory. Member of Furniture History Society, SSCR and Provincial Furniture History Society.

WHYTOCK & REID
Sunbury House, Belford Mews, Edinburgh **Lothian EH4 3DN**
TEL   031 226 4911
FAX   031 226 4595
OPEN   9–5.30 Mon–Fri; 9–12.30 Sat.

Specialise in restoring 18th and 19th century furniture, re–upholstery, polishing and gilding.

PROVIDE Home Inspections. Free Estimates. Collection/Delivery Service available. SPEAK TO David Reid. This workshop is in the Scottish Conservation Directory. SEE Carpets.

DAPHNE FRASER
Glenbarry, 58 Victoria Road, Lenzie, Glasgow, **Strathclyde G66 5AP**
TEL   041 776 1281
OPEN   By Appointment.

Specialise in restoring ornate mirror frames.

PROVIDE Free Estimates.
SPEAK TO Daphne Fraser.
This workshop is in the Scottish Conservation Directory.
SEE Collectors (Dolls; Toys), Oil Paintings, Picture Frames.

ROBERT HOWIE AND SON
19 High Street, Mauchline, **Strathclyde**
TEL   0290 50556
OPEN   8–5 Mon–Fri.

Specialise in restoring painted furniture, specialised finishes.

PROVIDE Home Inspections. Free Estimates. Chargeable Collection/Delivery Service.
SPEAK TO Robert Howie.
This workshop is in the Scottish Conservation Directory.

PIERS KETTLEWELL CABINETMAKERS
10 Robertson Street, Barrhead, **Strathclyde G78 1QW**
TEL   041 881 8166
OPEN   By Appointment.

Specialise in restoring antique furniture and making furniture to commission.

PROVIDE Home Inspections. Free Estimates. Collection/Delivery Service by arrangement.
SPEAK TO Piers Kettlewell.
This workshop is in the Scottish Conservation Directory.

FRAN MALLOY
Suite 1, 66 Dora Street, Glasgow, **Strathclyde G40 4DP**
TEL   041 551 0616
OPEN   8.30–6 Mon–Sat.

Specialise in restoring antique furniture of all periods.

PROVIDE Home Inspections. Free/Chargeable Estimates. Free/Chargeable Collection/Delivery Service.
SPEAK TO Fran Malloy.
This workshop is in the Scottish Conservation Directory.

THE OLD CURIOSITY SHOP
27–29 Crown Street, Ayr, **Strathclyde KA8 8AG**
TEL   0292 280222
OPEN   8–5 Mon–Fri; 10–3 Sat.

Specialise in restoring antique furniture, repairs, re–upholstery and polishing. Also manufacture hand–made furniture.

PROVIDE Home Inspections. Refundable Estimates. Free Collection/Delivery Service locally.
SPEAK TO Brian Kelly.
This workshop is in the Scottish Conservation Directory.

WESTPORT GALLERY
3 Old Hawkhill, Dundee, **Tayside DD1 5EU**
TEL   0382 21751
OPEN   9–5 Mon–Fri.

Specialise in restoring antique furniture and wood–carving.

PROVIDE Free Estimates. Chargeable Collection/Delivery Service.
SPEAK TO Neil Livingstone.
SEE Arms, Oil Paintings, Picture Frames, Silver.

IRENA ANTIQUES
111 Broad Street, Barry, **South Glamorgan CF6 8SX**
TEL   0446 747626 or 732517
OPEN   10–4 Mon–Fri.

Specialise in restoring antique furniture,

including painted and lacquered work, cane and rush seating.

PROVIDE Free Estimates. Free Collection/Delivery Service.
SPEAK TO Irena Halabuda.
Mrs Halabuda is a specialist in painted work in the manner of Angelica Kaufmann.
SEE Porcelain.

WINSTON JAMES RESTORATIONS
Pendalog Hall, Llanfyllin, **Powys SY22 5ET**
TEL   0691 648229
FAX   0691 648678
OPEN   10–5 Mon–Fri.

Specialise in restoring seat and case furniture, including veneering, carving, French polishing, gilding, decorative

paintwork. Exact replicas of any case furniture made to order.

PROVIDE Home Inspections. Free Estimates. Free Collection/Delivery Service.
SPEAK TO Miss K. Beazley or Mr W. James.
Established 1968.

SNOWDONIA ANTIQUES
Station Road, Llanrwst, **Gwynedd LL26 QEP**
TEL   0492 640789
OPEN   9–5.30 Mon–Sat or By Appointment.

Specialise in restoring period furniture.

PROVIDE Home Inspections. Chargeable Estimates. Chargeable Collection/Delivery Service.
SPEAK TO Mr J. Collins.
SEE Clocks.

CLOCKS, WATCHES, BAROMETERS

DO

Identify weights when moving longcase clocks so that they can go back on the same
pulley
Allow hours to strike when moving hands forward
Use wax polish, not silicon sprays, on wooden cases
Keep fitted boxes for clocks and watches, as this can enhance resale value
For insurance purposes, keep a photograph and details such as serial numbers of all
clocks and watches you own

DON'T

Turn hands backwards
Move any clock without securing or removing the pendulum
Clean carriage clocks or gilt cases with metal polish
Clean brass inlay on wood with metal polish
Touch silvered chapter rings – fingermarks may result

D. J. DAVIS
13 Castle Street, Thornbury, Bristol,
Avon BS12 1HA
TEL   0454 412430
OPEN   By Appointment.

Specialise in restoring clock cases,
including wood–turning, locks, some
metalwork and clock movement repairs.
All aspects of cleaning, polishing and
finishing covered.

PROVIDE Home Inspections. Free
Estimates. Free Local
Collection/Delivery Service.
SPEAK TO David Davis.
Mr Davis is a member of the Guild of
Master Craftsmen and a director of the
local museum.
SEE Furniture.

JOHN AND CAROL HAWLEY
'The Orchard', Clevedon Lane, Clapton
Wick, Clevedon, **Avon BS21 7AG**
TEL   0275 852052
OPEN   By Appointment.

Specialise in repairing and restoring all
types of antique clocks. Do not
undertake watches.

PROVIDE Home Inspections. Free Local
Estimates. Free Collection/Delivery
Service.
SPEAK TO John or Carol Hawley.
They are CMBHI and MBWCG

DAVID MITCHELL
45 St. Michael's Road, Bedford,
Bedfordshire MK40 2LZ
TEL   0234 359976
OPEN   9–6 Mon–Fri or By
          Appointment.

Specialise in restoring clock cases.

PROVIDE Home Inspections.
Free/Chargeable Estimates.
Chargeable Collection/Delivery Service.
SPEAK TO David Mitchell.
Member of UKIC and BAFRA.
SEE Oil Paintings, Furniture.

ASHLEY ANTIQUES AND FURNITURE
Unit 43, Hungerford Arcade,
Hungerford, **Berkshire RG17 0DL**
TEL   0672 20481
OPEN   9.30–5.30 Daily.

Specialise in restoring clocks.

PROVIDE Home Inspections. Free
Estimates. Free Local
Collection/Delivery Service.
SPEAK TO Robert Duff.
SEE Furniture.

D. N. CARD
1A Chester Street, Caversham, Reading,
Berkshire RG4 8JH
TEL   0734 470777
OPEN   9–12.30, 2–5 Mon–Fri or By
          Appointment.

Specialise in restoring antique clocks,
watches and barometers.

PROVIDE Home Inspections. Free
Estimates. Chargeable
Collection/Delivery Service.
SPEAK TO David Card.
Mr Card is CMBHI. This workshop is
included on the register of conservators
maintained by the Conservation Unit of
the Museums and Galleries Commission.
SEE Collectors (Mechanical Music).

HAMILTON HAVERS
58 Conisboro Avenue, Caversham
Heights, Reading, **Berkshire RG4 7JE**
TEL   0734 473379
OPEN   By Appointment.

Specialise in restoring Boulle,
marquetry, ivory, tortoiseshell, mother-
of-pearl, brass, lapis lazuli and malachite
on clock–cases.

PROVIDE Free/Chargeable Estimates.
SPEAK TO Hamilton Havers.
SEE Furniture, Silver.

S. J. BIRT & SON
21 Windmill Street, Brill, Aylesbury, **Buckinghamshire HP18 9TG**
TEL   0844 237440
OPEN   By Appointment.

Specialise in restoring clocks, barometers and tower clocks.

PROVIDE Home Inspections. Free Estimates. Free Collection/Delivery Service.
SPEAK TO Mr S. J. Birt.
SEE Collectors (Mechanical Music).

ALAN MARTIN
Farthing Cottage, Clickers Yard, Yardley Road, Olney, **Buckinghamshire MK46 5DX**
TEL   0234 712446
OPEN   9–5 Mon–Sat; By Appointment Sun.

Specialise in repairing antique clocks and pocket watches.

PROVIDE Home Inspections. Free/Chargeable Estimates. Free Collection/Delivery Service.
SPEAK TO Alan Martin.
Mr Martin is MBHI and a Member of the Clock and Watchmakers' Guild.

TINGEWICK ANTIQUES CENTRE

Main Street, Tingewick, **Buckinghamshire MK18 4PB**
TEL   0280 847922
OPEN   10.30–5 Mon–Sat; 11–5 Sun.

Specialise in restoring metalware on clocks.

PROVIDE Home Inspections. Free Estimates. Collection/Delivery Service by arrangement.
SPEAK TO Rosemarie or Barry Smith. SEE Furniture

DODDINGTON HOUSE ANTIQUES
2 Benwick Road, Doddington, Nr. March, **Cambridgeshire PE15 OTG**
TEL   0354 740755
OPEN   10–6 Mon–Sat.

Specialise in restoring clock–cases and barometers.

PROVIDE Refundable Estimates. Free Collection/Delivery Service.
SPEAK TO Brian or Lynette Frankland.
SEE Furniture.

A. ALLEN ANTIQUE RESTORERS
Buxton Rd, Newtown, Newmills, Via Stockport, **Cheshire SK12 3JS**
TEL   0663 745274
OPEN   8–5 Mon–Fri; 9–12 Sat.

Specialise in mending and repairing longcase clocks.

PROVIDE Home Inspections. Free/Chargeable Estimates. Collection/Delivery Service.
SPEAK TO Tony Allen.
SEE Furniture, Picture Frames, Silver.

PETER D. BOSSON
10B Swan St, Wilmslow, **Cheshire SK9 1HE**
TEL   0625 525250 and 527857
OPEN   10–12.45, 2.15–5 Tues–Sat.

Specialise in restoring barographs, barometers, clocks.

PROVIDE Home Inspections. Free Estimates. Free Local Collection/Delivery Service.
SPEAK TO Peter Bosson.
SEE Collectors (Scientific Instruments).

MILL FARM ANTIQUES
50 Market Street, Disley, Stockport, **Cheshire SK12 2DT**
TEL   0663 764045
OPEN   9–6 Mon–Sat.

Specialise in restoring antique clocks and barometers.

PROVIDE Home Inspections. Free Estimates. Free Collection/Delivery Service.
SPEAK TO F. E. Berry.
SEE Collectors (Mechanical Music).

DEREK RAYMENT ANTIQUES
Orchard House, Barton Road, Barton, Nr. Farndon, **Cheshire SY14 7HT**
TEL   0829 270 429
OPEN   By Appointment.

Specialise in repairing and restoring antique barometers.

PROVIDE Home Inspections. Free Estimates.
SPEAK TO Derek or Tina Rayment.
Members of BADA.

THE OLD MAN ANTIQUES
Coniston, **Cumbria LA21 8DU**
TEL   05394 41389
OPEN   9.30–5.30 Daily from Easter to 5 November. By appointment only during winter months.

Specialise in repairing and restoring wheel (mercury) barometers.
SPEAK TO Ron or Yvonne Williams.

JOHN M. PENDLEBURY
4 Meadow Grove, Grange–over–Sands, **Cumbria LA11 7AT**
TEL   05395 35201
OPEN   9–5 Mon–Fri By Appointment Only.

Specialise in restoring clocks and barometers.

PROVIDE Home Inspections. Free Local Estimates. Free Collection/Delivery Service.
SPEAK TO John M. Pendlebury.
Mr Pendlebury is MBHI

DERBYSHIRE CLOCKS
104 High Street West, Glossop, **Derbyshire SK13 8BB**
TEL   0457 862677
OPEN   1–5 Mon–Sat; 1–4.30 Sun; closed Tues.

Specialise in restoring antique clocks and barometers.

PROVIDE Home Inspections. Refundable Estimates. Free Collection/Delivery Service.
SPEAK TO Terence Peter Lees.

C. REYNOLDS
The Spindles, Tonge, Melbourne, **Derbyshire DE7 1BD**
TEL   0332 862609 and 0836 752602
OPEN   By Appointment.

Specialise in restoring verge movement watches 1780–1880.

PROVIDE Home Inspections. Chargeable Estimates.
SPEAK TO Mr T. Reynolds.

JOHN SMITH & SONS
Midland Clock Works, 27 Queen Street, Derby, **Derbyshire DE1 3DU**
TEL   0332 45569
FAX   0332 290642
OPEN   8–5 Mon–Fri.

Specialise in restoring clocks and barometers, expert in longcase, bracket and case restoration.

PROVIDE Home Inspections. Free Estimates (in workshop). Chargeable Collection/Delivery Service.
SPEAK TO Mr David Higginbotham. Mr Higginbotham is MBHI. This workshop is included on the register of conservators maintained by the Conservation Unit of the Museums and Galleries Commission.

BAROMETER WORLD
Quicksilver Barn, Merton, Okehampton,
Devon EX20 3DS
TEL   08053 443
OPEN   8–5 Mon–Sat.

Specialise in restoring antique
barometers.

PROVIDE Home Inspections by
arrangement. Free Estimates.
Chargeable Collection/Delivery Service.
SPEAK TO Philip Collins.
Member of BAFRA. This workshop is
included on the register of conservators
maintained by the Conservation Unit of
the Museums and Galleries Commission.

CLIVE AND LESLEY COBB
Newhouse Farm, Bratton Fleming,
Barnstaple, **Devon EX31 4RT**
TEL   0598 710465
OPEN   9–5.30 Daily.

Specialise in restoring painted clock
dials.

PROVIDE Home Inspections. Free
Estimates. Chargeable
Collection/Delivery Service.
SPEAK TO Clive Cobb.
Established over twenty years. Member
of UKIC and the Guild of Master
Craftsmen. This workshop is included on
the register of conservators maintained
by the Conservation Unit of the
Museums and Galleries Commission.
SEE Furniture.

LAURIE PENMAN
Castle Workshop, 61 High Street,
Totnes, **Devon TQ9 5PB**
TEL   0803 866344
FAX   0803 866344
OPEN   8a.m.–6p.m. Mon–Sat.
         Sunday by appointment.
         Telephone anytime.

Specialise in repairing and restoring
clocks.

PROVIDE Home Inspections. Free
Estimates.
SPEAK TO Laurie Penman.

Also provide workshop tuition and a
correspondence course. Internationally
recognised horologist.

CLARE SPICER
The Old Hare and Hounds, Fore Street,
Witheridge, Tiverton, **Devon
EX16 8AH**
TEL   0884 860 135
OPEN   9–4 Mon–Fri.

Specialise in restoring and conserving
clock dials.

PROVIDE Local Home Inspections. Free
Estimates.
SPEAK TO Clare Spicer.
SEE Porcelain.

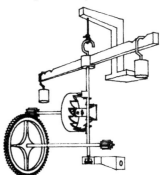

LAURENCE G. WOOTTON
2 Church Street, South Brent, **Devon TQ10 9AB**
TEL   0364 72553
OPEN   By Appointment (telephone between 9.30a.m.–12.30p.m.)

Specialise in repairing clocks and watches.

PROVIDE Home Inspections.
SPEAK TO Laurence Wootton

MICHAEL BARRINGTON
The Old Rectory, Warmwell, Dorchester, **Dorset DT2 8HQ**
TEL   0305 852104
OPEN   By Appointment.

Specialise in restoring longcase clock-cases.

PROVIDE Local Free Estimates. Free/Chargeable Collection/Delivery Service.
SPEAK TO Michael Barrington.
Member of BAFRA.
SEE Collectors (Musical Instruments, Toys), Furniture.

THE CHETTLE GUILD
The Stables, Chettle House, Chettle, Blandford, **Dorset DT11 8DB**
TEL   0258 89576
OPEN   9–6 Mon–Sat.

Specialise in restoring clocks.

PROVIDE Home Inspections. Free Estimates. Free Local Collection/Delivery Service.
SPEAK TO Alastair or Andrew Arnold.
SEE Arms, Furniture, Collectors (Scientific Instruments).

D. J. JEWELLERY
166–168 Ashley Road, Parkstone, Poole, **Dorset BH14 9BY**
TEL   0202 745148
OPEN   9.30–5 Mon–Sat.

Specialise in repairing antique clocks.

PROVIDE Home Inspections. Free Estimates. Chargeable Collection/Delivery Service.
SPEAK TO Dennis O'Sullivan.

GOOD HOPE ANTIQUES
2 Hogshill Street, Beaminster, **Dorset DT8 3AE**
TEL   0308 862119
OPEN   9.30–5 Mon–Sat; closed Wed.

Specialise in restoring barometers and clocks, especially longcase, bracket and English wall clocks.

PROVIDE Chargeable Estimates. Chargeable Collection/Delivery Service.
SPEAK TO David Beney.

TOLPUDDLE ANTIQUE RESTORERS
The Stables, Tolpuddle, Dorchester, **Dorset DT2 7HF**
TEL   0305 848739
OPEN   9–6 Mon–Fri; 12–5 Sat.

Specialise in restoring clocks and barometers.

PROVIDE Home Inspections. Free Estimates. Free Collection/Delivery Service.
Member of BAFRA.
SEE Furniture.

THE COLLECTOR
Douglas House, 23–25 The Bank, Barnard Castle, **Durham DL12 8PH**
TEL   0833 37783
OPEN   10–5 or By Appointment.

Specialise in restoring clocks.

PROVIDE Home Inspections. Refundable Estimates. Chargeable Collection/Delivery Service.
SPEAK TO Robert Jordan or Paul Hunter.
Also provide a full design service.
SEE Furniture

DAVID, JEAN & JOHN ANTIQUES

587 London Road, Westcliff, **Essex SS0 9PQ**

TEL   0702 339106
FAX   0268 560563
OPEN   10–5 Mon–Sat; closed Wed.

Specialise in clock and watch repairs
PROVIDE Home Inspections. Refundable Estimates. Free Collection/Delivery Service.
SPEAK TO David Howard.
SEE Furniture.

LITTLEBURY ANTIQUES

58–60 Fairycroft Road, Saffron Walden, **Essex CB10 1LZ**

TEL   0799 527961
FAX   0799 527961
OPEN   8.30–5.15 Mon–Fri; Sat By Appointment.

Specialise in restoring barometers and clocks of all periods.
PROVIDE Home Inspections. Free Estimates. Free/Chargeable Collection/Delivery Service.
SPEAK TO N. H. D'Oyly.
SEE Furniture.

SMALLCOMBE CLOCKS

Regency House, Globe Industrial Estate, Rectory Road, Grays, **Essex RM17 6ST**

TEL   0375 379980
FAX   0375 390286
OPEN   8.30–5 Mon–Fri.

Specialise in repairing and restoring longcase clocks.
PROVIDE Home Inspections. Free Estimates. Free/Chargeable Collection/Delivery Service.
SPEAK TO Brett Smallcombe or Tony Holland.

KEITH BAWDEN

Mews Workshop, Montpellier Retreat, Cheltenham, **Gloucestershire GL50 2XG**

TEL   0242 230320
OPEN   7–4.30 Mon–Fri.

Specialise in conserving and restoring antique clocks.
PROVIDE Free Estimates. Home Inspections. Local Collection/Delivery Service.
SPEAK TO Keith Bawden.
SEE Furniture, Oil Paintings, Porcelain, Silver.

WILLIAM COOK CABINETMAKER

Primrose Cottage, 11 Northfield Road, Tetbury, **Gloucestershire GL8 8HD**

TEL   0666 502877
OPEN   9–5 Mon–Fri.

Specialise in restoring clock–cases, including gilding.
PROVIDE Free Estimates.
SPEAK TO William or Ruth Cook.

KEITH HARDING'S WORLD OF MECHANICAL MUSIC

Oak House, High Street, Northleach, **Gloucestershire GL54 3EU**

TEL   0451 860181
FAX   0451 861133
OPEN   10–6 Daily.

Specialise in restoring clocks.
PROVIDE Home Inspections. Free Estimates. Free Local Collection/Delivery Service.
SPEAK TO Keith Harding.
SEE Collectors (Mechanical Music).

ANDREW LELLIOTT

6 Tetbury Hill, Avening, Tetbury, **Gloucestershire GL8 8LT**

TEL   0453 835783 or 0453 832652
OPEN   By Appointment.

Specialise in restoring 18th century English clock–cases.

PROVIDE Home Inspections. Free Estimates. Free Collection/Delivery Service. Full Insurance Cover.
SPEAK TO Andrew Lelliott.
Member of BAFRA. This workshop is included on the register of conservators maintained by the Conservation Unit of the Museums and Galleries Commission.
SEE Furniture.

CLIVE JOHN RAMMELL

Magpie Cottage, Wick Lane, Apperley, **Gloucestershire GL19 4DS**
TEL   0452 780527
OPEN   8.30–6 Mon–Sat.

Specialise in restoring antique clocks.

PROVIDE Home Inspections. Chargeable Estimates. Chargeable Collection/Delivery Service.
SPEAK TO Clive Rammell.
Member of UKIC and BHI.

GODFREY ROBERTSON

Fourwinds, Ablington, Bibury, Cirencester, **Gloucester GL7 5NX**
TEL   0258 740355
FAX   0285 740355 (On Demand Only)
OPEN   By Appointment.

Specialise in restoring clock cases and barometers.

PROVIDE Home Inspections. Free/Chargeable Estimates. Chargeable Collection/Delivery Service.
SPEAK TO Godfrey Robertson.
Member of BAFRA and UKIC.
SEE Furniture

BRYAN CLISBY ANTIQUE CLOCKS

Andwells Antiques, The Row, Hartley Wintney, **Hampshire RG27 8NY**
TEL   0252 716 436
OPEN   9–5.30 Mon–Sat.

Specialise in restoring antique clocks and barometers.

PROVIDE Home Inspections. Free Estimates. Chargeable Collection/Delivery Service.
SPEAK TO Bryan Clisby.

EVANS AND EVANS

40 West Street, Alresford, **Hampshire SO24 9AU**
TEL   0962 732170
OPEN   9–1, 2–5 Fri–Sat; By Appointment Mon–Thur.

Specialise in restoring good English and French clocks.

PROVIDE Home Inspections. Refundable Estimates. Free Collection/Delivery Service.
SPEAK TO David or Noel Evans.

GERALD MARSH ANTIQUE CLOCKS LTD

32A The Square, Winchester, **Hampshire SO23 9EX**
TEL   0962 844443
OPEN   9.30–5 Mon–Sat.

Specialise in restoring antique English and French clocks, watches and barometers.

PROVIDE Home Inspections. Free Estimates. Collection/Delivery Service.
SPEAK TO Gerald Marsh or D. Dipper.
Member of Worshipful Company of Clockmakers, Fellow of British Horological Institute, Member of NAWCC (USA) and BADA.
SEE **Oxfordshire.**

A. W. PORTER

High Street, Hartley Witney, Nr. Basingstoke, **Hampshire RG27 8NY**
TEL   025 126 2676
FAX   025 126 2064
OPEN   9–5.30 Mon–Fri; 9.30–5 Sat.

Specialise in restoring antique clocks, watches and barometers.

PROVIDE Home Inspections. Free
Estimates. Chargeable
Collection/Delivery Service.
SPEAK TO Mr Porter.
Established 1844.
SEE Silver.

J. A. PRADO (PRADO CABINETMAKER AND RESTORER)
Great Weir House, The Great Weir,
Alresford, **Hampshire SO24 9DB**
TEL   0962 732896
FAX   0962 734233
OPEN   By Appointment.

Specialise in restoring English clock–
cases 1660 to 1815 with emphasis on
marquetry and brass inlay.

PROVIDE Home Inspections. Free
Estimates. Chargeable
Collection/Delivery Service.
SPEAK TO Mr J. A. Prado. This workshop
is included on the register of
conservators maintained by the
Conservation Unit of the Museums and
Galleries Commission.
SEE Furniture

THE BAROMETER SHOP
4 New Street, Leominster, **Hereford &
Worcester HR6 8BT**
TEL   0568 613652
OPEN   9–5.30 Mon–Sat.

Specialise in restoring barometers and
clocks.

PROVIDE Home Inspections. Free
Estimates. Free Collection/Delivery
Service.
SPEAK TO Richard Cookson.
Mr Cookson is CMBHI.
SEE Furniture, Collectors (Scientific
Instruments).

HANSEN CHARD ANTIQUES
126 High Street, Pershore, **Hereford &
Worcester WR10 1EA**
TEL   0386 553423
OPEN   10–5 Tues, Wed, Fri, Sat or By
       Appointment.

Specialise in restoring clocks and
barometers.

PROVIDE Home Inspections. Free
Estimates. Free Local
Collection/Delivery Service.
SPEAK TO P. W. Ridler.
Member of BHI.

THE CLOCK SHOP
161 Victoria Street, St Albans,
Hertfordshire AL1 3TA
TEL   0727 856633
OPEN   10.30 –6.30 Mon–Fri; 10.30–4
       Sat; closed Thur.

Specialise in restoring antique and
modern clocks, watches and barometers.

PROVIDE Free Estimates. Chargeable
Collection/Delivery Service.
SPEAK TO Mr P. E. Setterfield.

COUNTRY CLOCKS
3 Pendley Bridge Cottages, Tring
Station, Tring, **Hertfordshire HP23
5QU**
TEL   044282 5090
OPEN   By Appointment.

Specialise in restoring antique clocks,
including movements, dials and cases.
No watch repairs.

PROVIDE Home Inspections. Free
Estimates. Free Local
Collection/Delivery Service.
SPEAK TO Terence Cartmell.

W. B. GATWARD & SON LTD
20 Market Place, Hitchin,
Hertfordshire SG5 1DU
TEL   0462 434273
OPEN   9.15–5.15 Mon–Sat; closed
       Wed.

Specialise in repairing and restoring antique clocks and watches.

PROVIDE Local Home Inspections. Free Estimates. Chargeable Collection/Delivery Service.
Speak to Miss Gatward or Mr Hunter.
SEE Silver.

CHARLES PERRY RESTORATIONS LTD
Praewood Farm, Hemel Hempstead Road, St Albans, **Hertfordshire AL3 6AA**
TEL   0727 853487
FAX   0727 846668
OPEN   Mon–Fri 8.30–6; By Appointment Sat.

Specialise in restoring clocks.

PROVIDE Home Inspections. Free Estimates. Chargeable Collection/Delivery Service.
SPEAK TO John Carr.
Mr Carr is a member of BAFRA and the Guild of Master Craftsmen.
By Appointment to HM Queen Elizabeth II, Antique Furniture Restorers.
This workshop is included on the register of conservators maintained by the Conservation Unit of the Museums and Galleries Commission.
SEE Furniture, Books, Collectors (Ship Models, Toys)

HERITAGE RESTORATIONS
24 Castle Street, Berkhamsted, **Hertfordshire HP4 2DW**
TEL   0442 873819
OPEN   10–5 Daily.

Specialise in restoring clocks and watches.

PROVIDE Free Estimates. Home Inspections.
SPEAK TO John Wilshire.
SEE Furniture, Porcelain.

HOWARD ANTIQUE CLOCKS
33 Whitehorse Street, Baldock, **Hertfordshire SG7 6QF**
TEL   0462 892385
OPEN   9.30–5 Tues–Sat.

Specialise in restoring and repairing antique clocks.

PROVIDE Home Inspections. Free Estimates. Free Local Collection/Delivery Service.
SPEAK TO Mr D. Howard.
Mr Howard is CMBHI.

OLD ROPERY ANTIQUES
East Street, Kilham, Nr. Driffield, **North Humberside YO25 0ST**
TEL   026282 233
OPEN   9.30–5 Mon–Sat.

Specialise in restoring antique clocks.

PROVIDE Home Inspections. Chargeable Estimates. Free Collection/Delivery Service.
SPEAK TO John Butterfield.
SEE Collectors (Scientific Instruments), Furniture.

ROBIN FOWLER (PERIOD CLOCKS)
Washingdales, Washing Dale Lane, Aylesby, Grimsby, **South Humberside DN37 7LH**
TEL   0472 751335
OPEN   By Appointment.

Specialise in restoring antique clocks and barometers, also supply and restore all types of turret clocks.

PROVIDE Home Inspections. Free Estimates. Free Collection/Delivery Service.
SPEAK TO Robin Fowler.

Work guaranteed for five years in the case of spring–driven movements and ten years for weight–driven movements

A. & S. ALLEN
40 Clarendon Way, Chislehurst, **Kent BR7 6RF**
TEL   0689 826345
OPEN   9–5 Mon–Fri.

Specialise in restoring clock dials.

PROVIDE Free Estimates. Collection/Delivery Service by arrangement.
SPEAK TO Adrian Allen.
SEE Porcelain.

ANTIQUE RESTORATIONS
The Old Wheelwright's Shop, Brasted Forge, Brasted, Westerham, **Kent TN16 1JL**
TEL   0959 563863
FAX   0959 561262
OPEN   9–5 Mon–Fri; 10–1 Sat.

Specialise in restoring longcase and bracket clocks.

PROVIDE Refundable Estimates. Free Collection/Delivery Service.
SPEAK TO Raymond Konyn.
Member of BAFRA and the Antique and Fine Art Disasters Emergency Mobile Unit.
SEE Furniture, Lighting.

BENEDICT CLEGG
Rear of 20 Camden Road, Tunbridge Wells, **Kent TN1 2PT**
TEL   0392 548095
OPEN   8.30–5.30 Mon–Fri or By Appointment.

Specialise in restoring clock cases.

PROVIDE Home Inspections. Free Estimates. Chargeable Collection/Delivery Service.
SPEAK TO Benedict Clegg.
SEE Furniture.

KEITH DAVIS
14 Little Buckland Avenue, Maidstone, **Kent ME16 0BG**
TEL   0622 679034
OPEN   8.30–5.30 Mon–Fri.

Specialise in restoring antique clocks and barometers.

PROVIDE Home Inspections. Free Estimates. Free Local Collection/Delivery Service.
SPEAK TO Keith Davis.
Member of AHS and Freeman of the Clockmakers' Company. This workshop is included on the register of conservators maintained by the Conservation Unit of the Museums and Galleries Commission.

THE GALLERY
Clock Repairs, South Goodwin House, St Margaret's Bay, **Kent CT15 6DT**
TEL   0304 853287
FAX   0304 853488
OPEN   By Appointment.

Specialise in restoring antique clocks, watches, barometers and barographs. Clock and barometer case restoration, including lacquered and japanned cases to museum quality, re–silvering. Very fine replica clocks and barometers made to order.
PROVIDE Home Inspections. Free Estimates. Free Collection/Delivery Service.
SPEAK TO Anthony Gray.
Mr Gray is MBHI and a member of UKIC.

BRUCE LUCKHURST
Little Surrenden Workshops, Bethersden, **Kent TN26 3BG**
TEL   0233 829589
OPEN   9–5 Mon–Fri.

Specialise in clocks cases of all kinds.

PROVIDE Home Inspections. Chargeable Estimates. Chargeable Collection/Delivery Service.
SPEAK TO Bruce Luckhurst.
Member of BAFRA and UKIC. This workshop is included on the register maintained by the Conservation Unit of the Museums and Galleries Commission.
SEE Furniture, Musical Instruments.

GERRY WILBY
32 West Reach, Whitstable, **Kent CT5 1EG**
TEL 0227 274736
OPEN By Appointment.

Specialise in restoring longcase and painted clock dials.

PROVIDE Free Estimates.
SPEAK TO Gerry Wilby.
Member of UKIC. This workshop is included on the register of conservators maintained by the Conservation Unit of the Museums and Galleries Commission.

DROP DIAL ANTIQUES
Last Drop Village, Hospital Road, Bolton, **Lancashire**
TEL 0204 307186 workshop.
    0257 480995
OPEN 12–5 Daily.

Specialise in restoring antique clocks, including dials and movements, although casework is limited. Restoring mercury but not aneroid barometers.

PROVIDE Free Estimates.
SPEAK TO Mr or Mrs I. Roberts.

COLIN D. FISHER
61 High Street, Chapeltown, Turton, Bolton, **Lancashire BL7 OEW**
TEL 0204 853428
OPEN 9–5 Mon, Wed, Fri, Sat or By Appointment.

Specialise in restoring antique clocks, especially longcase and Vienna and

bracket clocks. Parts can be made to order and dials restored.

PROVIDE Home Inspections. Free Estimates. Collection/Delivery Service.
SPEAK TO C. D. Fisher.
Member of the British Watch and Clockmakers' Guild and the Antiquarian Horological Association. This workshop is included on the register of conservators maintained by the Conservation Unit of the Museums and Galleries Commission.

HARROP FOLD CLOCKS
Harrop Fold, Bolton–by–Bowland, Nr. Clitheroe, **Lancashire BB7 4PJ**
TEL 02007 665
OPEN By Appointment.

Specialises in restoring antique longcase clocks.

PROVIDE Home Inspections. Free Estimates. Free Collection/Delivery Service.
SPEAK TO Mr F. Robinson.

ERIC SMITH ANTIQUE RESTORATIONS
Park Road Church, Park Road, Darwen, **Lancashire BB3 2LD**
TEL 0254 776222
OPEN 9–6 Mon-Fri or By Appointment.

Specialise in restoring longcase clocks.

PROVIDE Home Inspections. Free Estimates. Chargeable Collection/Delivery Service.
SPEAK TO Eric Smith
Member of UKIC.
SEE Furniture.

N. BRYAN-PEACH ANTIQUES
28 Far Street, Wymeswold, Loughborough, **Leicestershire LE12 6TZ**
TEL 0509 880425
OPEN 9–6 Mon–Sat.

Specialise in restoring clocks and barometers, re–silvering, dial repair.

PROVIDE Home Inspections.
SPEAK TO Mr N. Bryan–Peach.

ELLIOTT NIXON
42 Lytton Road, Clarendon Park, Leicester, **Leicestershire LE2 1WL**
TEL   0533 703227
OPEN   9–6 Mon–Sat.

Specialise in a full restoration and conservation service for clocks and watches.

PROVIDE Home Inspections. Free Estimates. Free Local Collection/Delivery Service.
SPEAK TO Elliott Nixon BA.
Mr Nixon is FBHI and Regional Horological Conservator to the National Trust. This workshop is included on the register of conservators maintained by the Conservation Unit of the Museums and Galleries Commission.
SEE Collectors (Scientific Instruments).

E. CZAJKOWSKI & SON
96 Tor–O–Moor Road, Woodhall Spa, **Lincolnshire LN10 6SB**
TEL   0526 352895
OPEN   9–5 Mon–Fri.

Specialise in restoring clocks and barometers.

PROVIDE Home Inspections. Free Estimates. Free Local Collection/Delivery Service.
SPEAK TO Mr M. J. Czajkowski.
Member of COSIRA and UKIC, West Dean trained. This workshop is included on the register maintained by the Conservation Unit of the Museums and Galleries Commission.
SEE Furniture.

GRANTHAM CLOCKS
30 Lodge Way, Grantham, **Lincolnshire NG31 8DD**
TEL   0476 61784
OPEN   By Appointment.

Specialise in repairing and restoring all types of antique clocks.

PROVIDE Home Inspections. Free Estimates. Free Collection/Delivery Service.
SPEAK TO Roy Conder.
Member of BHI

O. COMITTI & SON LTD
656 Forest Road, **London E17 3ED**
TEL   081 509 0011
FAX   081 521 3320
OPEN   9–5 Mon–Fri.

Specialise in repairing and restoring mercury and aneroid barometers and clocks, including casework.
SPEAK TO Simon Barker.
Established 1850.

BOSWELL AND DAVIS
The Holywell Centre, 1 Phipp Street, **London EC2A 4PS**
TEL   071 739 5738
FAX   071 729 9882
OPEN   9–6 Mon–Fri.

Specialise in restoring longcase clocks.

PROVIDE Home Inspections. Free Estimates. Free Collection/Delivery Service
SPEAK TO David Boswell.
SEE Furniture.

NORTH LONDON CLOCK SHOP LTD
72 Highbury Park, **London N5 2XE**
TEL   071 226 1609
OPEN   9–6 Mon–Fri; 9–1 Sat.

Specialise in repairing and restoring all types of antique clocks and barometers.

PROVIDE Home Inspections. Free Estimates.
SPEAK TO Derek Tomlin.
Mr Tomlin is CMBHI.

**SPECIALIST ANTIQUARIAN HOROLOGISTS AND RESTORERS OF
FINE FURNITURE, ANTIQUES AND OBJETS D'ART**

RESTORATION WORKSHOPS,
4 GROVE END, GROVE HILL, SOUTH
WOODFORD, LONDON E18 2LE
081 530 5570

* High-quality antique clock repair and restoration. Also the old or not so old.

* Free estimates.

* Collection, delivery and setting up service free of charge.

* Full movement repair and restoration work undertaken. Case work, cabinet work, dial work, repairing and re-silvering, re-gilding, polishing and lacquering.

* Carriage clock repairs, enamel dial restoration, wheel and pinion cutting and replacement services. Clock-making to commissions and clocks (copy) made to order. Period lacquered clock cases and furniture restored to museum standard.

* Clock material, parts and spares made and supplied to order. Facsimile/copy of 18th Century tavern clocks made to order for interior designers/boardrooms/decorators. Work carried out on premises by qualified staff.

* Workshop open to inspection.

PAYMENT METHODS Cash, Cheque.

TRADE ASSOCIATIONS Craft Member of the British Horological Institute. This workshop is included on the register maintained by The Conservation unit of the Museums and Galleries Commission.

MOBILE TEL: **0860 487830**

PROP. C. D. BENT CMBHI,
CRAFT MEMBER OF THE
BRITISH HOROLOGICAL INSTITUTE

CLIFFORD J. TRACY
6–40 Durnford Street, **London N15 5NQ**
TEL   081 800 4773 or 4774
FAX   081 800 4351
OPEN   7.30–5 Mon–Thur; 7.30–4 Fri.

Specialise in restoring clock–cases and movements.

PROVIDE Home Inspections. Free Estimates. Free Collection/Delivery Service.
SPEAK TO Clifford Tracy.
Member of BAFRA and the UKIC. Will do minor repairs on site.
SEE Furniture.

W. PAIRPOINT & SONS LTD
10 Shacklewell Road, **London N16 7TA**
TEL   071 254 6362
FAX   071 254 7175
OPEN   8.30–5.30 Mon–Fri.

Specialise in regilding carriage clocks.

PROVIDE Free Estimates. Free Collection/Delivery Service in the London area.
SPEAK TO Eric Soulard.
SEE Silver.

B. C. METALCRAFTS
69 Tewkesbury Gardens, **London NW9 OQU**
TEL   081 204 2446
FAX   081 206 2871
OPEN   By Appointment.

Specialise in restoring and repairing French clocks and clock sets.
SPEAK TO F. Burnell or M. A. Burnell.
SEE Silver.

R. E. ROSE
731 Sidcup Rd, **London SE9 3SA**
TEL   081 859 4754
OPEN   8.30–5.30 Mon–Sat; closed Thur.

Specialise in restoring antique clocks and barometers.

PROVIDE Free Estimates.
SPEAK TO Ron Rose.
Mr Rose is FBHI.

NEWCOMBE & SON
89 Maple Rd, **London SE20 8UL**
TEL   081 778 0816
OPEN   7.15–5.30 Mon–Fri.

Specialise in repairing and restoring antique clocks and barometers, including silvering and gilding service, enamel and painted clock faces, brass and wood frets, clock hands in brass or steel.

PROVIDE Home Inspections. Free Estimates. Free Collection/Delivery Service.
SPEAK TO Mike Newcombe.

SOMLO ANTIQUES
7 Piccadilly Arcade, **London SW1Y 6NA**
TEL   071 499 6526
FAX   071 499 0603
OPEN   10–5.30 Mon–Fri.

Specialise in repairing vintage wrist–watches, antique pocket watches, technical and decorative enamel watches.

PROVIDE Home Inspections. Free/Chargeable Estimates.
SPEAK TO George Somlo.

BIG BEN CLOCKS
5 Broxholme House, New Kings Road, **London SW6 4AA**
TEL   071 736 1770
FAX   071 384 1957
OPEN   9–5 Mon–Fri.

Specialise in repairing and overhauling all types of antique clocks.

PROVIDE Home Inspections. Chargeable Collection/Delivery Service.
SPEAK TO Roger Lascelles.
SEE Silver.

AUBREY BROCKLEHURST
124 Cromwell Road, **London SW7 4ET**
TEL   071 373 0319
OPEN   9–1, 2–5.30 Mon–Fri; 10–1 Sat.

Specialise in restoring and repairing antique English and French clocks.

PROVIDE Home Inspections. Free Estimates. Chargeable Collection/Delivery Service.
SPEAK TO Aubrey Brocklehurst, Ms Gill or Mrs Leonard.
Mr Brocklehurst is a member of BADA and he and Ms Gill and Mrs Leonard are all FBHIs.
SEE Furniture.

THE CLOCK CLINIC LTD
85 Lower Richmond Road, **London SW15 1EU**
TEL   081 788 1407
FAX   081 780 2838
OPEN   9–6 Tues–Fri; 9–1 Sat.

Specialise in restoring antique clocks, barometers and barographs.

PROVIDE Chargeable Home Inspections. Free Estimates in shop.
Chargeable Collection/Delivery Service.
SPEAK TO Robert Pedler.
Mr Pedler is FBHI.

JOHN WALKER
64 South Molton Street, **London W1Y 1HH**
TEL   071 629 3487
OPEN   8.30–5.15 Mon–Fri.

Specialise in repairing and restoring antique and modern clocks and watches.

PROVIDE Home Inspections. Free Estimates. Chargeable Collection/Delivery Service
SPEAK TO John Walker or Steve Martin.
This family firm was established in 1830.
Mr Walker is FBHI.
SEE Silver.

WILLIAM MANSELL
24 Connaught Street, **London W2 2AF**
TEL   071 723 4154
OPEN   9–6 Mon–Fri and Sat a.m.

Specialise in repairing and restoring antique clocks, wrist–watches, pocket watches.

PROVIDE Home Inspections. Free Estimates. Free Collection/Delivery Service.
SPEAK TO Bill Salisbury.
This is a small, established business which dates back to 1864.
SEE Silver.

BADGER ANTIQUES
12 St Mary's Road, **London W5 5ES**
TEL   081 567 5601
OPEN   10–6 Mon–Sat.

Specialise in restoring clocks and pocket watches.

PROVIDE Home Inspections. Free Estimates. Free Collection/Delivery Service.
SPEAK TO Michael Allders.
SEE Furniture.

ROY BENNETT
22 Cuckoo Lane, **London W7 3EY**
TEL   081 840 6911
OPEN   By Appointment.

Specialise in restoring antique clocks and watches.

PROVIDE Free Estimates. Chargeable Collection/Delivery Service.
SPEAK TO Roy Bennett.
Member of BWCMG.

RODERICK ANTIQUE CLOCKS
23 Vicarage Gate, **London W8 4AA**
TEL   071 937 8517
FAX   071 937 8517
OPEN   10–5.15 Mon–Fri; 10–4 Sat, By Appointment.

Specialise in restoring antique clocks, including carriage, bracket, skeleton and decorative French, ormolu and longcase clocks.

PROVIDE Free Estimates.
SPEAK TO Roderick Mee.
Mr Mee is a member of LAPADA.

IGOR TOCIAPSKI
39 Ledbury Road, **London W11 2AA**
TEL　　071 229 8317
OPEN　　10–5 Tues–Fri.

Specialise in repairing antique clocks.

PROVIDE Home Inspections. Free Estimates. Chargeable Collection/Delivery Service.
SPEAK TO Igor Tociapski.

DAVID NEWELL
55 Shelton Street, **London WC2H 9HE**
TEL　　071 836 1000
FAX　　071 240 9764
OPEN　　10–6 Mon–Fri By Appointment.

Specialises in restoring antique clocks and watches, particularly French clocks. Barometers and barographs are also restored.

PROVIDE Free Estimates.
Mr Newell is FBHI.
SPEAK TO David Newell.
SEE Collectors (Mechanical Music)

J. G. TREVOR–OWEN
181–193 Oldham Rd, Rochdale, **Greater Manchester OL16 5QZ**
TEL　　0706 48138
OPEN　　1.30–7 Mon–Fri or By Appointment.

Specialise in restoring clocks.

PROVIDE Home Inspections, Refundable Estimates.
SPEAK TO J. G. Trevor–Owen.
SEE Oil Paintings, Collectors (Musical Instruments).

R. W. BAXTER
Joel House, 43 Hoghton Street, Southport, **Merseyside PR9 OPG**
TEL　　0704 537377
OPEN　　9–1, 2–5.30 Mon–Fri.

Specialise in restoring antique clocks, carriage, longcase, bracket, French. Brass dials resilvered and pocket watches and modern clocks and watches repaired.

PROVIDE Home Inspections. Free Estimates. Free Collection/Delivery Service.
SPEAK TO R. W. Baxter.
Mr Baxter is FBHI. This workshop is included on the register of conservators maintained by the Conservation Unit of the Museums and Galleries Commission.

THE CLOCK SHOP
7 The Quadrant, Hoylake, Wirral, **Merseyside L47 2AY**
TEL　　051 632 1888
OPEN　　9–5.30 Mon–Fri.

Specialise in restoring antique clocks.

PROVIDE Home Inspections. Free Estimates. Collection/Delivery Service by arrangement.
SPEAK TO Kevin Whay.
Mr Whay is MBHI and MBWCG.

BARNT GREEN ANTIQUES
93 Hewell Road, Barnt Green, Birmingham, **West Midlands B45 8NL**
TEL　　021 445 4942
OPEN　　9–5 30 Mon–Fri; 9–1 Sat.

Specialise in restoring and conserving longcase clocks, gilding.

PROVIDE Home Inspections. Free Estimates. Chargeable Collection/Delivery Service.
SPEAK TO Mr P. Slater.
Member of BAFRA.
SEE Furniture.

F. S. BUGGINS trading as FIELDHOUSE BROS.
40 Castlecroft Gardens, Wolverhampton, **West Midlands WV3 8LN**
TEL   0902 761148
OPEN   9–5 Mon–Sat; closed Thur.

Specialise in restoring antique longcase clocks.

PROVIDE Home Inspections. Free Estimates. Free Collection/Delivery Service.
SPEAK TO Mr Buggins.
Mr Buggins is a CMBHI. This workshop is included on the register of conservators maintained by the Conservation Unit of the Museums and Galleries Commission.

OSBORNES ANTIQUES
91 Chester Road, New Oscott, Sutton Coldfield, **West Midlands B73 5BA**
TEL   021 355 6667
FAX   021 355 0666
OPEN   9–1 Mon; 9–1, 2–5 Tues, Wed; 9–1, 2–5.30 Thur, Fri; 9.15–12 Sat.

Specialise in repairing and restoring antique barometers, scientific glass-blowers and manufacture of replacement barometer parts.

PROVIDE Free Estimates.
SPEAK TO Mrs Osborne. Member of BSSG.

'AS TIME GOES BY'
Buxton Hill, Buxton, Norwich, **Norfolk NR10 5JF**
TEL   0603 666508
FAX   0603 665508
OPEN   9.30–5 Mon–Fri; 10–4 Sat.

Specialise in restoring antique clocks. Also make fine walnut longcase clocks.

PROVIDE Home Inspections. Free Estimates. Free/Chargeable Collection/Delivery Service.

SPEAK TO Stephen or Catherine Phillips. Member of BHI.

DAVID BARTRAM FURNITURE
The Raveningham Centre, Castell Farm, Beccles Road, Raveningham, Nr. Norwich, **Norfolk NR14 6NU**
TEL   050 846 721
OPEN   10–5.30 Daily.

Specialise in comprehensive antique restoration service, including clock cases.

PROVIDE Home Inspections. Free Estimates. Collection/Delivery Service.
SPEAK TO David Bartram.
Mr Bartram is a member of BAFRA and UKIC. This workshop is included on the register of conservators maintained by the Conservation Unit of the Museums and Galleries Commission.
SEE Silver, Furniture.

A.F.DUDLEY trading as 'THE FURNITURE CLINIC'.
Wykeham Hall, Saham Toney, Thetford, **Norfolk IP25 7ES**
TEL   0953 883208
FAX   0953 885800
OPEN   By Appointment.

Specialise in restoring barometers and clocks.

PROVIDE Home Inspections. Free Estimates. Free Collection/Delivery Service.
SPEAK TO Mr A. Dudley.
Members of the Guild of Master Craftsmen and the Association of Master Upholsterers.
SEE Collectors (Dolls, Toys, Mechanical Music), Furniture.

HARRISONS OF NORWICH
4 Capitol House, Heigham Street, Norwich, **Norfolk NR2 4TE**
TEL   0603 767573
OPEN   9–1, 2–5.30 Mon–Fri.

Specialise in restoring antique clock dials of all descriptions.

PROVIDE Free Estimates.
SPEAK TO Mr Roger L. Moll.
CMBHI, MBWCMG. This workshop is included on the register of conservators maintained by the Conservation Unit of the Museum and Galleries Commission.

RICHARD J. McPHEE CABINETMAKER
20 Muspole Street, Norwich, **Norfolk NR3 1DJ**
TEL   0603 667701
OPEN   8–1, 2–6 Mon–Fri; 8–1 Sat.

Specialise in restoration of clock movements.

PROVIDE Home Inspections. Free/Chargeable Estimates. Chargeable Collection/Delivery Service.
SPEAK TO Richard McPhee.
Member of UKIC and the Guild of Master Craftsmen. This workshop is included on the register of conservators maintained by the Conservation Unit of the Museums and Galleries Commission.
SEE Furniture.

PARRISS
20 Station Road, Sheringham, **Norfolk NR26 8RE**
TEL   0263 822661
OPEN   9.30–1, 2.15–5 Mon–Fri.

Specialise in repairing antique clocks.

PROVIDE Home Inspections. Chargeable Estimates. Free/Chargeable Collection/Delivery Service.
SPEAK TO J. H. Parriss.

WICKENDEN CLOCKS
53 Gorse Rd, Thorpe St Andrew, Norwich, **Norfolk NR7 OAY**
TEL   0603 32179
OPEN   9–5 Daily.

Specialise in restoring clocks and barometers.

PROVIDE Home Inspections. Free Estimates. Free Local Collection/Delivery Service.
SPEAK TO Eric Wickenden.
SEE Collectors (Mechanical Music).

R. C. WOODHOUSE MBHI
(Antiquarian Horologist),
10 Westgate, Hunstanton, **Norfolk PE36 5AL**
TEL   0485 532903
OPEN   11–5 Wed, Fri, Sat or By Appointment.

Specialise in restoring longcase, bracket and other good clocks from a carriage clock to a church/stable clock. Barometers also undertaken and small locks repaired and keys made.

PROVIDE Home Inspections. Free Estimates. Collection/Delivery Service.
SPEAK TO R. C. Woodhouse
Member of the UKIC, BHI and BWCMG.

GOODACRE ENGRAVING LTD
Thrumpton Avenue (off Chatsworth Avenue), Meadow Lane, Long Eaton, Nottingham, **Nottinghamshire NG10 2GB**
TEL   0602 734387
FAX   0602 461193
OPEN   8.30–5 Mon–Thur; 8.30–1.30 Fri.

Specialise in restoration of antique dials and movements, including painted dials.

PROVIDE Free Estimates.
Can produce castings on a one–off basis

ALISTAIR FRAYLING–CORK
2 Mill Lane, Wallingford, **Oxfordshire OX10 ODH**
TEL   0491 826221
OPEN   10–6 Mon–Fri; By Appointment Sat.

Specialise in restoring clock–cases.
PROVIDE Home Inspections. Free
Estimates. Chargeable
Collection/Delivery Service.
SPEAK TO Alistair Frayling–Cork.
Member of BAFRA.
SEE Furniture, Collectors (Musical
Instruments).

GERALD MARSH ANTIQUE CLOCKS LTD

Jericho House, North Aston,
Oxfordshire OX6 4HX
TEL 0869 40087
OPEN 9.30–5 Mon–Sat.

Specialise in restoring antique English
and French clocks, watches and
barometers.
PROVIDE Home Inspections. Free
Estimates. Collection/Delivery Service.
SPEAK TO Gerald Marsh
Member of Worshipful Company of
Clockmakers, Fellow of British
Horological Institute, Member of
NAWCC (USA) and BADA.
SEE **Hampshire**.

PETER A. MEECHAM

The Malt House, Milton–Under–
Wychwood, **Oxfordshire OX7 6JT**
TEL 0993 830215
FAX 0993 830039
OPEN 8.30–5 Mon–Fri.

Specialise in restoring and repairing
antique clocks, including verge
reconversions and the making of
replacement parts in a traditional and
sympathetic manner.
PROVIDE Home Inspections. Free
Estimates. Free Collection/Delivery
Service.
SPEAK TO P. A. Meecham.
Mr Meecham is CMBHI.

COLIN PIPER RESTORATION

Highfield House, The Greens, Leafield,
Witney, **Oxfordshire OX8 5NP**
TEL 0993 87593
OPEN 8–6 Mon–Sat.

Specialise in restoring longcase and
other clock cases, barometers.
PROVIDE Home Inspections.
Free/Chargeable Estimates.
Free/Chargeable Collection/Delivery
Service.
SPEAK TO Colin Piper.
SEE Furniture.

WEAVES AND WAXES

53 Church Street, Bloxham, Banbury,
Oxfordshire OX15 4ET
TEL 0295 721535
FAX 0295 271867
OPEN 9–1, 2–5.30 Tues–Fri; 9–1,2–4
Sat.

Specialise in restoring clocks.

PROVIDE Home Inspections.
Free/Chargeable Estimates. Chargeable
Collection/Delivery Service.
SPEAK TO Laurie Grayer.
SEE Furniture.

WITNEY RESTORATIONS

Workshop: Unit 17, Hanborough
Business Park, Main Road, Long
Hanborough, **Oxfordshire OX7 2LH**
Accounts and Enquiries: 96–100 Corn
Street, Witney, **Oxfordshire OX8 7BU**
TEL 0993 703902 accounts and
enquiries
0993 883336 workshop
FAX 0993 779852
OPEN 9.30–5 Mon–Fri.

Specialise in restoring and conserving
fine antique clocks.

PROVIDE Home Inspections. Free
Estimates. Chargeable
Collection/Delivery Service.
SPEAK TO Mr A. Smith or Mr. R. Woollen.
SEE Furniture

RICHARD HIGGINS

The Old School, Longnor, Nr.
Shrewsbury, **Shropshire SY5 7PP**
TEL 0743 718162
OPEN 8–6 Mon–Fri.

Specialise in restoring bracket, longcase and carriage clocks, including specialist works to movements, dials and cases. Also restore barometers.

PROVIDE Home Inspections. Free/Chargeable Estimates. Collection/Delivery Service by arrangement. SPEAK TO Richard Higgins. Member of BAFRA and UKIC. This workshop is included on the register of conservators maintained by the Conservation Unit of the Museums and Galleries Commission. SEE Furniture, Collectors (Mechanical Music).

F. C. MANSER & SON LTD
53–54 Wyle Cop, Shrewsbury, **Shropshire SY1 1XJ**
TEL   0743 351120
FAX   0743 271047
OPEN   9–5.30 Mon, Tues, Wed, Fri; 9–10 Thur; 9–5 Sat.

Specialise in restoring clocks, barometers, Boulle work.

PROVIDE Home Inspections. Free Estimates. Chargeable Collection/Delivery Service. SPEAK TO Paul Manser. Member of LAPADA and the Guild of Master Craftsmen. SEE Porcelain, Silver

EDWARD VENN ANTIQUE RESTORATIONS
52 Long Street, Williton, Taunton, **Somerset TA4 4QU**
TEL   0984 32631
OPEN   8.30–5.30 Mon–Fri.

Specialise in restoring barometers and longcase clocks.

PROVIDE Chargeable Estimates. Chargeable Collection/Delivery Service. SPEAK TO Mr Venn. SEE Furniture

A. C. PRALL RESTORATIONS
Highfield Farm, Uttoxeter Road, Draycott, **Staffordshire ST11 9AE**
TEL   0782 399022
OPEN   9–7 Mon–Fri.

Specialise in restoring clocks, including longcase and mantel.

PROVIDE Free Estimates. Free/Chargeable Collection/Delivery Service. SPEAK TO Mr Prall. SEE Furniture

ANTIQUE CLOCKS BY SIMON CHARLES
The Limes, 72 Melford Road, Sudbury, **Suffolk CO10 6LT**
TEL   0787 375931
OPEN   10–6 Mon–Sat.

Specialise in restoring early English clocks, including movements and cases.

PROVIDE Home Inspections. Free Estimates. Chargeable Collection/Delivery Service. SPEAK TO Simon Charles. Member of BWCMG.

E. T. MANSON
8 Market Hill, Woodbridge, **Suffolk IP12 4LU**
TEL   0394 380235
OPEN   10–5 Thur and Sat or By Appointment.

Specialise in restoring antique clocks, including wheel and pinion cutting, remaking of missing parts, repeating work.

PROVIDE Home Inspections. Free Estimates. Free Collection/Delivery Service. SPEAK TO E. T. Manson.

PEPPERS PERIOD PIECES
23 Churchgate Street, Bury St Edmunds,
Suffolk IP33 1RG
TEL   0284 768786
OPEN   10–5 Mon–Sat.

Specialise in restoring clocks.

PROVIDE Home Inspections. Refundable
Estimates.
Free/Chargeable Collection/Delivery
Service.
SPEAK TO M. E. Pepper.
Their restorers are West Dean trained.
SEE Furniture.

A. E. BOOTH & SON
9 High Street, Ewell, Epsom, **Surrey**
KT17 1SG
TEL   081 393 5245
OPEN   9–5 Mon–Fri.

Specialise in restoration of clocks.

PROVIDE Home Inspections.
Free/Refundable Estimates. Free
Collection/Delivery Service.
SPEAK TO D. J. Booth.
Member of BAFRA.
SEE Furniture.

B. S. ANTIQUES
39 Bridge Road, East Molesey, **Surrey**
KT8 9ER
TEL   081 941 1812
OPEN   10–5 Mon–Sat; closed Wed.

Specialise in repairing and restoring
antique clocks and barometers.

PROVIDE Home Inspections. Free
Estimates. Collection/Delivery Service
by arrangement.
SPEAK TO Stephen Anderman.

THE CLOCK SHOP
64 Church Street, Weybridge, **Surrey**
KT13 8DL
TEL   0932 840407 and 855503
OPEN   9.45–5.45 Mon–Sat.

Specialise in restoring antique clocks
and barometers, including casework.

PROVIDE Home Inspections. Free
Estimates. Free Collection/Delivery
Service.
SPEAK TO Mr Forster.

ROGER A. DAVIS
19 Dorking Rd, Great Bookham, **Surrey**
KT23 4PU
TEL   0372 457655 and 453167
OPEN   9.30–5.30 Tues, Thur, Sat.

Specialise in restoring antique clocks.

PROVIDE Home Inspections. Free
Estimates. Free Collection/Delivery
Service.
SPEAK TO Roger Davis.
Mr Davis is MBHI and MBWCMG.

E. HOLLANDER LTD
The Dutch House, Horsham Road,
South Holmwood, Dorking,
Surrey RH5 4NF
TEL   0306 888921
OPEN   8–4.50 Mon–Fri; Sat By
   Appointment.

Specialise in restoring 17th–19th
century clocks and watches as well as
barometers.

PROVIDE Home Inspections. Free
Estimates. Collection/Delivery Service
by arrangement.
SPEAK TO David Pay.
BADA and MBHI.

HOROLOGICAL WORKSHOPS
204 Worplesdon Road, Guildford,
Surrey GU2 6UY
TEL   0483 576496
OPEN   8.30–5.30 Mon–Fri; 9–12.30
   Sat.

Specialise in repairing antique clocks,
watches and barometers and restoring
turret clocks.

PROVIDE Home Inspections, Free

Estimates. Chargeable
Collection/Delivery Service.
SPEAK TO Mr M. D. Tooke.
Member of BADA.

JOHN KENDALL
156 High St, Old Woking, **Surrey**
GU21 9JH
TEL   0483 771310
OPEN   9–5 Mon–Fri.

Specialise in restoration of clock cases.

PROVIDE Home Inspections. Free
Estimates. Chargeable
Collection/Delivery Service.
SPEAK TO John Kendall.
SEE Furniture.

RICHARD LAWMAN–WARWICK ANTIQUE RESTORATIONS
32 Beddington Lane, Croydon, **Surrey**
CR0 4TB
TEL   081 688 4511
OPEN   9–6 Tues–Sat.

Specialise in clock restoration.

PROVIDE Home Inspections. Free
Estimates. Free Collection/Delivery
Service.
SPEAK TO Richard Lawman.
Member of the Guild of Master
Craftsmen. This workshop is included
on the register of conservators
maintained by the Conservation Unit of
the Museums and Galleries Commission.
SEE Furniture.

MANOR ANTIQUES AND RESTORATIONS
2 New Shops, High Street, Old Woking,
Surrey GU22 9JW
TEL   0483 724666
         MOB 0860 851956
FAX   0483 750366
OPEN   10–5 Mon–Fri; 10–4.30 Sat.

Specialise in clock repairs.

PROVIDE Home Inspections. Free
Estimates. Collection/Delivery Service.

SPEAK TO Alan Wellstead.
Member of the Guild of Master
Craftsmen.
SEE Furniture, Picture Frames.

SURREY CLOCK CENTRE
3 Lower Street, Haslemere, **Surrey**
GU27 2NY
TEL   0428 651313
OPEN   9–5 Wed; 9–1 Sat.

Specialise in restoring antique clocks
and barometers.

PROVIDE Home Inspections. Free
Estimates. Chargeable
Collection/Delivery Service.
SPEAK TO C. Ingrams or S. Haw.

SHAUN VICKERS
Foxgloves, Clock Barn Lane, Busbridge,
Godalming, **Surrey GU8 4AZ**
TEL   0483 429964
FAX   0483 424360
OPEN   9–6 Mon–Fri.

Specialise in restoring clock cases.

PROVIDE Home Inspections. Free
Estimates. Free Local
Collection/Delivery Service.
SPEAK TO Shaun Vickers.
SEE Picture Frames, Furniture.

JUDITH WETHERALL
trading as **J.B. SYMES**
28 Silverlea Gardens, Horley, **Surrey**
RH6 9BB
TEL   0293 775024
OPEN   8.30–5.30 Daily By
         Appointment Only.

Specialise in restoring japanned and
lacquered clock–cases, Boulle and inlay.

PROVIDE Free Local Home Inspections.
Free Estimates. Chargeable
Collection/Delivery Service.
SPEAK TO Judith Wetherall.
Member of UKIC and IIC. This
workshop is included on the register of
conservators maintained by the

Conservation Unit of the Museums and Galleries Commission.
SEE Furniture, Picture Frames, Porcelain

JOHN COWDEROY ANTIQUES

42 South Street, Eastbourne, **East Sussex BN21 4XB**
TEL   0323 720058
FAX   0323 410163
OPEN   9.30–1, 2.30–5 Mon, Tues, Thur, Fri; 9.30–1 Wed, Sat.

Specialise in restoring antique English and French clocks.

PROVIDE Home Inspections. Free Estimates. Chargeable Collection/Delivery Service.
SPEAK TO David or Richard Cowderoy. Member of LAPADA.
SEE Collectors (Mechanical Music), Furniture.

EASTBOURNE CLOCKS

9 Victoria Drive, Eastbourne, **East Sussex BN20 8JR**
TEL   0323 642650
OPEN   8.30–12.30, 2–5 Mon–Fri; 8.30–12.30 Sat.

Specialise in restoring and repairing antique and good quality clocks. They will make clocks and movements to order.

PROVIDE Home Inspections. Free Estimates. Free Collection/Delivery Service.
SPEAK TO Philip Wardale. Mr Wardale is CMBHI.

SIMON HATCHWELL ANTIQUES

94 Gloucester Rd, Brighton, **East Sussex BN1 4AP**
TEL   0273 691164
FAX   0273 691164
OPEN   9–1.30, 2.30–5 Mon–Fri; Sat By Appointment.

Specialise in restoring barometers.

PROVIDE Home Inspections. Free Estimates. Free Local Collection/Delivery Service.
SPEAK TO Simon or Allan Hatchwell. Member of LAPADA.

T. P. BROOKS

Sycamores, School Lane, Lodsworth, Petworth, **West Sussex GU28 9DH**
TEL   07985 248
OPEN   9–6 Mon–Fri or By Appointment.

Specialise in restoring 17th to 19th century clocks and barometers.

PROVIDE Home Inspections. Free Estimates. Free Collection/Delivery Service.
SPEAK TO Mr T. P. Brooks. Member of BHI and UKIC. This workshop is included on the register of conservators maintained by the Conservation Unit of the Museums and Galleries Commission.
SEE Collectors (Mechanical Music)

GARNER & CO.

Stable Cottage, Steyning Road, Wiston, **West Sussex BN44 3DD**
TEL   0903 814565
OPEN   9–5.30 Mon–Fri By Appointment.

Specialise in restoring clocks and dials.

PROVIDE Home Inspections. Estimates.
SPEAK TO Sid Garner.
SEE Furniture, Porcelain, Silver.

WEST DEAN COLLEGE

West Dean, Chichester, **West Sussex PO18 00Z**
TEL   0243 63 301
FAX   0243 63 342
OPEN   9–5 Mon–Fri.

Specialise in training conservators and restorers in the field of antique clocks.

They will also undertake restoration work.

PROVIDE Local Home Inspections. Free Estimates.
SPEAK TO Peter Sarginson.
SEE Books, Furniture, Porcelain, Silver

T. P. ROONEY CLOCKMAKER AND RESTORER
191 Sunderland Road, Harton Village, South Shields, **Tyne & Wear NE34 6AQ**
TEL   091 456 2950
OPEN   By Appointment.

Specialise in restoring and repairing antique and quality clocks, except turret and carriage, and will hand-make traditional clocks to commission.

PROVIDE Home Inspections. Free Estimates. Free Collection/Delivery Service,
SPEAK TO T. P. Rooney.
Mr Rooney is Grad. BHU, BADA Dip. This workshop is included on the register of conservators maintained by the Conservation Unit of the Museums and Galleries Commission

W. MAHONEY CLOCK & WATCH RESTORATION
15 Meadow Road, Newbold–on–Avon, Nr. Rugby, **Warwickshire CV21 1ER**
TEL   0788 546985
OPEN   6–6 Mon–Sat.

Specialise in restoring clocks and watches, including movements, dials, cases, silvering dials, painted dials, recutting wheels, pinions.

PROVIDE Home Inspections. Chargeable Estimates. Chargeable Collection/Delivery Service.
SPEAK TO William Mahoney.

TIME IN HAND
11 Church Street, Shipston–on–Stour, **Warwickshire CV36 4AP**
TEL   0608 62578
OPEN   9–1, 2–5.30 Mon–Sat.

Specialise in restoring fine clocks, barometers and antique mechanisms.

PROVIDE Home Inspections. Free Estimates. Chargeable Collection/Delivery Service.
SPEAK TO Francis Bennett or Alyson Clossick

COSBY FINE CLOCKS RESTORER
The Park House, Tockenham Wick, Nr. Wootton Bassett, Swindon, **Wiltshire SN4 7PQ**
TEL   0793 848945
OPEN   9–6 Mon–Sat By Appointment Only.

Specialise in restoring fine quality antique clocks, longcase, bracket, French mantel and table clocks, carriage clocks etc. Also automata clocks. Specialists in proper restoration of mechanical tower and stable (turret) clocks.

PROVIDE Local Home Inspections. Free/Chargeable Estimates. Chargeable Collection/Delivery Service.
SPEAK TO Mr Julian C. S. F. Cosby. MBWCG, Associate Member of the BHI, Member of the Antiquarian Horological Society. This workshop is included on the register of conservators maintained by the Conservation Unit of the Museums and Galleries Commission.

RESTORATIONS UNLIMITED
Pinkney Park, Malmesbury, **Wiltshire SN16 0NX**
TEL   0666 840888
OPEN   8.30–5 Mon–Fri; By Appointment Sat & Sun.

Specialise in restoring longcase and bracket clocks.

PROVIDE Home Inspections. Free Estimates. Free Collection/Delivery Service.
SPEAK TO Richard Pinchis.
SEE Furniture, Porcelain.

TIME RESTORED & CO.
18–20 High Street, Pewsey, **Wiltshire SN9 5AQ**
TEL   0672 63544
FAX   0672 63544
OPEN   By Appointment.

Specialise in restoring antique English and French clocks and barometers.

PROVIDE Home Inspections. Free Estimates. Free Collection/Delivery Service.
SPEAK TO J. H. Bowler–Reed.
SEE Collectors (Mechanical Music).

CHRIS WADGE CLOCKS
142 Fisherton Street, Salisbury, **Wiltshire SP2 7QT**
TEL   0722 334467
OPEN   9–5 Tues–Sat.

Specialise in repairing most types of clocks, especially anniversary clocks 1880–1970. They also repair barometers, barographs and pocket watches.

PROVIDE Home Inspections. Free Estimates. Chargeable Collection/Delivery Service.
SPEAK TO Chris or Patrick Wadge.

HAWORTH ANTIQUES
Harrogate Road, Huby, Nr. Leeds, **North Yorkshire LS17 OEF** and 26 Cold Bath Road, Harrogate, **North Yorkshire HG2 ONA**
TEL   0423 734293
          0423 521401
OPEN   10–5 Tues–Sat or By Appointment.

Specialise in restoring clocks, including white and brass dial movements and casework.

PROVIDE Home Inspections. Free Estimates. Chargeable Collection/Delivery Service.
SPEAK TO Glynn or June White.
They are MBWCMG.

G. D. HOPPER
Clock Work, 27 Elm Road, Ripon, **North Yorkshire HG4 2PE**
TEL   0765 602606
OPEN   9–5 Mon–Fri or By Appointment.

Specialise in restoring all types of antique and modern clocks and watches. Also service time–lock mechanisms and other special timers.

PROVIDE Home Inspections. Free Estimates. Chargeable Collection/Delivery Service.
SPEAK TO David Hopper.
CMBHI. This workshop is included on the register of conservators maintained by the Conservation Unit of the Museums and Galleries Commission.

DAVID MASON & SON
7–9 Westmoreland Street, Harrogate, **North Yorkshire HG1 5AY**
TEL   0423 567305
OPEN   9–5 Mon–Sat.

Specialise in repair of clocks, watches and barometers.

PROVIDE Home Inspections. Free Estimates. Collection/Delivery Service.
SPEAK TO John Mason.
Member of NAG, Yorkshire Goldsmiths Association, FGA.
SEE Silver.

JOHN PEARSON ANTIQUE CLOCK RESTORATION
Church Cottage, Birstwith, Harrogate, **North Yorkshire HG3 2NG**
TEL   0423 770828
OPEN   By Appointment.

Specialise in dial restoration, complete clock restoration including movement, case and dial.

PROVIDE Home Inspections. Free Estimates. Collection/Delivery Service. SPEAK TO John Pearson.

DAVID BARKER

Antique Clock Restoration, Inglenook, Ferncliffe Drive, Utley, Keighley, **West Yorkshire BD20 6HN**
TEL   0535 606306
OPEN   Mon–Sat By Appointment.

Specialise in restoring antique clocks and barometers.

PROVIDE Home Inspections. Free Estimates. Free/Chargeable Collection/Delivery Service. SPEAK TO David Barker. SEE Collectors (Mechanical Music).

ROBERT E. BARFOOT

9 York Parade, Belfast, **Co. Antrim BT15 3QZ**
TEL   0232 773108
OPEN   By Appointment.

Specialise in restoring English bracket and longcase clocks and French Boulle clocks.

PROVIDE Home Inspections. Free Estimates. Free Collection/Delivery Service. SPEAK TO Robert Barfoot. Member of IPCRA and BHI.

HARRY GILMORE

75 Osborne Park, Belfast, **Co. Antrim BT9 6JQ**
TEL   0232 084 661580
OPEN   By Appointment.

Specialise in maintaining and restoring French, English, American etc. antique clocks, Longcase, wall, bracket and carriage clocks sympathetically treated.

PROVIDE Home Inspections. Refundable Estimates. Collection/Delivery Service by arrangement. SPEAK TO Harry Gilmore. Member of IPCRA, BCWMG and BHI.

T. M. TUKE

18 Main Street, Greyabbey, Newtownards, **Co. Down**
TEL   024774 416
FAX   024774 250
OPEN   11–5 Mon–Sat; closed Thur.

Specialise in repairing clocks.

PROVIDE Home Inspections. Free Estimates. Free Collection/Delivery Service. SPEAK TO Tom Tuke. Mr Tuke is MBHI. SEE Silver.

K. AND M. NESBITT

21 Tobermore Road, Magherafelt, **Co. Londonderry BT45 5HB**
TEL   0648 32713
FAX   0648 82713
OPEN   By Appointment.

Specialise in restoring antique clocks and watches.

PROVIDE Home Inspections. Free Estimates. Chargeable Collection/Delivery Service. SPEAK TO Mr K. Nesbitt.

DAVID HEATH

'Fontaine', Sarshill, Kilmore, **Co. Wexford**
TEL   053 29722
OPEN   By Appointment.

Specialise in restoring antique English and American longcase, bracket and carriage clocks.

PROVIDE Home Inspections. Free Estimates. Collection/Delivery Service by arrangement. SPEAK TO David Heath.

ST JAMES'S GALLERY LTD

Smith Street, St Peter Port, **Guernsey, Channel Islands**

TEL   0481 720070
OPEN   9–5 Mon–Fri; 9–1 Sat or By Appointment.

Specialise in clock repairs.

PROVIDE Home Inspections. Chargeable Estimates. Collection/Delivery Service by arrangement.
SPEAK TO Mrs Whittam.
SEE Furniture, Porcelain.

GRANT LEES

98 Gala Park, Galashiels, Selkirkshire, **Borders TD1 1EZ**

TEL   0896 3721
OPEN   9–6 Mon–Sat; closed Wed and Sat a.m.

Specialise in restoring antique clocks, barometers, vintage wrist–watches.

PROVIDE Home Inspections. Free Estimates. Chargeable Collection/Delivery Service.
SPEAK TO Grant Lees.
This workshop is in the Scottish Conservation Directory.
SEE Furniture, Collectors (Mechanical Music).

J. TUBBECKE

Antique Clocks, 11 Island Street, Galashiels, **Borders TD1 1NZ**

TEL   0896 58958
OPEN   10–5 Mon–Fri; 10–1.30 Sat; closed Wed.

Specialise in restoring antique clocks and watches, including gear cutting, dial painting, case restoration. Missing parts hand–made.

PROVIDE Home Inspections. Free Estimates. Free Collection/Delivery Service.

SPEAK TO J. Tubbecke or T. Treeby.
This workshop is in the Scottish Conservation Directory.
SEE Collectors (Mechanical Music).

ECONOMIC ELECTRO-PLATING CO. LTD

3 Johnston Terrace, Edinburgh, **Lothian EH1 2PW**

TEL   031 225 6587
FAX   031 220 2546
OPEN   9–5 Mon–Fri.

Specialise in restoring antique clock cases.

PROVIDE Local Home Inspections. Free Estimates. Free Local Collection/Delivery Service.
SPEAK TO A. P. Robertson.
SEE Silver.

HAMILTON AND INCHES

87 George Street, Edinburgh, **Lothian EH2 3EY**

TEL   031 225 4898
FAX   031 220 6994
OPEN   9–5 Mon–Fri; 9–12.30 Sat.

Specialise in repairing clocks and watches.

PROVIDE Home Inspections. Free Estimates. Chargeable Collection/Delivery Service.
SPEAK TO Malcolm Gillan.
Member of NAG.
SEE Silver.

SIMON LOWMAN

112 Gilmore Place, Edinburgh, **Lothian EH3 9PL**

TEL   031 229 2129
OPEN   9–6 Mon–Fri

Specialise in repairing and restoring 18th century English and French bracket and longcase clocks as well as carriage clocks.

PROVIDE Home Inspections. Free Estimates. Chargeable Collection/Delivery Service.

SPEAK TO Simon Lowman.
Mr Lowman is MBHI. This workshop is in the Scottish Conservation Directory.

WILIAM MITCHELL CLOCK REPAIRER

42 Dundas Street, Edinburgh, **Lothian EH3 6JN**

TEL　　031 556 8000
OPEN　　9–1, 2–5 Mon–Sat or By Appointment.

Specialise in restoring clocks, antique and modern mechanical but not quartz.

PROVIDE Home Inspections. Free Estimates. Chargeable Collection/Delivery Service.
SPEAK TO William Mitchell.
This workshop is in the Scottish Conservation Directory.

KENNETH CHAPELLE ANTIQUE CLOCK RESTORER

26 Otago Lane, Glasgow, **Strathclyde G12 8PB**.

TEL　　041 334 7766
OPEN　　By Appointment.

Specialise in restoring fine antique clocks.

PROVIDE Home Inspections. Free Estimates. Chargeable Collection/Delivery Service.

SPEAK TO Kenneth Chapelle.
Mr Chapelle is FBHI. This workshop is in the Scottish Conservation Directory

TIM BRAMELD

Howell's House, Grosmont, **Gwent NP7 8BP**

TEL　　0981 240 940
OPEN　　By Appointment.

Specialise in repairing and restoring antique clocks, particularly regulators.

PROVIDE Home Inspections. Free Estimates. Chargeable Collection/Delivery Service.
SPEAK TO Tim Brameld.

SNOWDONIA ANTIQUES

Station Road, Llanrwst, **Gwynedd LL26 QEP**

TEL　　0492 640789
OPEN　　9–5.30 Mon–Sat or By Appointment.

Specialise in restoring longcase clocks.

PROVIDE Home Inspections. Chargeable Estimates. Chargeable Collection/Delivery Service.
SPEAK TO Mr J. Collins.
SEE Furniture

SILVER, JEWELLERY, OBJECTS OF VERTU AND METALWORK

SILVER

DO

Clean with soft rags and soap and water
Keep silver in felt bags
Store in a dry environment
Avoid stacking in cupboards
Use a soft toothbrush for cast ornament
Beware of wetting any items containing other materials such as iron or steel

DON'T

Overclean hallmarks
Leave salt, mustard etc in condiments
Put away cutlery while still warm from washing
Put rubber bands round cutlery
Put plated items in the dishwasher
Use liquid polish on inlaid items such as tortoiseshell, wood etc
Clean with any abrasive

JEWELLERY

DO

Remember that pearls are very sensitive to abrasion and corrosion – always store and wrap them separately and polish gently with a soft cloth after wearing
Keep all fitted boxes which bear a maker's or retailer's name
Have bead necklaces regularly restrung with silk
Keep insurance valuations up to date and understand exactly what is covered and where: losses overseas are often not

DON'T

Do the gardening or any other manual task while wearing jewellery
Waste gin on cleaning jewellery: warm water and a little detergent are preferable, applied with a soft toothbrush
Clean anything except gemstones and gold or platinum yourself
Apply hairspray or scent while wearing jewellery, particularly pearls

ANNE FINNERTY
62 Gainsborough Road, Southcote,
Reading, **Berkshire RG3 3BZ**
TEL   0734 588274
OPEN   By Appointment.

Specialise in restoring antique
beadwork, pearl and bead re–threading.

PROVIDE Free Estimates. Postal
Collection/Delivery Service.
SPEAK TO Anne Finnerty.

HAMILTON HAVERS
58 Conisboro Avenue, Caversham
Heights, Reading, **Berkshire RG4 7JE**
TEL   0734 473379
OPEN   By Appointment.

Specialise in restoring Boulle,
marquetry, ivory, tortoiseshell, mother–
of–pearl, brass, lapis–lazuli and malachite
objets d'art.

PROVIDE Free/Chargeable Estimates.
SPEAK TO Hamilton Havers.
SEE Clocks, Furniture.

STYLES SILVER
12 Bridge Street, Hungerford,
Berkshire RG17 OEH
TEL   0488 683922
OPEN   9.30–5.30 Tues–Sat; closed
       school holidays.

Specialise in repairing and cleaning
English 18th–20th century silverware

PROVIDE Free Estimates.
SPEAK TO Derek Styles.

JOHN ARMISTEAD
Malham Cottage, Bellingdon, Nr.
Chesham, **Buckinghamshire
HP5 2UR**
TEL   0494 758209
OPEN   9–5 Mon–Fri.

Specialise in repairing metalwork,
including brass candlesticks, chandeliers,
fire irons, polishing, plating, casting.

PROVIDE Home Inspections, Free
Estimates. Collection/Delivery
Service by arrangement.
SPEAK TO John Armistead.
Member of the Guild of Master
Craftsmen and UKIC. This workshop is
included on the register of conservators
maintained by the Conservation Unit of
the Museums and Galleries Commission.
SEE Furniture.

BUCKIES JEWELLERS
31 Trinity Street, Cambridge,
Cambridgeshire CB2 1TB
TEL   0223 357910
OPEN   9.45–5 Tues–Sat.

Specialise in repairing and restoring
jewellery and silverware.

PROVIDE Home Inspections. Refundable
Estimates. Chargeable
Collection/Delivery Service.
SPEAK TO Peter R. Buckie.

IAN FALCON HAMMOND
50 Kings Road, Eaton Socon, St Neots,
Cambridgeshire PE19 3DB
TEL   0480 212794
OPEN   By Appointment.

Specialise in restoring Oriental and
European ivories, tortoiseshell, mother–
of–pearl, fans, meershaum pipes, snuff
boxes, Japanese shibyama and netsuke.

PROVIDE Home Inspections. Chargeable
Estimates. Chargeable
Collection/Delivery Service.
SPEAK TO Ian Hammond.

A. ALLEN ANTIQUE RESTORERS
Buxton Rd, Newtown, Newmills, Via
Stockport, **Cheshire SK12 3JS**
TEL   0663 745274
OPEN   8–5 Mon–Fri; 9–12 Sat.

Specialise in restoring Boulle work,
inlay, gilding and metalwork.

PROVIDE Home Inspections.
Free/Chargeable Estimates.
Collection/Delivery Service.
SPEAK TO Tony Allen.
SEE Clocks, Furniture, Picture Frames.

THE TEXTILE RESTORATION STUDIO
20 Hargreaves Road, Timperley,
Altrincham, **Cheshire WA15 7BB**
TEL   061 904 9944
FAX   061 903 9144
OPEN   9.30–5 Mon–Fri.

Specialise in cleaning, conserving and
repairing of antique fans.
They also undertake framing and
mounting for display.

PROVIDE Home Inspections. Free
Estimates. Collection/Delivery
Service by arrangement.
SPEAK TO Jacqueline Hyman.
Established 1982. Member of UKIC.
This workshop is included on the register
of conservators maintained by the
Conservation Unit of the Museums and
Galleries Commission.
SEE Carpets, Collectors (Dolls), Lighting

DOMINO RESTORATIONS
TEL   05394 45751
OPEN   By Appointment Only.

Specialise in restoring metalware,
jewellery and objets d'art.

PROVIDE Home Inspections.
Free/Chargeable Estimates.
Free/Chargeable Collection/Delivery
Service.
SPEAK TO Roy or June Hargreaves.
SEE Porcelain

D. J. JEWELLERY
166–168 Ashley Road, Parkstone, Poole,
Dorset BH14 9BY
TEL   0202 745148
OPEN   9.30–5 Mon–Sat.

Specialise in repairing antique jewellery.

PROVIDE Home Inspections. Free
Estimates. Chargeable
Collection/Delivery Service.
SPEAK TO Dennis O Sullivan.
SEE Clocks.

GEORGIAN GEMS
28 High Street, Swanage, **Dorset**
BH19 2NU
TEL   0929 424697
OPEN   9.30–1, 2.15–5 Daily; closed Sun
         summer; closed Mon p.m. and
         Thur winter.

Specialise in repairing antique jewellery.

PROVIDE Home Inspections. Free
Estimates. Chargeable
Collection/Delivery Service.
SPEAK TO Brian Barker.
Member of the Gemmological
Association and the National Association
of Goldsmiths.

HEIRLOOMS ANTIQUE JEWELLERS
21 South Street, Wareham, **Dorset**
BH20 4LR
TEL   0929 554207
OPEN   9–5 Mon–Sat, closed Wed.

Specialise in restoring and repairing
antique jewellery and silver, except
watches.

PROVIDE Free Estimates. Valuations.
SPEAK TO Michael or Gabrielle Young

MICHAEL MALLESON
Trent Smithy, Rigg Lane, Trent,
Sherborne, **Dorset DT9 4SS**
TEL   0935 850957
OPEN   9–5 Mon–Fri; By Appointment
         Sat.

Specialise in restoring historical
wrought and cast iron work, including
chandeliers, locks, firedogs, door
furniture.

PROVIDE Home Inspections. Chargeable
Estimates. Chargeable

Collection/Delivery Service.
SPEAK TO Michael Malleson.
Member of BABA.

MILLSIDE ANTIQUE RESTORATION
Parndon Mill, Parndon Mill Lane,
Harlow, **Essex CM20 2HP**
TEL   0279 428148
FAX   0279 415075
OPEN   10–5 Mon–Fri.

Specialise in cleaning and restoring
enamels, including snuff boxes and
cloisonné work as well as ivory
enamelling.

PROVIDE Home Inspections.
Free/Chargeable Estimates. Chargeable
Collection/Delivery Service.
SPEAK TO David Sparks or Angela
Wickliffe-Philp.
SEE Oil Paintings, Picture Frames,
Porcelain.

PETER SHORER
40 Devonshire Road, Ilford, **Essex
IG2 7EW**
TEL   081 590 8364
OPEN   By Appointment.

Specialise in refurbishment of jewellery
and small metalwork, trophies etc.
Reproduction of antiquities. own design
made up or designed to order.

PROVIDE Chargeable Home Inspections.
Free/Chargeable Estimates.
Chargeable Collection/Delivery Service.
SPEAK TO Peter or Michael Shorer.
This workshop is included on the register
of conservators maintained by the
Conservation Unit of the Museums and
Galleries Commission.

KEITH BAWDEN
Mews Workshop, Montpellier Retreat,
Cheltenham, **Gloucestershire
GL50 2XS**
TEL   0242 230320
OPEN   7–4.30 Mon–Fri.

Specialise in conserving and restoring all
aspects of metalwork.

PROVIDE Free Estimates. Home
Inspections. Local Collection/Delivery
Service.
SPEAK TO Keith Bawden.
SEE Clocks, Furniture, Oil Paintings,
Porcelain

ATELIER FINE ART CASTINGS LTD
Hulfords Lane, Nr. Hartley Wintney,
Hampshire RG27 8AG
TEL   0252 844388
OPEN   8.30–5 Mon–Fri.

Specialise in restoring bronze, brass,
copper and lead art work. Bronze casting
and restoration of most other metalwork
undertaken.

PROVIDE Home Inspections. Free
Estimates. Chargeable
Collection/Delivery Service.
SPEAK TO Valerie.
Work can be collected in London from
The Sladmore Gallery, 32
Bruton Place, London W1X 7AA.
TEL   071 499 0365.
SEE Porcelain.

DOUGLAS J. LINCOLN
Athgarvan House, Shawford,
Winchester, **Hampshire SO21 2AA**
TEL   0962 712662
OPEN   By Appointment.

Specialise in restoring silverware,
especially engraved and chased work.
They can also provide engraving services
for lettered plaques.

PROVIDE Local Home Inspections. Free
Estimates. Chargeable
Local Collection/Delivery Service.
SPEAK TO Douglas Lincoln.
Visiting Tutor at West Dean. This
workshop is included on the register of
conservators maintained by the
Conservation Unit of the Museums and
Galleries Commission.
SEE Furniture.

A. W. PORTER
High Street, Hartley Witney, Nr.
Basingstoke, **Hampshire RG27 8NY**
TEL   025 126 2676
FAX   025 126 2064
OPEN   9–5.30 Mon–Fri; 9.30–5 Sat.

Specialise in restoring jewellery and
silverware.

PROVIDE Home Inspections. Free
Estimates. Chargeable
Collection/Delivery Service.
SPEAK TO Mr Porter.
Established 1844.
SEE Clocks.

STANLEY THORNE
Hursley Antiques, Hursley, Nr.
Winchester, **Hampshire SO21 2JY**
TEL   0962 775488
OPEN   10–6 Mon–Sat.

Specialise in repairs and restoration to
brass, copper, spelter, bronze, pewter,
commissions taken, vases lamped, brass
or lead liners made, lanterns made to
pattern or sketch.

PROVIDE Local Home Inspections. Free
Estimates. Local Free
Colection/Delivery Service.
SPEAK TO Stanley Thorne.

W. B. GATWARD & SON LTD
20 Market Place, Hitchin,
Hertfordshire SG5 1DU
TEL   0462 434273
OPEN   9.15–5.15 Mon–Sat; closed
       Wed.

Specialise in repairing and restoring
antique jewellery and silver.

PROVIDE Local Home Inspections. Free
Estimates. Chargeable
Collection/Delivery Service.
Speak to Miss Gatward or Mr Hunter.
SEE Clocks.

WILLIAM H. STEVENS
8 Eton Avenue, East Barnet,
Hertfordshire EN4 8TU
TEL   081 449 7956
OPEN   9–5.30 Mon–Fri.

Specialise in restoring Japanese and
Chinese works of art, including enamels,
lacquer, ivory, horn, mother–of–pearl,
soapstone and jade. They also restore
Blue John.

PROVIDE Home Inspections. Free
Estimates. Free
Collection/Delivery Service.
SPEAK TO John, Robin or Daniel Stevens.
This is the fifth generation of a family
firm founded in 1836.
SEE Porcelain.

BEEBY & POWELL
2–6 Basement, Victoria Street,
Rochester, **Kent ME1 1XH**
TEL   0634 830764
OPEN   By Appointment.

Specialise in restoring antique silver and
gold objects.

PROVIDE Home Inspections. Free
Estimates. Free Collection/Delivery
Service.
SPEAK TO Jonathan Beeby or Jim Powell.
Member of the Guild of Master
Craftsmen.

HENWOOD DECORATIVE METAL STUDIOS
The Bayle, Folkestone, **Kent CT20 1SQ**
TEL   0303 250911 or 245730
FAX   0303 850224
OPEN   8.30–5 Mon–Fri.

Specialise in restoring any non–ferrous
metalwork; antiques, church altarware,
door furniture and domestic tableware.
They can undertake any service allied to
non–ferrous metals i.e. repairs,
replacement, re-polishing, electro-
plating, lacquering, engraving. Can also

manufacture to suit client's own requirements, either small run or one off.

PROVIDE Local Home Inspections. Free Estimates. Local Free Collection/Delivery Service.
SPEAK TO Mr P. J. Rose.
Member of UKIC, Federation of Master Craftsmen and National Church Craft Association.
SEE Porcelain.

SARGEANT RESTORATIONS
21 The Green, Westerham, **Kent TN16 1AX**
TEL   0959 62130
OPEN   8.30–5.30 Mon–Sat.

Specialise in restoring, cleaning and wiring metal chandeliers, candelabra and general light fittings.

PROVIDE Home Inspections. Free Estimates. Chargeable Collection/Delivery Service.
SPEAK TO Ann, David or Denys Sargeant.
SEE Porcelain

CHARLES HOWELL JEWELLER
2 Lord Street, Oldham, **Lancashire OL1 3EY**
TEL   061 624 1479
OPEN   9.15–5 Mon–Sat.

Specialise in restoring Victorian and Edwardian jewellery and silverware.

PROVIDE Free Estimates.
SPEAK TO Mr N. G. Howell.
Member of NAG.

BARRY M. WITMOND
42 Wragby Road, Bardney, **Lincolnshire LN3 5XL**
TEL   0526 398338
OPEN   By Appointment.

Specialise in restoring English and Continental silver plate.

PROVIDE Home Inspections. Free/Chargeable Estimates. Collection/Delivery Service Available.
SPEAK TO Barry Witmond

DAVID TURNER
4 Atlas Mews, Ramsgate Road, **London E8 2NA**
TEL   071 249 2379
OPEN   10–6 Mon–Fri.

Specialise in restoring metalwork and metal light fittings.

PROVIDE Home Inspections. Free Estimates. Free Collection/Delivery Service
SEE Furniture, Porcelain.

RUPERT HARRIS
Studio 5, 1 Fawe Street, **London E14 6PD**
TEL   071 987 6231 and 515 2020
FAX   071 987 7994
OPEN   9–6 Mon–Fri.

Specialise in conserving fine and decorative metalwork. Advice also given on display, storage, environmental control, security of outdoor sculpture, emergency and disaster planning and salvage.

PROVIDE Home Inspections. Chargeable Estimates. Chargeable Collection/Delivery Service.
SPEAK TO Rupert Harris.
Member of UKIC and IIC. This workshop is included on the register of conservators maintained by the Conservation Unit of the Museums and Galleries Commission.
SEE Porcelain.

EDWARD BARNARD & SONS LTD
54 Hatton Garden, **London EC1N 8HN**
TEL   071 405 5677
FAX   071 405 6604
OPEN   9–5 Mon–Fri.

Specialise in repairing and restoring antique and modern silver and gold ware.

PROVIDE Home Inspections. Free Estimates, Free Collection/Delivery Service in Central London.
SPEAK TO C. Ashenden or J. Padgett.

R. HOLT & CO. LTD
98 Hatton Garden, London EC1N 8NX
TEL   071 405 5286 or 0197
FAX   071 430 1279
OPEN   9.30–5.30 Mon–Fri.

Specialise in cutting and re–cutting gemstones and restoring and repairing gemset items and carvings.

PROVIDE Home Inspections. Free Estimates.
SPEAK TO R. Holt or M. R. Howard. Members of Guild of Master Craftsmen, British Jewellers Association and the Gemmological Association of Great Britain. Members of the London Diamond Bourse.

KEMPSON AND MAUGER
Studio 26, 63 Clerkenwell Road, London EC1M 5NP
TEL   071 251 0578
OPEN   By Appointment.

Specialise in restoring enamel on precious metals.

PROVIDE Free Estimates.
SPEAK TO Mr Hamilton.

RICHARD LAWTON LTD
33 Greville Street, London EC1 8TB
TEL   071 228 5139
OPEN   9–3 Mon–Fri By Appointment.

Specialise in restoring silver and silver plate. Replating, gilding, rebristling of hairbrushes, cigarette boxes relined, frames rebacked, cutlery rebladed, new handles on tea or coffee pots. Blue glass liners supplied.

PROVIDE Home Inspections. Free Estimates. Free Local/Collection Delivery Service. Chargeable Postal Service outside London.
SPEAK TO Richard Lawton.

C. J. VANDER LTD
Dunstan House, 14A St Cross Street, London EC1N 8XD
TEL   071 831 6741
FAX   071 831 9695
OPEN   9–5.30 Mon–Fri.

Specialise in repairing and restoring high quality antique and second–hand silver and Victorian electroplate.

PROVIDE Free Estimates.
SPEAK TO Mr R. F. H. Vander.
Established 1886.

PETER CHAPMAN ANTIQUES Incorporating CHAPMAN RESTORATIONS
10 Theberton Street, London N1 0QX
TEL   071 226 5565
FAX   081 348 4846
OPEN   9.30–6 Mon–Sat.

Specialise in repairing bronze and other metalwork and will convert objects into lamps.

PROVIDE Home Inspections. Refundable Estimates. Chargeable Collection/Delivery Service.
SPEAK TO Peter Chapman or Tony Holohan.
SEE Furniture, Oil Paintings, Picture Frames, Porcelain.

W. PAIRPOINT & SONS LTD
10 Shacklewell Road, London N16 7TA
TEL   071 254 6362
FAX   071 254 7175
OPEN   8.30–5.30 Mon–Fri.

Specialise in restoring Old Sheffield and EPNS plate.

PROVIDE Free Estimates, Free Local Collection/Delivery Service.
SPEAK TO Eric Soulard.
SEE Clocks.

WAKELY AND WHEELER LTD
10 Shacklewell Road, **London N16 7TA**
TEL   071 254 6362
FAX   071 254 7175
OPEN   8.30–9.30 Mon–Fri.

Specialise in restoring and repairing antique and other silverware.

PROVIDE Free Estimates.
SPEAK TO F. J. P. Legget.
They have been established for 200 years.

STAMFORD SILVER REPAIRS
The Workshop, Scope Antiques Emporium, 64–66 Willesden Lane. **London NW6 7SX**
TEL   071 328 5833
OPEN   10–6 Mon–Sat.

Specialise in repairing silver, including removing dents and engravings, replacing missing parts. They will also repair good quality brass and copper objects.

PROVIDE Free Estimates.
SPEAK TO Donald Stamford.

WELLINGTON GALLERY
1 St John's Wood High Street, **London NW8 7NG**
TEL   071 586 2620
OPEN   10–5.30 Mon–Sat.

Specialise in restoring silver and Sheffield plate.

PROVIDE Home Inspections. Free Estimates. Chargeable Collection/Delivery Service.
SPEAK TO Mrs Maureen Barclay or Mr K. J. Barclay.
Member of LAPADA.
SEE Porcelain, Oil Paintings, Furniture.

B. C. METALCRAFTS
69 Tewkesbury Gardens, **London NW9 0QU**
TEL   081 204 2446
FAX   081 206 2871
OPEN   By Appointment.

Specialise in restoring and repairing antique lighting decor and all types of conversion to electricity.

SPEAK TO F. Burnell or M. A. Burnell. They are Members of DLA.
SEE Clocks.

VERDIGRIS ART METALWORK RESTORERS
Arch 280 or 290, Crown Street, **London SE5 0UR**
TEL   071 703 8373
OPEN   9–5 Mon–Fri.

Specialise in restoring bronzes, chandeliers, door furniture, ormolu, pewter and spelter, monumental bronzes, including modern works.

PROVIDE Free Estimates.
SPEAK TO Gerard Bacon.

WILKINSON PLC
5 Catford Hill, **London SE6 4NU**
TEL   081 314 1080
FAX   081 690 1524
OPEN   9–5 Mon–Fri.

Specialise in restoring chandeliers.

PROVIDE Home Inspections. Free Estimates. Chargeable Collection/Delivery Service.
SPEAK TO Peter Prickett, Jane Milnes or David Wilkinson.
SEE Porcelain.

THE FAN MUSEUM
12 Crooms Hill, **London SE10 8ER**
TEL   081 858 7879 or 305 1441
OPEN   11–4.30 Tues–Fri; 12–4.30 Sat, Sun; closed Mon.

Specialise in conserving and restoring all types of fans.

PROVIDE Inspections at museum. Free Estimates. Delivery Service.

SPEAK TO Mrs Alexander.

RELCY ANTIQUES
9 Nelson Road, Greenwich, **London SE10 9JB**

TEL   081 858 2812
FAX   081 293 4135
OPEN   10–6 Mon–Sat.

Specialise in restoring antique metalwork, including copper, brass, silver and ormolu.

PROVIDE Home Inspections. Free/Chargeable Estimates. Collection/Delivery Service by arrangement.

SPEAK TO Robin Challis.

SEE Collectors (Scientific Instruments), Furniture, Oil Paintings.

CRAWLEY STUDIOS
39 Wood Vale, **London SE23 3DS**

TEL   081 299 4121
FAX   081 299 0756
OPEN   9–6.15 Mon–Fri.

Specialise in restoring Tôle and papier mâché objects.

PROVIDE Home Inspections. Free Estimates. Chargeable Collection/Delivery Service.

SPEAK TO Marie Louise Crawley. Member of BAFRA, UKIC and the Guild of Master Craftsmen.

SEE Furniture.

ELIZABETH HANLEY
35 Elizabeth Street, **London SW1W 9RP**

TEL   071 730 8480
FAX   071 259 9752
OPEN   9.30–5.30 Mon–Fri.

Specialise in restoring objects of vertu.

PROVIDE Home Inspections. Free Estimates. Chargeable Collection/Delivery Service.

SPEAK TO Elizabeth Hanley.

SEE Porcelain.

BOURBON–HANBY ANTIQUES
Chelsea Antiques Market, 245–253 Kings Road, **London SW3 5EL**

TEL   071 352 2106
OPEN   10–6 Mon–Sat.

Specialise in repairing antique jewellery.

PROVIDE Home Inspections. Free Estimates. Free Collection/Delivery Service.

SPEAK TO Mr Barrett.

CHRISTINE SCHELL
15 Cale Street, **London SW3 3QS**

TEL   071 352 5563
OPEN   10–5.30 Mon–Fri.

Specialise in restoring tortoiseshell, silver and pique work, refurbishing dressing–table sets and photograph frames.

PROVIDE Home Inspections. Free/Chargeable Estimates.

SPEAK TO Christine Schell.

JOHN HEAP
No.1 The Polygon, **London SW4 0JG**

TEL   071 627 4498
OPEN   By Appointment.

Specialise in restoring enamels, cane handles.

PROVIDE Home Inspections. Free Estimates. Free Collection/Delivery Service.

SPEAK TO John Heap.

SEE Furniture, Porcelain.

CHRISTOPHER WRAY'S LIGHTING EMPORIUM
600 Kings Road, **London SW6 2DX**

TEL   071 736 8434
FAX   071 731 3507
OPEN   9.30–6 Mon–Sat.

Specialise in restoring original Victorian and Edwardian light fittings.

PROVIDE Free Estimates. Chargeable Collection/Delivery Service.
SPEAK TO Curos Khawlari.
SEE Porcelain.

COLIN BOWLES LTD
Unit 15, Heliport Estate, Bridges Court, **London SW11 3RE**
TEL　071 738 2559
OPEN　9–4 Mon–Fri.

Specialise in restoring antiquities and works of art.

PROVIDE Home Inspections. Free Estimates. Free Collection/Delivery Service.
SPEAK TO Colin Bowles.

COMPTON HALL RESTORATION
Unit A, 133 Riverside Business Centre, Haldane Place, **London SW18 4UQ**
TEL　081 874 0762
OPEN　9–5 Mon–Fri.

Specialise in restoring Tôle, papier mâché and penwork.

PROVIDE Home Inspections. Free Estimates. Collection/Delivery Service by arrangement.
SPEAK TO Lucinda Compton, Jane or Henrietta Hohler.
Member of BAFRA and UKIC.
SEE Furniture.

PLOWDEN AND SMITH LTD
190 St Ann's Hill, **London SW18 2RT**
TEL　081 874 4005
FAX　081 874 7248
OPEN　9–5.30 Mon–Fri.

Specialise in restoring and conserving gold and silver.

PROVIDE Home Inspections. Free Estimates. Free/Chargeable Collection/Delivery Service.

SPEAK TO Bob Butler.
SEE Oil Paintings, Furniture, Porcelain, Display.

BLOOMFIELD CERAMIC RESTORATIONS LTD
43 Portland Place, **London W1N 3AG**
TEL　071 580 5761
FAX　071 636 1625
OPEN　By Appointment.

Specialise in restoring antique European and Oriental objets d'art.

PROVIDE Free Estimates.
SPEAK TO Steven P. Bloomfield.
SEE Porcelain.

A. & B. BLOOMSTEIN LTD
Bond Street Silver Galleries, 111–112 New Bond Street, **London W1Y OBQ**
TEL　071 493 6180
FAX　071 495 3493
OPEN　9–5 Mon–Fri.

Specialise in restoring antique silver, Victorian plate and old Sheffield plate.

PROVIDE Free Estimates. Free Collection/Delivery Service.
SPEAK TO Alfred Bloomstein.
Member of LAPADA and BADA.

BRUFORD & HEMING LTD
28 Conduit Street, London **W1R 9TA**
TEL　071 499 7644
FAX　071 493 5879
OPEN　9.30–5.30 Mon–Fri.

Specialise in restoring antique jewellery and antique domestic silver, especially flatware. They also specialise in matching up missing items of antique cutlery.

PROVIDE Home Inspections. Free Estimates. Free Collection/Delivery Service.
SPEAK TO Alan Kinsey.
Member of BADA and NAG, they have

traded from the same address since 1858.

HADLEIGH JEWELLERS

30A Marylebone High Street, **London W1M 3PP**

TEL   071 935 4074
OPEN   9.30–5.30 Mon–Fri; 9.30–5 Sat.

Specialise in repairing and restoring antique jewellery and stones.

PROVIDE Free Estimates.
SPEAK TO Mr J. Aldridge.

GEOFFREY HAGGAR

58 Davies Street, **London W1Y 1LB**

TEL   071 409 1418
OPEN   9.30–4 Daily.

Specialise in restoring all types of jewellery.

PROVIDE Home Inspections. Free Estimates. Free Collection/Delivery Service.
SPEAK TO Geoffrey Haggar.

HANCOCKS AND CO

1 Burlington Gardens, **London W1X 2HP**

TEL   071 493 8904
FAX   071 493 8905
OPEN   9.30–5.30 Mon–Fri; 10.30–4.30 Sat.

Specialise in repairing and restoring fine antique and period jewellery.

PROVIDE Home Inspections. Free Estimates. Chargeable Collection/Delivery Service.
SPEAK TO Stephen Burton, Duncan Semmens or Ian Morton.

HARVEY & GORE

4 Burlington Gardens, **London W1X 1LH**

TEL   071 493 2714
FAX   071 493 0324
OPEN   9.30–5 Mon–Fri.

Specialise in restoring fine antique and period jewellery, antique silver and old Sheffield plate.

PROVIDE Free/Chargeable Estimates.
SPEAK TO Brian Norman.
Member of BADA. Established 1720.

HENNELL OF BOND STREET LTD

12 New Bond Street, **London W1Y OHE**

TEL   071 629 6888
FAX   071 493 8158
OPEN   9.30–5.30 Tues–Sat.

Specialise in restoring modern and antique silver, old Sheffield plate.

PROVIDE Home Inspections. Free Estimates. Free Collection/Delivery Service.
SPEAK TO Stephen Condell.

W. SITCH & CO. LTD

48 Berwick Street, **London W1V 4JD**

TEL   071 437 3776
OPEN   8.30–5.30 Mon–Fri; 9–1 Sat.

Specialise in restoring late 19th century lighting.

PROVIDE Home Inspections. Free Estimates. Free/Chargeable Collection/Delivery Service.
SPEAK TO Ron Sitch.
SEE Porcelain.

JOHN WALKER

64 South Molton Street, **London W1Y 1HH**

TEL   071 629 3487
OPEN   8.30–5.15 Mon–Fri.

Specialise in repairing and restoring antique and modern jewellery.

PROVIDE Home Inspections. Free Estimates. Chargeable Collection/Delivery Service.
SPEAK TO John Walker or Steve Martin.
FBHI. Established 1830.
SEE Clocks.

H. J. HATFIELD & SON
42 St Michael's Street, **London W2 1QP**
TEL   071 723 8265
FAX   071 706 4562
OPEN   9–1 and 2–5 Mon–Fri.

Specialise in restoring metalwork and lacquer.

PROVIDE Home Inspections. Free Estimates.
SPEAK TO Philip Astley–Jones.
SEE Furniture.

WILLIAM MANSELL
24 Connaught Street, **London W2 2AF**
TEL   071 723 4154
OPEN   9–6 Mon–Fri; 10–1 Sat.

Specialise in repairing and restoring silverware and antique jewellery.

PROVIDE Home Inspections. Free Estimates. Free Collection/Delivery Service.
SPEAK TO Bill Salisbury.
Established 1864.
SEE Clocks.

S. LAMPARD & SON LTD
32 Notting Hill Gate, **London W11 3HX**
TEL   071 229 5457
OPEN   11–6 Mon, Tues, Thur, Fri.

Specialise in restoring antique jewellery and silver.

PROVIDE Home Inspections. Free Estimates.
SPEAK TO Mr J. R. Barnett.

ROSEMARY COOK RESTORATION
78 Stanlake Road, **London W12 7HJ**
TEL   081 749 7977
OPEN   By Appointment.

Specialise in restoring painted objects.

PROVIDE Home Inspections. Free Estimates. Free Local Collection/Delivery Service.
SPEAK TO Rosemary Cook.
SEE Furniture, Porcelain.

PHOEBE MASON
17 Russell Road, **London W14 8HU**
TEL   071 602 5694
OPEN   By Appointment Only.

Specialise in restoring objects in stone, plaster, resin, wood and plastics.

PROVIDE Home Inspections. Free/Chargeable Estimates. Free/Chargeable Collection/Delivery Service.
SPEAK TO Phoebe Mason.
SEE Furniture, Picture Frames.

S. J. SHRUBSOLE LTD
43 Museum Street, **London WC1A 1LY**
TEL   071 405 2712
OPEN   9–5.30 Mon–Fri.

Specialise in repairing antique silver and old Sheffield plate.

PROVIDE Free Estimates.
SPEAK TO Mr C. J. Shrubsole.
Member of the Antique Plate Committee, Goldsmith Hall.

HAMPTON UTILITIES (B'HAM) LTD
15 Pitsford Street, Hockley, Birmingham, **West Midlands B18 6LJ**
TEL   021 554 1766
OPEN   8–4 Mon–Fri.

Specialise in restoring and repairing antique and modern silver, including plating and gilding.

PROVIDE Free Estimates. Chargeable Collection/Delivery Service.
SPEAK TO C. Harrison.
SEE Furniture, Picture Frames.

CATHERINE MEADS

37 Cadbury Road, Moseley,
Birmingham, **West Midlands B13 9BH**
TEL 021 449 4840
OPEN 9–7 Mon–Fri.

Specialise in restoring domestic and ethnographic items, including North American, Indian and Aboriginal artefacts.

PROVIDE Home Inspections. Free Estimates. Free Local Collection/Delivery Service.
SPEAK TO Catherine Meads.
Member of UKIC. This workshop is included on the register of conservators maintained by the Conservation Unit of the Museums and Galleries Commission.
SEE Frames.

MAUREEN ANN ROBSON
Dip Cons. CSD (Design Management)

Studio, 29 Park Avenue, Hockley, Birmingham,
West Midlands B18 5ND
TEL 021 551 1937
OPEN By Appointment.

Specialise in restoring metals, papier mâché and inlaid mother-of-pearl, freshly excavated artefacts and ethnographic material.

PROVIDE Free Estimates. Chargeable Collection/Delivery Service.
SPEAK TO Consultant Conservator.
SEE Porcelain

DAVID BARTRAM FURNITURE

The Raveningham Centre, Castell Farm, Beccles Road, Raveningham,
Nr. Norwich, **Norfolk**
TEL 050 846 721
OPEN 10–5.30 Daily.

Specialise in comprehensive antique restoration, including metalwork.

PROVIDE Home Inspections. Free Estimates. Collection/Delivery Service.
SPEAK TO David Bartram.
SEE Clocks, Furniture.

PETER HOWKINS

135 King Street, Great Yarmouth,
Norfolk NR30 2PQ
TEL 0493 844639
OPEN 9–5.30 Mon–Sat or By Appointment.

Specialises in restoring antique jewellery and silver.

PROVIDE Home Inspections.
SPEAK TO Valerie Howkins or Thomas Burn.
Member of NAG.
SEE Furniture (different address).

PENNY LAWRENCE

Fairhurst Gallery, Bedford Street,
Norwich, **Norfolk NR2 1AS**
TEL 0603 632064
OPEN 9–5 Mon–Fri.

Specialise in restoring and conserving objets d'art.

PROVIDE Home Inspections. Free Estimates. Free/Chargeable Collection/Delivery Service.
SPEAK TO Penny Lawrence.
This workshop is included on the register of conservators maintained by the Conservation Unit of the Museums and Galleries Commission.
SEE Furniture, Oil Paintings, Picture Frames.

MARIANNE MORRISH

South Cottage Studio, Union Lane, Wortham Ling, Diss,
Norfolk IP22 ISP
TEL 0379 643831
OPEN 10–4 Mon–Fri.

Specialise in restoring objets d' art.

PROVIDE Home Inspections. Free Estimates. Chargeable

Collection/Delivery Service.
SPEAK TO Marianne Morrish.
Member of the Guild of Master
Craftsmen.
SEE Porcelain.

ARTISTRY AND METAL
Sherwood Forge, Oakset Drive,
Welbeck, Nr. Worksop,
Nottinghamshire S80 3LW
TEL   0909 486029
OPEN   8–5 Mon–Fri.

Specialise in interior iron and metalwork
repoussage and relevage, fine knives and
damascus, restoration and conservation
of architectural ironwork, etching.

PROVIDE Home Inspections. Refundable
Estimates. Chargeable
Collection/Delivery Service.
SPEAK TO F. J. M. Craddock.
Mr Craddock is a Master Bladesmith and
a Member of UKIC and BABA.

HOWARDS OF BURFORD
51 High Street, Burford, **Oxfordshire
OX18 4QA**
TEL   0993 823172
OPEN   9.30–5.30 Mon–Sat.

Specialise in repairing and restoring
antique and modern silver and jewellery.

PROVIDE Home Inspections. Free
Estimates. Free Collection/Delivery
Service.
SPEAK TO Robert Light

ROGER BOLTON–SMITH
Meadowside, Bushmoor, Nr. Craven
Arms, **Shropshire SY7 8DW**
TEL   0694 781233
OPEN   By Appointment.

Specialise in restoring Himalayan,
South–East Asian, Chinese and Buddhist

Art in wood, bronze, iron, fabric, ivory,
precious metal and stones.

PROVIDE Home Inspections. Chargeable
Estimates. Chargeable
Collection/Delivery Service.
SPEAK TO Roger Bolton-Smith.
Member of UKIC.

F. C. MANSER & SON LTD
53–54 Wyle Cop, Shrewsbury,
Shropshire SY1 1XJ
TEL   0743 351120
FAX   0743 271047
OPEN   9–5.30 Mon–Wed, Fri; 9–1
        Thur; 9–5 Sat.

Specialise in restoring light fittings and
silverware.

PROVIDE Home Inspections. Free
Estimates. Chargeable
Collection/Delivery Service.
SPEAK TO Paul Manser.
Member of LAPADA and Guild of
Master Craftsmen.
SEE Clocks, Porcelain

T. R. BAILEY
11 St Andrew's Road, Stogursey,
Bridgwater, **Somerset TA5 1TE**
TEL   0278 732887
OPEN   By Appointment.

Specialise in providing fine quality and
hardwood handles and accessories for
silverware.

PROVIDE Free Estimates.
Collection/Delivery Service by
arrangement.
SPEAK TO Tim Bailey.
SEE Furniture

ROGER & SYLVIA ALLAN
The Old Red Lion, Bedingfield, Eye,
Suffolk IP23 7LQ
TEL   0728 628 491
OPEN   By Appointment.

Specialise in restoring painted snuff–boxes and ceramics.

PROVIDE Home Inspections. Free Estimates.
SPEAK TO Roger Allan.
SEE Oil Paintings, Furniture.

BRIAN R. BROOKES
Brookes Forge Flempton, Flempton, Bury St Edmunds,
Suffolk IP28 6EN
TEL 0284 728473
OPEN 2.30–6 Mon–Fri.

Specialise in making and restoring chandeliers together with a wide variety of decorative ironwork. Brass castings are produced from clients' patterns; these can be patinated to match colour and tone of original. Details of patterns are accurately copied. Single items can be undertaken.

PROVIDE Home Inspections. Free Estimates. Free Collection/Delivery Service.
SPEAK TO Brian Brookes.
Member of IIC and UKIC. This workshop is included on the register of conservators maintained by the Conservation Unit of the Museums and Galleries Commission.

SUFFOLK BRASS
Thurston, Bury St. Edmunds, **Suffolk IP31 3SN**
TEL 0359 30888 and 0379 898670
OPEN 9–6 Mon–Fri; 9–12 Sat.

Specialise in casting brass by the hot wax or sand process from original brassware for furniture fittings. Also make hand–forged iron fittings.

PROVIDE Free Estimates. Free Collection/Delivery Service (same day).
SPEAK TO Mark Petts or Thane Meldrum.
SEE Lighting

CRY FOR THE MOON
31 High Street, Godalming, **Surrey GU7 1AU**
TEL 0483 426201
FAX 0483 860117
OPEN 9.30–5.30 Mon–Sat.

Specialise in restoring antique and fine jewellery and silver.

PROVIDE Free Estimates
SPEAK TO Mr Ackroyd or Mr Hibbert.

NORMAN FLYNN RESTORATIONS
37 Lind Road, Sutton, **Surrey SM1 4PP**
TEL 081 661 9505
OPEN 7.45–3.30 Mon–Fri.

Specialise in restoring antique and modern enamel.

PROVIDE Home Inspections. Free Estimates. Free Collection/Delivery Service each week to London.
SPEAK TO Norman Flynn.
SEE Porcelain.

S. L. HEZSELTINE AND CO. (SILVERSMITHS)
"Nice Things" House, Station Road, Gomshall **Surrey GU5 9NS**
TEL 081 642 6388
MOB 083 130 7080
FAX 081 642 6388
OPEN By Appointment only.

Specialise in restoring all forms of silver, gold and jewellery. Supply and fit new combs and mirrors to silver backs, renovate perfume sprays including new puffers, ink–stand liners, repair teapot handles and undertake hand engraving. They also give talks on silver.
Also supply blue glass liners and new mirrors.

PROVIDE Home Inspections. Free Estimates. Free Collection/Delivery Service.
SPEAK TO S. L. Hezseltine.
Mr Hezseltine is a Master Silversmith.

PRECISION PARTS COMPANY

Keystone House, Plaistow Road, Dunsfold, **Surrey GU8 4PF**
TEL   0483 200445
OPEN   By Appointment.

Specialise in restoring lanterns, chandeliers or other antique light fittings, design and manufacture of a wide range of metal parts asociated with the above.

PROVIDE Home Inspections. Free Estimates.
SPEAK TO Vincent Lee–Brown.
Member of UKIC and Fellow of RGS. This workshop is included on the register of conservators maintained by the Conservation Unit of the Museums and Galleries Commission.
SEE Furniture.

RICHARD QUINNELL LTD

Rowhurst Forge, Oxshott Road, Leatherhead, **Surrey KT22 OEN**
TEL   0372 375148
FAX   0372 386516
OPEN   9–5 Mon–Fri.

Specialise in restoring metal – wrought iron, cast iron, steel, stainless steel, copper, bronze, brass, aluminium, lead, spelter and occasionally precious metals.

PROVIDE Home Inspections. Chargeable Estimates. Chargeable Collection/Delivery Service.
SPEAK TO Richard Quinnell MBE. Founder Member British Artist Blacksmiths Association. This workshop is included on the register of conservators maintained by the Conservation Unit of the Museums and Galleries Commission.

R. SAUNDERS

71 Queens Road, Weybridge, **Surrey KT13 9UQ**
TEL   0932 842601
OPEN   9.15–5 Mon–Sat; closed Wed.

Specialise in restoring and cleaning English silver.

PROVIDE Home Inspections. Free Estimates. Free Collection/Delivery Service.
SPEAK TO J. B. Tonkinson.
SEE Furniture, Porcelain, Oil Paintings.

SIMPSON DAY RESTORATION

Studio 13, Acorn House, Cherry Orchard Road, Croydon, **Surrey CR0 6BA**
TEL   081 681 8339
OPEN   9.30–6 Mon–Fri.

Specialise in restoring Canton enamels.

PROVIDE Free Estimates.
SPEAK TO Sarah Simpson or Sarah Day.
SEE Porcelain.

DAVID CRAIG

Toll Cottage, Station Road, Durgates, Wadhurst, **East Sussex TN5 6RS**
TEL   0892 782188
OPEN   9–5.30 Mon–Fri.

Specialise in restoring enamels.

PROVIDE Free Estimates. Free Collection/Delivery Service in London area.
SPEAK TO David Sutcliffe.
SEE Porcelain.

RECOLLECTIONS (EST 1973)

1A Sydney Street, Brighton, **East Sussex BN1 4EN**
TEL   0273 681517
OPEN   10.30–5 Mon–Sat.

Specialise in polishing and repairing metalwork, including brass and copper, including Victorian table lamps and fire fenders.

SPEAK TO Bruce Bagley or Peter Tooley.

YELLOW LANTERN ANTIQUES LTD
34 & 34B Holland Road, Hove, **East Sussex BN3 1JL**
TEL   0273 771572
OPEN   9.30–1, 2.15–5.30 Mon–Fri; 9–1, 2.15–4.30 Sat.

Specialise in cleaning ormolu and bronze.
PROVIDE Home Inspections. Free Estimates. Free Collection/Delivery Service.
SPEAK TO Mr or Mrs B. R. Higgins. Member of LAPADA.
SEE Furniture.

GARNER & CO.
Stable Cottage, Steyning Road, Wiston, **West Sussex BN44 3DD**
TEL   0903 814565
OPEN   9–5.30 Mon–Fri By Appointment.

Specialise in repairing lead and brass objects as well as conserving and repairing metal chandeliers.
PROVIDE Home Inspections. Estimates.
SPEAK TO Sid Garner.
SEE Clocks, Furniture, Porcelain.

SUGG LIGHTING LIMITED
Sussex Manor Business Park, Gatwick Road, Crawley, **West Sussex RH10 2GD**
TEL   0293 540111
FAX   0293 540114
OPEN   By Appointment.

Specialise in restoring traditional gas and electric pendant lights.
PROVIDE Free Estimates.
SPEAK TO Sales Office.
SEE Lighting.

WEST DEAN COLLEGE
West Dean, Chichester, **West Sussex PO18 00Z**
TEL   0243 63 301
FAX   0243 63 342
OPEN   9–5 Mon–Fri.

Specialise in training conservators and restorers in the field of fine metalwork, which they will also restore.
PROVIDE Local Home Inspections. Free Estimates.
SPEAK TO Peter Sarginson.
SEE Books, Clocks, Furniture, Porcelain

DAVID MOULSON
The Gorralls, Cold Comfort Lane, Alcester, **Warwickshire B49 5PU**
TEL   0789 764092
OPEN   By Appointment.

Specialise in restoring antique pewter.
PROVIDE Home Inspections. Free Estimates. Chargeable Collection/Delivery Service.
SPEAK TO David Stephen Moulson. Member of UKIC. This workshop is included on the register of conservators maintained by the Conservation Unit of the Museums and Galleries Commission.

MARK THOMAS STEVENS
70 Saltisford, Warwick, **Warwickshire CV34 4TT**
TEL   0926 495542
OPEN   9–5.30 Mon–Fri.

Specialise in restoring silver, Old Sheffield Plate, EPNS.
Also make modern and reproduction silverware.

PROVIDE Free Estimates.
SPEAK TO Mark Stevens.
This workshop is included on the register of conservators maintained by the Conservation Unit of the Museums and Galleries Commission.

HECTOR COLE IRONWORK
The Mead, Great Somerford, Chippenham, **Wiltshire SN15 5JB**
TEL   0249 720485
OPEN   By Appointment – best to phone in the evenings

Specialise in restoring and renovating antique ironwork using wrought iron. Also make reproductions of medieval ironwork.

PROVIDE Free Estimates.
SPEAK TO Hector Cole.

SARUM METALCRAFT

31 Sarum Business Park, Portway, Salisbury, **Wiltshire SP4 6EA**
TEL   0722 411461
FAX   0722 411461
OPEN   9–4 Mon–Fri.

Specialise in repairing and making Tôle ware.

PROVIDE Home Inspections. Free/Chargeable Estimates. Free/Chargeable Collection/Delivery Service.
SPEAK TO Mr Francis Russell.

SHENSTONE RESTORATIONS

23 Lansdown Road, Swindon, **Wiltshire SN1 3NE**
TEL   0793 644980
OPEN   By Appointment.

Specialise in restoring smaller decorative items, including marquetry and inlay. They work in bone, mother–of–pearl, ebony and ivory and its substitutes as well as Boulle marquetry.

PROVIDE Local Home Inspections. Chargeable Estimates. Chargeable Collection/Delivery Service.
SPEAK TO Blair Shenstone.
SEE Furniture

PHOEBE CLEMENTS

19 Middlethorpe Drive, York, **North Yorkshire YO2 2NG**
TEL   0904 708279
OPEN   By Appointment.

Specialise in restoring metal items of silver, gold and copper, especially its alloys bronze and brass, pewter.

PROVIDE Home Inspections. Free/Chargeable Estimates. Free Collection/Delivery Service.
SPEAK TO Phoebe Clements.
This workshop is included on the register of conservators maintained by the Conservation Unit of the Museums and Galleries Commission.
SEE Furniture, Arms.

RON FIELD (METALWORK)

Rowhouse House, Wykeham, Scarborough, **North Yorkshire YO13 9QG**
TEL   0723 862640
OPEN   9–5.30 Mon–Fri or By Appointment.

Specialise in repairing and restoring antique and vintage metalwork of all types, including mechanical antiques and particularly items of interior decor.

PROVIDE Home Inspections. Free/Refundable Estimates. Free/Chargeable Collection/Delivery Service.
SPEAK TO Ron Field.
Member of the Guild of Master Craftsmen.

DUNCAN GRIMMOND

The Old Granary, Uppercourt Terrace, Ripon, **North Yorkshire HG4 1PD**
TEL   0765 600982
OPEN   10–4 Thur or By Appointment.

Specialise in restoring jewellery, silverware, ivory, tortoiseshell, mother-of-pearl, non-wood inlay and non-ferrous metalwork.

PROVIDE Home Inspections by arrangement. Chargeable Collection/Delivery Service.
SPEAK TO Duncan Grimmond.

DAVID MASON & SON
7–9 Westmoreland Street, Harrogate,
North Yorkshire H91 5AY
TEL   0423 567305
OPEN   9–5 Mon–Sat.

Specialise in repairing jewellery.

PROVIDE Home Inspections. Free
Estimates. Collection/Delivery
Service.
SPEAK TO John Mason.
Member of NAG, Yorkshire Goldsmiths
Association and FGA.
SEE Clocks.

NIDD HOUSE ANTIQUES
Nidd House, Bogs Lane, Harrogate,
North Yorkshire HG1 4DY
TEL   0423 884739
OPEN   9–5 Mon–Fri or By
    Appointment.

Specialise in restoring lead castings and
pewter work.

PROVIDE Home Inspections. Free Local
Estimates. Chargeable
Collection/Delivery service.
SPEAK TO Mr D. Preston.
Members of the Guild of Master
Craftsmen and UKIC. This workshop is
included on the register of conservators
maintained by the Conservation Unit of
the Museums and Galleries Commission.
SEE Porcelain, Furniture, Collectors
(Scientific Instruments)

G. P. S.
3 Woodseats Road, Sheffield, **South
Yorkshire S8 0PD**
TEL   0742 581777
FAX   0742 581777
OPEN   9–5 Mon–Fri.

Specialise in restoring silver, silverplate,
copper, brass, pewter, old Sheffield plate
etc.

PROVIDE Home Inspections. Free
Estimates. Free Collection/Delivery
Service.

SPEAK TO Mr C. Rattigan.
Member of UKIC. Mr. Rattigan is
Silversmith to the Chatsworth House
Estate.

GILLIAN SALMON
71 Park Grange Croft, Sheffield, **South
Yorkshire S2 3QJ**
TEL   0742 730451
OPEN   9–5.30 Mon–Sat.

Specialise in metal restoration, including
gold, silver, bronze, lead and alloys.
Repatriation and finishing.

PROVIDE Home Inspections. Free
Estimates. Free/Chargeable
Collection/Delivery Service.
SPEAK TO Gillian Salmon.
Member of UKIC.

T. M. TUKE
18 Main Street, Greyabbey,
Newtownards, **Co. Down**
TEL   024774 416 or 252
FAX   024774 250
OPEN   11–5 Mon–Sat; closed Thur.

Specialise in repairing silver.

PROVIDE Home Inspections. Free
Estimates. Free
Collection/Delivery Service.
SPEAK TO Tom Tuke.
Member of BHI.
SEE Clocks.

J. BYRNE & SONS
23 South Anne Street, Dublin 2, **Co.
Dublin**
TEL   01 6718709
OPEN   9–5.30 Mon–Sat.

Specialise in restoring, repairing and
reproducing jewellery.

PROVIDE Free Estimates.
SPEAK TO Jim or Richard Byrne.

DESMOND TAAFFE
51 Dawson Street, Dublin 2, **Co. Dublin**
TEL   01 6719609
OPEN   9–5.30 Mon–Fri.

Specialise in restoring antique and domestic silver and churchware.

PROVIDE Free Estimates.
SPEAK TO Desmond Taaffe.

OLD ST ANDREWS GALLERY
9 Albany Place, St Andrews, **Fife KY16 9HH**
and 10 Golf Place, St Andrews, **Fife KY16 9JA**
TEL   0334–7840 and 0334–78712
OPEN   10–5 Mon–Fri.

Specialise in repairing silver and jewellery.

PROVIDE Home Inspections. Free Estimates. Free Collection/Delivery Service.
SPEAK TO Mr or Mrs Brown.
SEE Sporting Equipment (Golf).

GALLERY
48A Union Street, Aberdeen, **Grampian AB2 1HS**
TEL   0224 625909
OPEN   9–5.30 Mon–Sat.

Specialise in repairing and restoring jewellery. They also make jewellery.

PROVIDE Home Inspections. Free Estimates.
SPEAK TO Michael Gray.

GILES PEARSON
Brightmony House, Auldern, **Highland IV12 5PP**
TEL   0667 55550
OPEN   9–6 Daily.

Specialise in cane handles for silver and silver–plated tea and coffee pots.

PROVIDE Home Inspections. Free Estimates. Collection/Delivery Service by arrangement.
SPEAK TO Giles Pearson.
This workshop is in the Scottish Conservation Directory.
SEE Furniture.

THURSO ANTIQUES
Drill Hall, 21 Sinclair Street, Thurso, **Highland**
TEL   0847 63291
FAX   0847 62824
OPEN   10–5 Mon–Fri; 10–1 Sat.

Specialise in cleaning and redesigning jewellery.

PROVIDE Free Estimates. Collection/Delivery Service by arrangement.
SPEAK TO G. Atkinson.
SEE Oil Paintings.

ECONOMIC ELECTRO–PLATING CO LTD
3 Johnston Terrace, Edinburgh, **Lothian EH1 2PW**
TEL   031 225 6587
FAX   031 220 2546
OPEN   9–5 Mon–Fri.

Specialise in restoring decorative metal finises, chandeliers, gold and silver plating, Georgian silver.

PROVIDE Local Home Inspections. Free Estimates. Free Local Collection/Delivery Service.
SPEAK TO A. P. Robertson.
SEE Clocks.

HAMILTON AND INCHES
87 George Street, Edinburgh, **Lothian EH2 3EY**
TEL   031 225 4898
FAX   031 220 6994
OPEN   9–5 Mon–Fri; 9–12.30 Sat.

Specialise in restoring gold and silver antique and modern jewelley and objects.

PROVIDE Home Inspections. Free Estimates. Collection/Delivery Service.
SPEAK TO Kevin Williams.
Member of NAG.
SEE Clocks.

HOUNDWOOD ANTIQUES RESTORATION
7 West Preston Street, Edinburgh, **Lothian EH8 9PX**
TEL   031 667 3253
OPEN   By Appointment.

Specialise in restoring objets d'art, including ormolu, bronze and pewter.

PROVIDE Home Inspections. Free Estimates. Chargeable Collection/Delivery Service.
SPEAK TO Mr A. Gourlay.
SEE Furniture, Porcelain.

CPR ANTIQUES AND SERVICES
96 Main Street, Barrhead, Glasgow, **Strathclyde G78 1SE**
TEL   041 881 5379
OPEN   10–1, 1.30–5 Mon–Sat; closed Tues.

Specialise in restoring brass, copper, spelter and pewter, chrome stripped, spare parts made for certain items.

PROVIDE Free Estimates.
SPEAK TO Mrs C. Porterfield.

WESTPORT GALLERY
3 Old Hawkhill, Dundee, **Tayside DD1 5EU**
TEL   0382 21751
OPEN   9–5 Mon–Fri.

Specialise in repairing jewellery.

PROVIDE Free Estimates. Chargeable Collection/Delivery Service.
SPEAK TO Neil Livingstone.
SEE Arms, Furniture, Oil Paintings, Picture Frames

CARPETS, TEXTILES AND COSTUME

DO

Roll up rather than fold textiles where possible
Store fine lace rolled in acid-free tissue paper
Ask any laundry how much they will charge for cleaning your Victorian damask linen
tablecloth – prices can range from two pounds to twenty-two pounds a cloth!
Remember that while plain household or damask linen is extremely tough and durable,
lace- or crochet-trimmed cloths need more careful handling
Place fine linen inside a large stocking or pair of tights before machine washing
Starch linen when washing it – tablecloths especially will stay cleaner and crisper longer
Wash fine lace, crochet and pina cloths in soap flakes or a very mild liquid soap

DON'T

Hang embroidered silk work, pictures, samplers or indeed any textile in direct sunlight
Despair when buying discoloured antique linen – plain or damask linen is very tough and can
withstand being washed at boiling point, or on the 90°C programme in the washing machine
Be put off using well-known high-street laundries for cleaning plain table and bed linen. They are
often considerably cheaper than the 'specialist' laundries
Forget old-fashioned 'blue' added to linen during a wash will help to achieve the snowy, crisp look

JENNIFER GILL
Context, 56 Colston Street, Bristol,
Avon BS1 5AZ
TEL 0272 276285
OPEN 10–7 Mon–Fri By Appointment.

Specialise in restoring all flat and three-dimensional textiles, especially 17th century crewel work bed curtains and stumpwork caskets with display covers, mirror surrounds and pictures. Samplers including their frames or new conservation framing, including UV glass, also frames dummies for costume display cases.

PROVIDE Home Inspections. Free Estimates. Free/Chargeable Collection/Delivery Service.
SPEAK TO Jennifer Gill.
Member of SPAB.

FIONA HUTTON & FRANCES LENNARD
Textile Conservation, Ivy House Farm, Banwell, **Avon BS24 6LB**
TEL 0934 822449
FAX 0934 823565
OPEN 9–5 Mon–Fri.

Specialise in restoring all types of textiles damaged by accident, poor storage or bad display conditions, including painted and printed textiles, woven tapestries, embroideries, upholstery and costume.

PROVIDE Home Inspections. Chargeable Estimates. Chargeable Collection/Delivery Service.
SPEAK TO Fiona Hutton or Frances Lennard. Members of UKIC. This workshop is included on the register of conservators maintained by the Conservation Unit of the Museums and Galleries Commission.

ANGELA BURGIN FURNISHING AND DESIGN LTD
6–8 Gordon Street, Luton,
Bedfordshire LU1 2QP
TEL 0582 22563
FAX 0582 30413
OPEN 8–5 Mon–Thur or By Appointment.

Specialise in offering a highly specialised conservation service on all periods of curtaining.

PROVIDE Home Inspections. Free Estimates. Free Collection/Delivery Service.
SPEAK TO Angela Burgin.
Ms Burgin is a Member of the Association of Master Upholsterers.
SEE Furniture

THE TEXTILE RESTORATION STUDIO
20 Hargreaves Road, Timperley, Altrincham, **Cheshire WA15 7BB**
TEL 061 904 9944
FAX 061 903 9144
OPEN 9.30–5 By Appointment.

Specialise in cleaning, conserving and repairing all types of antique textiles, including samplers, canvas and bead work, tapestry, white work, embroidery, costume and ecclesiastical furnishings and vestments, lace, flags and banners. Framing and for display undertaken. Advice given on safe storage.

PROVIDE Home Inspections. Free Estimates. Collection/Delivery Service by arrangement. Illustrated lectures and study days available by arrangement.
SPEAK TO Jacqueline or Michael Hyman. Established 1982. Member of UKIC. This workshop is included on the register of conservators maintained by the Conservation Unit of the Museums and Galleries Commission.
SEE Collectors (Dolls), Silver, Lighting

EVELINE HARTLEY
Orientis, Digby Road, Sherborne,
Dorset DT9 3NR
TEL   0935 816479 or 813274
OPEN   10.15–12.45, 2.30–4.30 Tues,
Thur, Fri, Sat or By
Appointment.

Specialise in restoring Oriental rugs
(excluding Chinese), textiles and
embroideries.

PROVIDE Home Inspections. Free
Estimates. Free Collection/Delivery
Service.
SPEAK TO Mrs Hartley.
Member of the Rug Restorers
Association.

MARK CRAWLEY
Manor House Farm, 3 East Green,
Heighington, **Durham DL5 6PP**
TEL   0325 313256
OPEN   By Appointment.

Specialise in restoring small leather
items, including clock cases, photo
frames etc.

PROVIDE Home Inspections. Free
Estimates. Chargeable
Collection/Delivery Service.
SPEAK TO Mark Crawley.
Member of the Society of Bookbinders.
SEE Books.

ALLYSON McDERMOTT (INTERNATIONAL CONSERVATION CONSULTANTS)
Lintz Green Conservation Centre, Lintz
Green House, Lintz Green, Rowlands
Gill, **Durham NE39 1NL**
TEL   0207 71547 or 0831 104145 or
0831 257584
FAX   0207 71547
OPEN   9–5.30 Mon–Fri.

Specialise in conservation of historic
hangings, painted textiles and screens.

PROVIDE Home Inspections. Free
Estimates. Chargeable
Collection/Delivery Service.
SPEAK TO Allyson Mc Dermott or Gillian
Lee. They have a Southern Regional
Office at 45 London   Road,
Cheltenham, **Gloucestershire**.
SEE Art Researchers, Oil Paintings,
Lighting, Picture Frames, Specialist
Photographers.

ANNABEL WYLIE
The Coach House, Thorrington Road,
Great Bentley, Colchester, **Essex
CO7 8QR**
TEL   0206 251518
OPEN   By Appointment.

Specialise in conserving all types of fine
historic textiles, including furnishing and
household textiles, embroidery, costume
and costume accessories, painted and
printed textiles, flags and banners.
Display services and condition surveys
can also be provided.

PROVIDE Home Inspections.
Free/Chargeable Estimates. Chargeable
Collection/Delivery Service.
Member of UKIC. This workshop is
included on the register of conservators
maintained by the Conservation Unit of
the Museums and Galleries Commission.
SPEAK TO Annabel Wylie.

COCOA
7 Queens Circus, Montpellier,
Cheltenham, **Gloucestershire
GL50 1RX**
TEL   0242 233588
OPEN   10–5 Mon–Sat.

Specialise in restoring antique lace,
wedding gowns, linens, antique veils.
SPEAK TO P. A. O'Sullivan.

THE LADIES' WORK SOCIETY LIMITED

Delabere House, New Road, Moreton–in–Marsh, **Gloucestershire GL56 OAS**
TEL   0608 50447
OPEN   10–1, 2–5 Mon–Fri; 10–1 Wed;
          10–1, 2–4 Sat.

Specialise in designing needlework for period furniture and conserving antique textiles.

PROVIDE Local Home Inspections. Refundable Estimates. Chargeable Collection/Delivery Service.
SPEAK TO Stanley Duller.

ERIC PRIDE ORIENTAL RUGS

44 Suffolk Road, Cheltenham, **Gloucestershire GL50 2AQ**
TEL   0242 580822
OPEN   10–5 Tues–Fri.

Specialise in cleaning and restoring old handwoven rugs, carpets, kilims and tapestries, both European and Oriental.

PROVIDE Free Estimates.
SPEAK TO Eric Pride.

ELIZABETH W. TAYLOR

Cirencester Workshops (Brewery Arts), 9A Brewery Court, Cirencester, **Gloucestershire GL7 1JH**
TEL   0285 641177
OPEN   9–5 Mon–Fri; By Appointment
          Sat.

Specialise in restoring Oriental rugs and carpets.

PROVIDE Free Estimates.
SPEAK TO Elizabeth Taylor.
Member of the Rug Restorers Association

WENDY YEOMANS

5 St. John's Road, Cove, Farnborough, **Hampshire GU13 8QP**
Workshop, 32 Minley Road, Cove, Farnborough, **Hampshire**
TEL   0252 512186
OPEN   9–5 Mon–Fri or By
          Appointment.

Specialise in restoring antique textiles, especially antique bed hangings, ornate canopies, embroideries and tapestries.

PROVIDE Home Inspections. Free Estimates. Chargeable Collection/Delivery Service.
SPEAK TO Wendy Yeomans.
Member of UKIC.

WENDY TOULSON

Bank Villa, Kingswood, Kington, **Hereford & Worcester HR5 3HG**
TEL   0544 231442
OPEN   By Appointment Only.

Specialise in conserving all fine historic textiles. Also carries out surveys of collections, advises on preventative conservation, storage and exhibition mounting.

PROVIDE Home Inspections. Free/Chargeable Estimates.
SPEAK TO Wendy Toulson.
Member of IIC, UKIC and the Museums Association. This workshop is included on the register of conservators maintained by the Conservation Unit of the Museums and Galleries Commission.

NICOLA WARREN

Willow House, 16 Bridge Street, Kington, **Hereford & Worcester HR5 3DL**
TEL   0544 230251
OPEN   By Appointment.

Specialise in restoring antique and Oriental rugs, kilims, sumachs, embroideries etc.

PROVIDE Chargeable Estimates.
SPEAK TO Nicola Warren
Member of the Rug Restorers
Association

JO BOOSEY
The Tun House, Whitwell, Hitchin,
Hertfordshire SG4 8AG
TEL   0438 871563
OPEN   By Appointment.

Specialise in restoring Oriental rugs.

PROVIDE Home Inspections by
arrangement. Free/Chargeable
Estimates. Free/Chargeable
Collection/Delivery Service.
SPEAK TO Jo Boosey.
Member of UKIC and Rug Restorers
Association.

HERTFORDSHIRE CONSERVATION SERVICE
Seed Warehouse, Maidenhead Yard, The
Wash, Hertford, **Hertfordshire
SG14 1PX**
TEL   0992 588966 or 504662
ANS   0992 588966
FAX   0992 503184
OPEN   9–6 Mon–Fri By Appointment.

Specialise in restoring leather, livery and
wall hangings.

PROVIDE Home Inspections.
Free/Chargeable Estimates. Chargeable
Collection/Delivery Service.
SPEAK TO J. M. Macqueen.
This workshop is included on the register
of conservators maintained by the
Conservation Unit of the Museums and
Galleries Commission.
SEE Collectors (Dolls), Lighting,
Furniture, Porcelain, Oil Paintings,
Picture Frames

DORE TEXTILE AND COSTUME CLEANING AND CONSERVATION
271 Sandown Road, Deal, **Kent
CT14 6QU**
TEL   0304 373684
OPEN   By Appointment

Specialise in the specialist cleaning,
conservation, display and storage of
textile and costume objects.

PROVIDE On–Site Inspections by
arrangement. Free/Chargeable
Estimates. Chargeable
Collection/Delivery Service.
SPEAK TO Judith or Bernard Dore.

DESMOND AND AMANDA NORTH
The Orchard, Hale Street, East Peckham,
Kent TM12 5JB
TEL   0622 871353
OPEN   By Appointment.

Specialise in cleaning and undertaking
some repairs to old Oriental rugs and
carpets.

PROVIDE Chargeable Home Inspections.
Chargeable Estimates.
SPEAK TO Desmond or Amanda North.

PERSIAN RUG SHOP
Vines Farm, Matthews Lane, West
Peckham, Maidstone, **Kent ME18 5JS**
TEL   0732 850228
OPEN   9–5.30 Daily By Appointment.

Specialise in cleaning and restoring
Oriental rugs and carpets.

PROVIDE Home Inspections. Chargeable
Estimates. Chargeable
Collection/Delivery Service.
SPEAK TO Rod King.

PEARCE RUGS & FRINGES

The Cottage, Hamilton Lane, Scraptoft, Leicester, **Leicestershire LE7 9SB**
TEL   0533 414941
OPEN   By Appointment.

Specialise in cleaning, repairing and renovating Oriental rugs. Can also re–weave, clean and repair other types of carpeting.

PROVIDE Home Inspections. Chargeable Estimates. Chargeable Collection/Delivery Service.
SPEAK TO Mr B. W. Pearce.
Also supply a mail order service for carpet fringes.

TATTERSALL'S

14 Orange Street and 2 Bear Yard, Orange Street, Uppingham, **Leicestershire LE15 9SQ**
TEL   0572 821171
OPEN   9.30–5 Tues–Sat; closed Mon & Thur.

Specialise in restoring antique and old Persian rugs.

PROVIDE Home Inspections. Free Estimates. Chargeable Collection/Delivery Service.
SPEAK TO Janice Tattersall.
SEE Furniture.

DUNCAN WATTS ORIENTAL RUGS

36 Edinburgh Close, Market Harborough, **Leicestershire LE16 7QQ**
TEL   0858 462620
OPEN   9–5 Mon–Sat; closed Wed.

Specialise in restoring Oriental rugs.

PROVIDE Home Inspections. Free Estimates. Free Collection/Delivery Service.
SPEAK TO Duncan Watts.

WENDY A. CUSHING LTD

410 Greenheath Business Centre, 31 Three Colts Lane, **London E2 6JB**
TEL   071 739 5909
FAX   071 729 5130
OPEN   9–5.30 Mon–Fri.

Specialise in restoring trimmings for furnishings.

PROVIDE Home Inspections. Free Estimates.
SPEAK TO Wendy Cushing.

POPPY SINGER

213 Brooke Road, **London E5 8AB**
TEL   081 806 3742
OPEN   By Appointment.

Specialise in conserving all types of fine historic textile, including furnishing and household textiles, embroidery, costume and costume accessories, painted and printed trextiles, flags and banners. Display services and condition surveys can also be provided.

PROVIDE Home Inspections. Free/Chargeable Estimates. Chargeable Collection/Delivery Service.
SPEAK TO Poppy Singer.
Member of UKIC. This workshop is included on the register of conservators maintained by the Conservation Unit of the Museums and Galleries Commission.

R. D. ROBINS UPHOLSTERY LTD

50A Bignold Road, **London E7 0EX**
TEL   081 503 1153
FAX   081 503 1153
OPEN   7.30–5 Mon–Fri.

Specialise in restoring and cleaning needlework.

PROVIDE Home Inspections. Free Estimates. Chargeable Collection/Delivery Service.
SPEAK TO Mr B. S. Ansell.

Member of Association of Master
Upholsterers.
SEE **London SW19**
SEE Furniture.

of conservators maintained by the
Conservation Unit of the Museums and
Galleries Commission.
SEE **London W4**

BEHAR PROFEX LTD
The Alban Building, St Albans Place,
Upper Street, **London N1 0NX**
TEL   071 226 0144
OPEN   8–6 Mon–Thur; 8–5 Fri.

Specialise in cleaning, conserving and
restoring Oriental and European hand–
made carpets, rugs, textiles and
tapestries.

PROVIDE Home Inspections. Free
Estimates within M25 area.
Collection/Delivery Service.
SPEAK TO Robert Behar.
This family firm has been established for
over seventy years and is a member of
the UKIC. This workshop is included on
the register of conservators maintained
by the Conservation Unit of the
Museums and Galleries Commission.

CAMU AND GOLDBERG TEXTILE CONSERVATION
36 Woodland Gardens, **London
N10 3UA**
TEL   081 883 0300
OPEN   9–6 Mon–Fri or By
        Appointment.

Specialise in restoring historic and
antique textiles, including tapestries,
furnishing textiles, curtains, rugs and
carpets, embroideries, canvas work,
banners, painted textiles, samplers,
wedding veils, costume. They have
purpose–built facilities for the safe
cleaning of large and small textiles. Most
of the work is based on hand–sewing of
objects on to appropriate support fabrics
after cleaning.

PROVIDE Home Inspections.
Free/Refundable Estimates. Local
Collection/Delivery Service.
SPEAK TO Naomi Goldberg.
This workshop is included on the register

DAVID J. WILKINS ORIENTAL RUGS
27 Princess Road, **London NW1 8JR**
TEL   071 722 7608
OPEN   9.15–5 Mon–Fri.

Specialise in all types of repairs and
cleaning of Oriental rugs.

PROVIDE Home Inspections. Free
Estimates. Chargeable
Collection/Delivery Service.
SPEAK TO David or Alice Wilkins.

JANIE LIGHTFOOT
24 Cholmondeley Avenue, **London
NW10 5XN**
TEL   081 961 5469 or 081 963 1532
FAX   089 961 6020
OPEN   9–5 Mon–Fri.

Specialise in restoring tapestry, Oriental
rugs and textiles, shoes, embroideries,
costume, flags, banners, needlepoint,
Aubusson, ecclesiastical and church
pieces etc.

PROVIDE Free/Chargeable Estimates.
Free/Chargeable Collection/Delivery
Service.
SPEAK TO Janie Lightfoot.

MAYORCAS LTD
38 Jermyn Street, **London SW1Y 6DN**
TEL   071 629 4195
OPEN   9.30–5.30 Mon–Fri; 10–1 Sat.

Specialise in cleaning and repairing
antique textiles, tapestry, needlework,
silks, damasks, carpets and rugs.

PROVIDE Discretionary Home
Inspections. Collection/Delivery
Service.
SPEAK TO Andrew Morley Stephens.
Member of BADA.

WATTS & CO
7 Tufton Street, **London SW1P 3QE**
TEL   071 233 0424
FAX   071 233 1130
OPEN   9–5 Mon–Fri.

Specialise in restoring church embroidery and reproducing antique textiles. Special commissions undertaken.
PROVIDE Free Estimates. Chargeable Collection/Delivery Service.
SPEAK TO Shelagh Scott.

CHELSEA ORIENTAL CARPETS
Chenil Galleries, 181–183 Kings Road, **London SW3 5EB**
TEL   071 351 6611
OPEN   10–6 Mon–Sat.

Specialise in restoring antique Persian, Russian and Turkish carpets.
PROVIDE Home Inspections. Free/Chargeable Estimates.
SPEAK TO N. Sonmez.

HAROUT BARIN
57A New Kings Road, **London SW6 4SE**
TEL   071 731 0546
FAX   071 384 1620
OPEN   9.30–6 Mon–Sat.

Specialise in cleaning and restoring Oriental carpets, European tapestries, Aubussons and needlepoints.
PROVIDE Home Inspections. Free Estimates. Free Collection/Delivery Service.
SPEAK TO Harout Barin.

LUNN ANTIQUES LTD
86 New Kings Road, **London SW6 4LU**
TEL   071 736 4638
FAX   071 371 7113
OPEN   10–6 Mon–Sat.

Specialise in restoring antique linen and lace.
PROVIDE Home Inspections. Free Estimates. Chargeable Collection/Delivery Service.
SPEAK TO Mr or Mrs Lunn.

MARTIN CLARKE ANTIQUE CARPET RESTORATION
Unit S6, 245A Coldharbour Lane, **London SW9 8RR**
TEL   071 924 0452
OPEN   9–6 Mon–Sat.

Specialise in restoring Oriental rugs and carpets, including Aubussons and European tapestries. Cleaning and conservation service, including custom spinning and natural dyeing.
PROVIDE Home Inspections. Free Estimates. Free Local Collection/Delivery Service.
SPEAK TO Martin Clarke or Miranda Dutta–Scholler.

THE KILIM WAREHOUSE LTD
28A Pickets Street, **London SW12 8QB**
TEL   081 675 3122
FAX   081 675 8494
OPEN   10–6 Mon–Fri; 10–4 Sat.

Specialise in cleaning and restoring kilims and flatweaves.
PROVIDE Chargeable Estimates.
SPEAK TO Jose Luczyc-Wyhowska.

R. D. ROBINS UPHOLSTERY LTD
1–9 Tennyson Road, **London SW19 8SH**
TEL   081 540 0711
FAX   081 503 1153
OPEN   7.30–5 Mon–Fri.

Specialise in restoring and cleaning needlework.
PROVIDE Home Inspections. Free

Estimates. Chargeable
Collection/Delivery Service.
SPEAK TO Mr B. S. Ansell.
Member of Association of Master
Upholsterers.
SEE **London E7**
SEE Furniture.

RAYMOND BENARDOUT
18 Grosvenor Street, **London W1X
9FD**
TEL   071 355 4531
FAX   071 491 9710
OPEN   9–5.30 Mon–Fri.

Specialise in cleaning and restoring
carpets, rugs, tapestries and needlework,
including Aubussons.

PROVIDE Home Inspections.
Free/Chargeable Estimates. Chargeable
Collection/Delivery Service.
SPEAK TO Raymond Benardout.

MARIA DE BOTELLO
48 New Cavendish Street, **London
W1M 7LE**
TEL   071 935 1360
OPEN   By Appointment Only.

Specialise in restoring most tapestries
and textiles from 1400 to 1900, largely
17th and 18th century.

PROVIDE Local Home Inspections.
Chargeable Estimates.
SPEAK TO Maria de Botello.
Member of UKIC.

ESSIE CARPETS
62 Piccadilly, **London W1V 9HL**
TEL   071 493 7766
FAX   071 495 3456
OPEN   9.30–6.30 Sun–Fri; closed Sat.

Specialise in restoring Persian carpets
and Oriental rugs.

PROVIDE Home Inspections. Chargeable
Collection/Delivery Service.

KENNEDY CARPETS
9A Vigo Street, **London W1X 1AL**
TEL   071 439 8873
FAX   071 437 1201
OPEN   9.30–6 Mon–Sat.

Specialise in restoring decorative
European and Oriental carpets 1850–
1920 and fine 19th century Indian
carpets and rugs.

PROVIDE Free Estimates.
SPEAK TO Mr M. Kennedy.

SHAIKH & SON (ORIENTAL RUGS) LTD
16 Brook Street, **London W1Y 1AA**
TEL   071 629 3430
OPEN   10.30–6.30 Mon–Sat.

Specialise in repairing and cleaning
Oriental rugs.

PROVIDE Home Inspections. Free
Estimates. Free Collection/Delivery
Service.
SPEAK TO Mr A. Shaikh.

FRANSES CONSERVATION
11 Spring Street, **London W2 3RA**
TEL   071 262 1153
FAX   071 706 1892
OPEN   9–5 Mon–Fri.

Specialise in cleaning, conserving and
restoring fine carpets, needlework and
tapestries, including Aubussons and
Savonneries.

PROVIDE Home Inspections by
arrangement. Free Estimates.
Chargeable Collection/Delivery Service.
SPEAK TO Spencer Franses.

CAMU AND GOLDBERG TEXTILE CONSERVATION
37 Alexandra Road, **London W4 1AX**
TEL   081 995 9539
OPEN   9–6 Mon–Fri or By
          Appointment.

Specialise in restoring historic and antique textiles, including tapestries, furnishing textiles, curtains, rugs and carpets, embroideries, canvas work, banners, painted textiles, samplers, wedding veils, costume. They have purpose–built facilities for the safe cleaning of large and small textiles. Most of the work is based on hand–sewing of objects on to appropriate support fabrics after cleaning.

PROVIDE Home Inspections. Free/Refundable Estimates. Local Collection/Delivery Service.
SPEAK TO Melanie Camu.
This workshop is included on the register of conservators maintained by the Conservation Unit of the Museums and Galleries Commission.
SEE **London N10**

FRANCOISE BROUGH
Maida Vale, **London W9**
TEL   071 289 8708
OPEN   10–6 Mon–Fri By Appointment.

Specialise in restoring fine rugs, carpets and kelims.

PROVIDE Home Inspections. Free Estimates. Collection/Delivery Service by arrangement.
SPEAK TO Francoise Brough.
Member of the Textile Society.

JACK FAIRMAN (CARPETS) LTD
218 Westbourne Grove, **London W11 2RH**
TEL   071 229 2262
FAX   071 229 2263
OPEN   10–6 Mon–Fri; 10–1 Sat.

Specialise in cleaning and repairing Oriental carpets, rugs and tapestries.

PROVIDE Home Inspections. Free Verbal Estimates. Free Collection/Delivery Service.
SPEAK TO Serina Page.

KASIA & ELA TEXTILE RESTORATION STUDIO
Unit 11, Kolbe House, 63 Jeddo Road, **London W12 9EE**
TEL   081 740 4977
OPEN   8–5 Mon–Fri.

Specialise in restoring flatweaves, including tapestries, Aubussons, needlework and kilims.

PROVIDE Home Inspections. Free Estimates. Free Collection/Delivery Service within London.
SPEAK TO Kasia Kolendarska or Ela Sosnowska.
Member of Rug Restorers Association

DANIELLE BOSWORTH
24 Ambleside Gardens, Wembley, **Middlesex HA9 8TL**
TEL   081 904 6121
OPEN   9.30–6.30 Mon–Fri.

Specialise in restoring textiles, including tapestries, embroideries, upholstrered textiles, banners.

PROVIDE Home Inspections. Free/Chargeable Estimates. Collection/Delivery Service by arrangement.
SPEAK TO D. Bosworth or L. Bosworth.
Member of UKIC and Fellow of IIC.

JENNY SARGINSON
38 Milton Road, Hampton, **Middlesex TW12 2LJ**
TEL   081 941 4791
OPEN   By Appointment.

Specialise in restoring textiles, including tapestries, rugs, carpets, furnishing textiles, embroideries, costume.

PROVIDE Home Inspections. Free Estimates. Chargeable Collection/Delivery Service.
SPEAK TO Jenny Sarginson.
Member of UKIC.

THE NATIONAL TRUST TEXTILE CONSERVATION WORKROOM

Blickling Hall, Blickling, Norwich,
Norfolk NR11 6NF
TEL   0263 733 471
FAX   0263 734 924
OPEN   9–5.30 Mon–Fri.

Specialise in conserving textiles, including costume and large woven tapestries. Will also survey collections.

PROVIDE Home Inspections. Chargeable Estimates.
SPEAK TO Ksynia Marko.
This is the first time their conservation services are being offered to non–Trust clients.

HARLEQUIN THUNDERSTRAND

Tasburgh Hall, Low Road, Lower
Tasburgh, Norwich, **Norfolk
NR15 1LT**
TEL   0508 471 575
FAX   0508 471 403
OPEN   9–5 Mon–Fri By Appointment.

Specialise in restoring and specialist cleaning of hand–woven rugs and carpets, including Persian, Turkish, North African, Chinese and English.

PROVIDE Home Inspections. Free Estimates. Chargeable Collection/Delivery Service.
SPEAK TO Walter Brew.
Member of Rug Restorers Association

CHRISTOPHER CALNAN

57 Park Avenue South, Northampton,
Northamptonshire NN3 3AB
TEL   0604 36496
FAX   0604 26337
OPEN   By Appointment.

Specialise in the conservation of historical leather objects with an emphasis on gilt and decorative leather.

PROVIDE Home Inspections.
Free/Chargeable Estimates. Chargeable Collection/Delivery Service.
SPEAK TO Christopher Calnan.

THE LEATHER CONSERVATION CENTRE

34 Guildhall Road, Northampton,
Northamptonshire NN1 1EW
TEL   0604 232723
FAX   0604 602070
OPEN   9–6 Mon–Fri.

Specialise in conservation of all types of leather, including costume.

PROVIDE Home Inspections. Chargeable Estimates. Chargeable Collection/Delivery Service.
SPEAK TO Christopher Calnan.
SEE Lighting, Furniture

MISS LYNDALL BOND

Textile Conservation Services, 3–4 West
Workshops, Tan Gallop,
Nottinghamshire S80 3LW
TEL   0909 481655
OPEN   By Appointment.

Specialise in conserving costume, embroideries, lace, banners, tapestry. On–site work.

PROVIDE Chargeable on–site inspections. Chargeable Estimates.
Chargeable Collection/Delivery Service.
SPEAK TO Lyndall Bond.

CHRISTOPHER LEGGE ORIENTAL CARPETS

25 Oakthorpe Road, Summertown,
Oxford, **Oxfordshire OX2 7BD**
TEL   0865 57572
FAX   0865 54877
OPEN   9.30–5 Mon–Sat.

Specialise in cleaning, conserving, restoring and re-weaving old and antique tribal rugs and carpets.

PROVIDE Home Inspections by arrangement. Free Estimates.
SPEAK TO Christopher or Ann Marie Legge.
Also provide courses on rugs and their repair and conservation.
Member of Rug Restorers Association

THE ANTIQUE RESTORATION STUDIO

The Old Post Office, Haughton, **Staffordshire ST18 9JH**

TEL   0785 780424
FAX   0785 780157
OPEN   9–5 Mon–Fri.

Specialise in restoring antique and modern textiles.

PROVIDE Home Inspections. Free Estimates. Free Collection/Delivery Service.
SPEAK TO D. P. Albright.
SEE Furniture, Porcelain, Oil Paintings.

THE CREATIVE COMPANY

Newport House, Newport Road, Stafford, **Staffordshire ST16 1DA**

TEL   0785 53744
FAX   0785 53744
OPEN   9–5 Sun–Sat By Appointment.

Specialise in restoring domestic, ecclesiastical and ceremonial embroidery and costume to enable future use. Do not conserve.

PROVIDE Home Inspections. Chargeable Estimates. Chargeable Collection/Delivery Service.
SPEAK TO Jane Dew.
Member of UKIC abd the Costume and Textile Society

LIZ FLINTOFF

27A Kings Road, Richmond, **Surrey TW10 6EX**

TEL   081 940 7856
OPEN   By Appointment.

Specialise in restoring textiles and speciality tapestries.

PROVIDE Home Inspections. Free Estimates.
SPEAK TO Liz Flintoff.
Member of UKIC.

CLARE GILCHRIST

37 West Street, Dorking, **Surrey RH4 1BU**

TEL   0306 876370 or 0483 35790
FAX   0483 202983
OPEN   10–5 Mon–Sat; closed Wed.

Specialise in restoring antique and semi–antique Oriental carpets and rugs.

PROVIDE Home Inspections. Free Estimates. Free Collection/Delivery Service.
SPEAK TO Adam M. R. Gilchrist or Clare Gilchrist.

THE ROYAL SCHOOL OF NEEDLEWORK

Apartment 12A, Hampton Court Palace, East Molesey, **Surrey KT8 9AU**

TEL   081 943 1432
FAX   081 943 4910
OPEN   9.30–4 Mon–Fri.

Specialise in restoring and conserving antique textiles, including large hand–woven tapestries, needlework rugs, samplers and stump work.

PROVIDE Chargeable Home Inspections. Free Estimates at the School. Chargeable Collection/Delivery Service.
SPEAK TO Mrs Elizabeth Elvin.

TEXTILE CONSERVATION CENTRE

Apartment 22, Hampton Court Palace, East Molesey, **Surrey KT8 9AU**

TEL   081 977 4943
FAX   081 977 9081
OPEN   9–5 Mon Fri.

Specialise in conserving early, historic and modern textiles.

Also train textile conservators.

PROVIDE Chargeable Consultative Visits. Free Estimates at the Centre.
SPEAK TO Nell Hoare, Director.

KAREL WEIJAND
Lion & Lamb Courtyard, Farnham, **Surrey GU9 7LL**
TEL   0252 726215
OPEN   9.30–5.30 Mon–Sat or By Appointment.

Specialise in full restoration, repair and cleaning service for antique Oriental rugs, hand–made carpets and textiles.

PROVIDE Home Inspections. Free Estimates. Chargeable Collection/Delivery Service.
SPEAK TO Karel Weijand.
Member of LAPADA.

DENNIS WOODMAN ORIENTAL CARPETS
105 North Road, Kew, **Surrey TW9 4HJ**
TEL   081 878 8182
OPEN   10–6 Mon–Sat; 10–2 Sun.

Specialise in restoring rugs and flat weaves.

PROVIDE Local Home Inspections. Free Estimates.
SPEAK TO Dennis Woodman.
Member of the Rug Restorers Association.

KATHARINE BARKER
St John's House Museum, St John's, Warwick, **Warwickshire CV34 4NF**
TEL   0926 412732
OPEN   9–5 Mon–Fri By Appointment.

Specialise in restoring textiles, including costume, embroideries, tapestries and banners.

PROVIDE Home Inspections. Free/Chargeable Estimates.
SPEAK TO Katharine Barker.

Ms Barker is an Associate of the Museums Association and a Member of UKIC. This workshop is included on the register of conservators maintained by the Conservation Unit of the Museums and Galleries Commission.

CARPET CONSERVATION WORKSHOP
2 Danebury Court, Sarum Business Park, Salisbury, **Wiltshire SB4 6EB**
TEL   0722 411854
FAX   0722 339161
OPEN   8–6 Mon–Fri or By Appointment.

Specialise in conservation of carpets, tapestries and general textiles.

PROVIDE Home Inspections. Free Estimates. Collection/Delivery Service by arrangement.
SPEAK TO Jonathan or Heather Tetley.
Member of UKIC. This workshop is included on the register of conservators maintained by the Conservation Unit of the Museums and Galleries Commission.

KATHRYN JORDAN
The Barn, Estate Yard, Castle Combe, Nr. Chippenham, **Wiltshire SN14 7HU**
TEL   0249 782142
FAX   0249 782233
OPEN   9–4 By Appointment Only.

Specialise in restoring Oriental rugs and carpets, kelims and woven textiles. Also cleaning and conserving rugs.

PROVIDE Home Inspections. Free/Chargeable Estimates. Free Collection/Delivery Service.
SPEAK TO Kathryn Jordan.

BART BLOK
41 Kirkgate, Knaresborough, **North Yorkshire HG5 8BZ**
TEL   0423 865414
FAX   0423 869 614
OPEN   8.30–5.30 Mon–Sat or By Appointment.

Specialise in the care, repair and restoration of rugs, kilims and woven artefacts from Europe and the Orient using where necessary hand–spun wool and natural dyes.

PROVIDE Home Inspections. Free Estimates. Collection/Delivery Service.
SPEAK TO Bart or Kay Blok.
Member of UKIC and Rug Restorers Association.

LONDON HOUSE ORIENTAL RUGS AND CARPETS
9 Montpellier Parade, Harrogate, **North Yorkshire HG1 2TJ**
TEL   0423 567167
OPEN   10–5.30 Tues–Sat.

Specialise in restoring and repairing Oriental rugs and carpets.

PROVIDE Free Estimates.
SPEAK TO Christian Ries.
SEE **West Yorkshire.**

GORDON REECE GALLERY
Finkle Street, Knaresborough, **North Yorkshire HG5 8AA**
TEL   0423 866219
FAX   0423 868044
OPEN   10.30–5 Mon–Sat; 2–5 Sun; closed Thur.

Specialise in restoring knotted Oriental rugs and kilims.

PROVIDE Free Estimates.
SPEAK TO Gordon Reece or Jane Munro.

W. E. FRANKLIN (SHEFFIELD) LTD
116–120 Onslow Road, Sheffield, **South Yorkshire S11 7AH**
TEL   0742 686161
FAX   0742 687324
OPEN   8.30–5.30 Mon–Fri or By Appointment.

Specialise in restoring carpets and rugs, including Orientals.

PROVIDE Free Estimates. Chargeable Collection/Delivery Service.
SPEAK TO William E. Franklin.
They have had fifty years' experience. Members of the Association of Cleaning and Restoration (USA), the National Carpet Cleaners Association, the Fabric Care Research Association and the Fire and Flood Academy. This workshop is included on the register of conservators maintained by the Conservation Unit of the Museums and Galleries Commission.

CAROLINE J. BOOTH TEXTILE CONSERVATOR
Popples Barn House, Widdop Road, Heptonstall, Hebden Bridge, **West Yorkshire HX7 7HD**
TEL   0422 842051
OPEN   10–5 Mon–Fri.

Specialise in a full range of services for small embroidered, woven and printed historic textiles, including samplers. Condition and conservation reports provided and advice given on handling, storage and display. Ms Booth uses traditional conservation techniques so that any work done is reversible.

PROVIDE Home Inspections. Chargeable Estimates. Chargeable Collection/Delivery Service.
SPEAK TO Caroline Booth.
SEE Collectors (Dolls).

LONDON HOUSE ORIENTAL RUGS AND CARPETS
238–240 High Street, Boston Spa, By Wetherby, **West Yorkshire LS23 6AD**
TEL   0937 845123
OPEN   10–5.30 Tues–Sun.

Specialise in restoring and repairing Oriental carpets and rugs.

PROVIDE Free Estimates.
SPEAK TO Martin or Inger Ries.
SEE **North Yorkshire.**

CATHY McCLINTOCK TEXTILE CONSERVATION

Unit 18, 204 Kilroot Park, Larne Road, Carrickfergus, **Co. Antrim**
TEL   096 03 51429
OPEN   By Appointment.

Specialise in restoring antique textiles, including tapestries, costume, linen, needlework and lace.

PROVIDE Home Inspections. Free/Chargeable Estimates.
SPEAK TO Cathy McClintock.
Member of IPCRA, UKIC, IIC and SSCR. This workshop is included on the register of conservators maintained by the Conservation Unit of the Museums and Galleries Commission.

BERTHA ANN WALKER

44 The Gables, Randalstown, **Co. Antrim BT41 3JY**
TEL   0265 42178
FAX   0265 42178
OPEN   By Appointment Mon–Sat.

Specialise in restoring textiles.

PROVIDE Home Inspections. Free/Chargeable Estimates.
SPEAK TO Bertha A. Walker.
Member of SMF, IMA and IPCRA.

JENNY SLEVIN

9 Innisboffin, Bailey View, Harbour Road, Dalkey, **Co. Dublin**
TEL   01 280 3429
OPEN   By Appointment.

Specialise in restoring embroidery and fans.

PROVIDE Home Inspections. Free/Chargeable Estimates.
Collection/Delivery Service by arrangement.
SPEAK TO Jenny Slevin.

Member of IPCRA.
SEE Porcelain, Furniture, Picture Frames, Collectors (Wax)

CHISHOLME ANTIQUES

5 Orrock Place, Hawick, **Borders TD9 0HQ**
TEL   0450 76928
OPEN   9–6 Mon–Fri.

Specialise in repairing and restoring antique tapestry and beadwork chair covers.

PROVIDE Home Inspections. Free Estimates. Chargeable Collection/Delivery Service.
SPEAK TO Mr Roberts.
SEE Furniture.

JAMES ANDERSON RITCHIE

Art Restoration Service, 6 Woodhill Place, Aberdeen, **Grampian AB2 4LF**
TEL   0224 310491
OPEN   9–5.30 or By Appointment.

Specialise in restoring samplers and cleaning tapestries.

PROVIDE Local Home Inspections. Free Estimates. Chargeable Collection/Delivery Service.
SPEAK TO J. Anderson Ritchie.
Member of SSCR. This workshop is in the Scottish Conservation Directory.
SEE Oil Paintings, Picture Frames.

JOHN MACLEAN

112 Thirlstane Street, Edinburgh, **Lothian EH9 1AS**
TEL   031 447 4225
OPEN   By Appointment.

Specialise in repairing and restoring Oriental rugs and carpets.

PROVIDE Home Inspections. Free Estimates. Free Collection/Delivery Service.

SPEAK TO John Maclean.
Member of Rug Restorers Association
and SSCR.

WHYTOCK & REID

Sunbury House, Belford Mews,
Edinburgh, **Lothian EH4 3DN**
TEL　　031 226 4911
FAX　　031 226 4595
OPEN　9–5.30 Mon–Fri; 9–12.30 Sat.

Specialise in restoring antique and 20th
century rugs and carpets.

PROVIDE Home Inspections. Free
Estimates. Free/Chargeable
Collection/Delivery Service.
SPEAK TO David Reid.
SEE Furniture

DAVID AND SARA BAMFORD

The Workhouse, Industrial Estate,
Presteigne, **Powys LD8 2UF**
TEL　　0544 267849
FAX　　0544 267849
OPEN　10–5.30 Mon–Sat By
　　　　Appointment Only.

Specialise in restoring conserving and
cleaning Oriental rugs and textiles. They
also remake hand–knotted rugs and
carpets at their workshops in Turkey.

PROVIDE Home Inspections. Free
Estimates. Free Local
Collection/Delivery Service.
SPEAK TO David or Sara Bamford.

BOOKS, MANUSCRIPTS, MAPS AND GLOBES

DO

Keep books in a room with a constant, preferably controlled, temperature – the cooler the better

Be careful with central heating, which tends to dry out books. Vellum and cloth-bound books tend to warp; leather bindings tend to weaken and crack at the joints

Keep leather bindings clean and supple with occasional applications of a leather dressing such as hide food

Ascertain the commercial value of a book before having it repaired. Although professional repairs are comparatively inexpensive, they may not be worthwhile unless a book is of sentimental importance

DON'T

Store books in a sunny room. If this is unavoidable, keep them in a shaded area, away from direct sunlight. Coloured leather fades in the sun and spines are particularly affected. Framed maps and manuscripts should also be protected from direct sunlight

Open leather-bound volumes carelessly – some hinges and joints will crack if a book is opened unnecessarily widely

Pack books too tightly on a shelf

Remove books from a shelf by hooking a forefinger over the head of the spine.

Remove or obscure early bookplates or erase signatures. Evidence of previous ownership (provenance) can add importance and value

Use adhesive tape to repair a book. The glue it contains is corrosive and leaves a stain which it is almost impossible to remove

GEORGE BAYNTUN

Manvers Street, Bath, Avon BA1 1JW
TEL　0225 466000
FAX　0225 482122
OPEN　9–1 Mon–Fri; 9.30–1 Sat By
　　　Appointment.

Specialise in restoring rare books and
fine bindings.

PROVIDE Home Inspections. Free
Estimates. Postal Service.
SPEAK TO George Bayntun.

BRISTOL-BOUND BOOKBINDING

14 Waterloo Street, Clifton, Bristol,
Avon BS8 4BT
TEL　0272 238279
OPEN　10–6 Tues–Sat.

Specialise in restoring leather and cloth
bindings, fine bindings and leather
repairs.

PROVIDE Free Estimates. Chargeable
Collection/Delivery Service.
SPEAK TO Mrs R. M. James.

CEDRIC CHIVERS

9 A/B Aldermoor Way, Longwell Green,
Bristol, **Avon BS15 7DA**
TEL　0272 352617
FAX　0272 618446
OPEN　8–4.30 Mon–Fri.

Specialise in refurbishment, repair and
rebinding of books and the repair and
conservation of paper.

PROVIDE Free Estimates. Chargeable
Collection/Delivery Service.
Established 1878.

AMANDA SLOPE BOOKBINDER

99A High Street, Great Missenden,
Buckinghamshire HP16 0BB
TEL　0494 891319
OPEN　10–4 Mon–Fri; 10–12 Sat;
　　　closed Thur.

Specialise in restoring bookbindings and
making embroidered book covers.

PROVIDE Home Inspections. Free
Estimates. Chargeable
Collection/Delivery Service.
SPEAK TO Amanda Slope.
Member of Society of Bookbinders and
Designer Bookbinders.

BRIGNELL BOOKBINDERS

2 Cobble Yard, Napier Street,
Cambridge, **Cambridgeshire
CB1 1HP**
TEL　0223 321280
OPEN　8.30–5 Mon–Fri; 8.30–12.30
　　　Sat.

Specialise in restoring all types of books
both old and new.

PROVIDE Home Inspections. Free
Estimates. Collection/Delivery Service.
SPEAK TO Barry Brignell.

DAVID ENGLISH

225 Carter Street, Fordham, Ely,
Cambridgeshire CB7 5JU
TEL　0638 720216
OPEN　8–5 Mon–Sat.

Specialise in repairing and restoring
antiquarian books, new bindings in
cloth, vellum, leather and paper.

PROVIDE Free Estimates.
SPEAK TO David English.

STOAKLEY BOOKBINDERS

67A Bridge Street, Cambridge,
Cambridgeshire CB2 1VR
TEL　0223 355941
OPEN　8.30–6 Mon–Fri; 9–1 Sat.

Specialise in fine bindings – all forms of
restoration, leather and cloth, journals,
theses, map mounting, desk–top
leathers, inlays, box making, traditional
hand binders.

PROVIDE Home Inspections. Free
Estimates. Chargeable
Collection/Delivery Service.
SPEAK TO Mr C. Elbden or Mr M.
Lawrence.
Established 1884.

SUSAN WOOD
27 Compton Street, Chesterfield,
Derbyshire S40 4TA
TEL   0629 57417
ANS   0629 57417
OPEN   By Appointment.

Specialise in restoring paper and
parchment documents, maps and plans,
seals and books.

PROVIDE Home Inspections. Free
Estimates. Free/Chargeable
Collection/Delivery Service.
SPEAK TO Susan Wood.
Member of IPC, Society of Archivists,
Society of Bookbinders, Designer
Bookbinders and IIC.

BOOKBUILD
The Gatehouse, West Charleton, Nr.
Kingsbridge, **Devon TQ7 2AL**
TEL   0548 531294
OPEN   9–5.30 Mon–Sat or By
           Appointment.

Specialise in restoring antiquarian
books, book housings, manuscript
housings and all associated items,
including albums, drop–back boxes etc.
They pay particular attention to period
detail and execute all work to National
Trust specifications. They also offer a
specialist design binding service for
unusual housing of letters and
documents. The primary emphasis of
their work is to retain as much as possible
of the original structure, material and
style.

PROVIDE Home Inspections.
Collection/Delivery Service.
SPEAK TO Colin Roberts or Judith Lamb.

Bookbuild is associated with both the
Society of Bookbinders and Book
Restorers and Designer Bookbinders.

CARI PALMER
Plainsfield Cottage, Withleigh, Tiverton,
Devon EX16 8JJ
TEL   0884 255500
OPEN   By Appointment.

Specialise in restoring books, archive
material and paper ephemera. Does not
restore fine bindings.

PROVIDE Local Home Inspections. Free
Estimates. Local Chargeable
Collection/Delivery Service.
SPEAK TO Cari Palmer.
Member of IPC. This workshop is
included on the register of conservators
maintained by the Conservation Unit of
the Museums and Galleries Commission.

FRANCIS BROWN CRAFT BOOKBINDER
24 Camden Way, Dorchester. **Dorset
DT1 2RA**
TEL   0305 266039
OPEN   9–12.30, 2–5.30 Mon–Fri.

Specialise in all types of bookbinding
and restoration, gold blocking, edge
gilding, box–making design.
SPEAK TO Francis Brown.

MARK CRAWLEY
Manor House Farm, 3 East Green,
Heighington, **Durham DL5 6PP**
TEL   0325 313256
OPEN   By Appointment.

Specialise in restoring books, leather and
cloth, design bindings, decorative boxes
and containers.

PROVIDE Home Inspections. Free
Estimates. Chargeable
Collection/Delivery Service.
SPEAK TO Mark Crawley.
Member of the Society of Bookbinders.
SEE Carpets.

ACORN PRESS BOOKBINDING SERVICES

103 London Road, Stanway, Colchester, **Essex CO3 5NY**
TEL   0206 46101
FAX   0206 571201
OPEN   9–5 Mon–Fri.

Specialise in the restoration and repair of books and bindings.

PROVIDE Home Inspections. Free Estimates. Chargeable Collection/Delivery Service.
SPEAK TO Brian Strudwick.
Member of the Guild of Master Craftsmen.

BEELEIGH ABBEY BOOKS

Beeleigh Abbey, Maldon, **Essex CM3 4AD**
TEL   0621 856308
FAX   0621 850064
OPEN   9–6 Mon–Thur; Fri By Appointment.

Specialise in fine bindings.

PROVIDE Home Inspections. Free Estimates. Free Collection/Delivery Service.
SPEAK TO Alan Liddell.
Member of ABA.

KEITH DEAN

Conservation Section, Essex Record Office, 3B Montrose Road, Chelmsford, **Essex CM2 6TE**
TEL   0245 492211 Ext. 55424
OPEN   9–5.30 Mon–Fri.

Specialise in restoring books, maps, documents, seals and parchment.

PROVIDE Free Estimates. Chargeable Collection/Delivery Service.
SPEAK TO Keith Dean (Senior Conservator).
Member of UKIC and the Society of Archivists. This workshop is included on the register of conservators maintained by the Conservation Unit of the Museums and Galleries Commission.

HELEN DURANT

Bookbinding and Restoration, Meadowsweet Cottage, Hyde Chase, Danbury, **Essex CM3 4LN**
TEL   0245 222655
OPEN   10–6 Mon–Fri.

Specialise in all styles of binding work, paper and leather repairs, map repairs, box making and craft bookbinding.

PROVIDE Free Estimates.
SPEAK TO Helen Durant.
Member of the Society of Bookbinders.

GRAINNE WHITTLEY CONSERVATION AND RESTORATION OF WORKS OF ART ON PAPER

2 Durban Villas, Bath Road, Nailsworth, **Gloucestershire GL6 0HJ**
TEL   0453 833687
OPEN   9–6 Mon–Sat.

Specialise in conservation and restoration of books, maps, screens, scrolls, Japanese tissue, wallpaper.

PROVIDE Home Inspections. Free Estimates. Free Collection/Delivery Service.
SPEAK TO Grainne Whittley (Miss).
Member of UKIC and IPC. BA (Hons) in Conservation from Camberwell College of Arts and Crafts.
SEE Oil Paintings, Picture Frames

THE BOOKBINDERY

St Michael's Abbey, Farnborough, **Hampshire GU14 7NQ**
TEL   0252 547573
OPEN   8.30–12, 1.30–5 Mon–Fri.

Specialise in hand-crafted bookbinding;

all types of bookbinding undertaken.

PROVIDE Free Estimates. Free Collection/Delivery Service on large consignments only.
SPEAK TO Mr L. Prior.
Benedictine monastery, holding craft certificates for the restoration of old books.

R. & L. LANCEFIELD
"Toad Hall", Burnetts Lane, Horton Heath, Eastleigh,
Hampshire SO5 7DJ
TEL   0703 692032
OPEN   9–5.30 Mon–Fri or By Appointment.

Specialise in restoring books and manuscripts – all types of conservation undertaken on these items, either single pieces or collections.

PROVIDE Home Inspections. Free Estimates. Free/Chargeable Collection/Delivery Service.
SPEAK TO Rex Lancefield.
Member of IPC. This workshop is included on the register of conservators maintained by the Conservation Unit of the Museums and Galleries Commission.
SEE Oil Paintings.

KATE NEWTON
Yew Tree Cottage, Logaston, Woonton, Hereford, **Hereford and Worcester HR3 6QH**
TEL   0544 327712
OPEN   9–5 Mon–Fri.

Specialise in restoring maps, plans, odd documents, archives, Japanese woodcuts.

PROVIDE Home Inspections. Free Estimates. Chargeable Collection/Delivery Service.
SPEAK TO Kate Newton.
Member of IPC.
SEE Oil Paintings.

LEONORA WEAVER
6 Aylestone Drive, Hereford,
Hereford & Worcester HR1 1HT
TEL   0432 267816
OPEN   By Appointment.

Specialise in restoring and hand–colouring maps.

PROVIDE Free Estimates. Collection/Delivery Service sometimes available.
SPEAK TO Leonora Weaver.
SEE Oil Paintings.

CHARLES PERRY RESTORATIONS LTD
Praewood Farm, Hemel Hempstead Road, St Albans, **Hertfordshire AL3 6AA**
TEL   0727 853487
FAX   0727 846668
OPEN   8.30–6 Mon–Fri; By Appointment Sat.

Specialise in restoring globes.

PROVIDE Home Inspections. Free Estimates. Chargeable Collection/Delivery Service.
SPEAK TO John Carr.
Mr Carr is a member of BAFRA and the Guild of Master Craftsmen.
By Appointment to HM Queen Elizabeth II, Antique Furniture Restorers.
This workshop is included on the register of conservators maintained by the Conservation Unit of the Museums and Galleries Commission.
SEE Furniture, Collectors (Ship Models, Toys)

NICHOLAS ARDIZZONE
4 Golden Street, Deal, **Kent CT14 6JU**
TEL   0304 361139
OPEN   8.30–5.30 Mon–Sat.

Specialise in restoring objects on paper, including documents.

PROVIDE Home Inspections. Free
Estimates. Chargeable
Collection/Delivery Service.
SPEAK TO Nicholas Ardizzone.
Member of IPC. Camberwell Graduate
(HNO).
SEE Oil Paintings.

FRAN BIRD PAPER CONSERVATOR

Hogtrough Cottage, Hogtrough Hill,
Brasted, Westerham, **Kent TN16 1NX**
TEL   0959 565163
FAX   0959 565163
OPEN   9–5 Mon–Fri or By
        Appointment.

Specialise in restoring archives, books,
maps and manuscripts.

PROVIDE Home Inspections. Free
Estimates. Local Free
Collection/Delivery Service.
SPEAK TO Fran Bird.
Member of IPC.
SEE Oil Paintings.

CASTLE FINE ART STUDIO

26 Castle Street, Dover, **Kent
CT16 1PW**
TEL   0304 206360
OPEN   10–1, 2–5.30 Mon–Fri; 10–1
        Sat.

Specialise in restoring archival material,
ephemera and maps.

PROVIDE Home Inspections. Free
Estimates. Free
Local/Collection/Delivery Service.
SPEAK TO Ms Deborah Colam.
Member of IPC. This workshop is
included on the register of conservators
maintained by the Conservation Unit of
the Museums and Galleries Commission.
SEE Oil Paintings, Picture Frames

LIBRARY CONSERVATORS

'Draycott', Green Lane, Temple Ewell,
Kent CT16 3AR
TEL   0304 823060 or 206360
OPEN   10–5.30 Mon–Sat.

Specialise in sending out teams of library
conservators to conserve and treat
historical book collections as a whole on–
site and will do surveys if required. Also
conserve maps.

PROVIDE Home Inspections.
Free/Chargeable Estimates.
Free/Chargeable Collection/Delivery
Service.
SPEAK TO Louise Drover or Deborah
Colam.
Member of IPC. This workshop is
included on the register of conservators
maintained by the Conservation Unit of
the Museums and Galleries Commission.
SEE OIl Paintings, Picture Frames.

G. & D. I. MARRIN & SONS

149 Sandgate Road, Folkestone, **Kent
CT20 2DA**
TEL   0303 253016
FAX   0303 850956
OPEN   9.30–5.30 Mon–Sat.

Specialise in restoring antiquarian books
and maps.

PROVIDE Home Inspections. Chargeable
Estimates. Chargeable
Collection/Delivery Service.
SPEAK TO John or Patrick Marrin.
Member of ABA and PBFA.
SEE Oil Paintings.

RICHARD ZAHLER

Lane House, Fowgill, Bentham,
Lancaster, **Lancashire LA2 7AH**
TEL   05242 61998
OPEN   9–6 Mon–Fri or By
        Appointment.

Specialise in restoring maps.

SPEAK TO Richard Zahler.
Member of UKIC and the Guild of
Master Craftsmen. This workshop is
included on the register maintained by
the Conservation Unit of the Museums
and Galleries Commission.
SEE Furniture, Oil Paintings, Picture
Frames

SUE RAWLINGS
17 Nithsdale Crescent, Market
Harborough, **Leicestershire
LE16 9HA**
TEL   0858 464605
OPEN   9–5.30 Mon–Fri.

Specialise in restoring books and
archives.

PROVIDE Home Inspections. Free
Estimates. Free Local
Collection/Delivery Service.
SPEAK TO Sue Rawlings.
Member of IPC. This workshop is
included on the register of conservators
maintained by the Conservation Unit of
the Museum and Galleries Commission.
SEE Oil Paintings.

RILEY, DUNN & WILSON
LTD
Pegasus House, 116–120 Golden Lane,
London EC1Y 0UD
TEL   071 251 2551
FAX   071 490 2338
OPEN   9–5 Mon–Fri.

Specialise in restoring antiquarian books
and paper conservation, including
manuscripts and maps. Also rebind and
repair bindings.

PROVIDE Home Inspections. Free
Estimates. Free Collection/Delivery
Service.
SPEAK TO the Office Manager.
SEE West Yorkshire, Central.
SEE Oil paintings.

COLLEGE OF ARMS
Queen Victoria Street, **London EC4V
4BT**
TEL   071 248 2762
OPEN   10–4 Mon–Fri.

Specialise in fine binding and paper
conservation, undertaken by the College
of Arms Conservation Department.
SPEAK TO the Head of Conservation.
SEE Heraldry.

DATA & ARCHIVAL
DAMAGE CONTROL
CENTRE
4 Bridge Wharf, 156 Caledonian Road,
London N1 9UU
TEL   071 837 8215
FAX   071 278 0221
OPEN   9–5 Mon–Fri.

Specialise in restoring corporate
records, books, papers, documents.

PROVIDE Chargeable
Collection/Delivery Service.
SPEAK TO Helene M. Donnelly.
Member of IPC, AIC, Forensic Science
Society, Society of Emergency Services
Officers.

THOMAS MILNE
55 Rosebery Road, **London N10 2LE**
TEL   081 883 4609
OPEN   Mon–Fri By Appointment.

Specialise in restoring maps, plans and
archives.

PROVIDE Home Inspections. Chargeable
Estimates. Chargeable
Collection/Delivery Service.
SPEAK TO Thomas Milne.
Member of UKIC and IPC.
Conservation Unit intern, Tate Gallery
London.
SEE Oil Paintings.

CATHERINE RICKMAN
ART CONSERVATION
11 Berkley Road, **London NW1 8XX**
TEL   071 586 0384
OPEN   9–6 Mon–Fri By Appointment.

Specialise in restoring manuscripts and philatelic materials.

PROVIDE Home Inspections. Free Verbal Estimates.
SPEAK TO Catherine Rickman.
Member of IPC, UKIC, IIC and AIC.
This workshop is included on the register of conservators maintained by the Conservation Unit of the Museums and Galleries Commission.
SEE Oil Paintings.

CELIA J. ALBERMAN AND DINAH SWAYNE
45A Montpelier Grove, **London NW5 2XG**
TEL   071 267 9909
OPEN   9.30–5.30.

Specialise in restoring books.

PROVIDE Home Inspections.
Free/Chargeable Estimates.
Collection/Delivery Service by arrangement.
SPEAK TO Celia Alberman or Dinah Swayne.
Member of IPC, Society of Bookbinders and Designer Bookbinders.

JANE ZAGEL
31 Pandora Road, **London NW6 1TS**
TEL   071 794 1663
OPEN   9–6 Mon–Fri.

Specialise in restoring books.

PROVIDE Home Inspections. Refundable Estimates. Chargeable Collection/Delivery Service.
SPEAK TO Jane Zagel.
This workshop is included on the register of conservators maintained by the Conservation Unit of the Museums and Galleries Commission.
SEE Oil Paintings, Specialist Photographers.

SANGORSKI & SUTCLIFFE/ZAEHNSDORF LTD
175R Bermondsey Street, **London SE1 3UW**
TEL   071 407 1244
FAX   071 357 7466
OPEN   9–4.30 Mon–Fri.

Specialise in restoring and repairing bookbinding.

PROVIDE Home Inspections. Free Estimates. Free Collection/Delivery Service.
SPEAK TO Janet Blake.
Make visitors' books, game books, cellar books and stationery items to individual specification.

KIM ELIZABETH LEYSHON PICTURE RESTORER
2 Walerand Road, **London SE13 7PG**
TEL   081 318 1277
OPEN   By Appointment.

Specialise in restoring terrestrial and celestial globes.

PROVIDE Home Inspections. Free Estimates. Free Collection/Delivery Service.
SPEAK TO Kim Leyshon.
Member of IPC, IIC and UKIC.
SEE Oil Paintings.

MARIE LOUISE LOPEZ
25 Crewys Road, **London SE15 2BJ**
TEL   071 358 9641
OPEN   By Appointment Mon–Sat.

Specialise in restoring all works of art on paper, including maps, wallpaper and parchment. Full documentation, photographs and condition reports supplied.

PROVIDE Home Inspections.
Free/Chargeable Estimates. Free Local Collection Delivery Service.
SPEAK TO Marie Louise Lopez.
Member of UKIC, IPC and Wallpaper

History Society. This workshop is
included on the register of conservators
maintained by the Conservation Unit of
the Museums and Galleries Commission.
SEE Oil Paintings.

CATHERINE HODGSON

265 Croxted Road, **London SE21 8NN**
TEL   081 761 2567
OPEN   By Appointment.

Specialise in repairing both cloth and
leather books. Will also design and bind
presentation books.

PROVIDE Home Inspections. Free
Estimates. Chargeable
Collection/Delivery Service.
SPEAK TO Catherine Hodgson.

CLARE REYNOLDS

20 Gubyon Avenue, **London SE24
ODX**
TEL   071 326 0458
OPEN   9–5 Mon–Fri.

Specialise in restoring archives,
manuscripts and parchment.

PROVIDE Home Inspections. Free
Estimates. Chargeable
Collection/Delivery Service.
SPEAK TO Clare Reynolds.
SEE Oil Paintings.

SHEPHERDS BOOKBINDERS LTD

76B Rochester Row, **London SW1P
1JU**
TEL   071 630 1184
FAX   071 931 0541
OPEN   9–5.30 Mon–Fri; 10.30–1 Sat.

Specialise in bookbinding restoration
and archive conservation.

PROVIDE Free Estimates.
SPEAK TO Jan Blake or Rob Shepherd.
Member of IPC and Society of
Bookbinders and Restorers.
SEE Oil Paintings.

BERNARD C. MIDDLETON

3 Gauden Road, **London SW4 6LR**
TEL   071 622 5388
FAX   071 498 2716
OPEN   9–6 Mon–Fri.

Specialise in the restoration of
antiquarian books and rebinding in
period styles.

PROVIDE Free Estimates.
SPEAK TO Bernard Middleton.

KING'S COURT GALLERIES

951–953 Fulham Road, **London
SW6 5HY**
TEL   071 610 6939
FAX   071 731 4737
OPEN   10–5.30 Mon–Sat.

Specialise in paper conservation and
restoration, including antique maps.

PROVIDE Home Inspections. Free
Estimates. Chargeable
Collection/Delivery Service.
SPEAK TO Mrs J. Joel.
Member of the Fine Art Trade Guild.
SEE **Surrey**
SEE Oil Paintings.

BRIGID RICHARDSON

91 Langthorne Street, **London SW6
6JS**
TEL   071 381 0198
OPEN   Mon–Sat By Appointment.

Specialise in conservation of documents,
manuscripts, prints and pages of old
books.

PROVIDE Home Inspections.
Free/Chargeable Estimates. Chargeable
Collection/Delivery Service.
SPEAK TO Brigid Richardson.
Member of IPC. This workshop is
included on the register of conservators
maintained by the Conservation Unit of
the Museums and Galleries Commission.
SEE Oil Paintings.

DORETTA MESHIEA

12A Ennismore Gardens, **London**
SW7 1AA
TEL   071 581 8397
FAX   071 499 1272
OPEN   10–5 Mon–Fri.

Specialise in restoring manuscripts, books and ephemera, archival storage and refurbishment of libraries and collections.

PROVIDE Home Inspections. Chargeable Estimates. Chargeable Collection/Delivery Service.
SPEAK TO Doretta Meshiea.
Member of IPC.
SEE Oil Paintings.

SYLVIA SUMIRA CONSERVATION OF GLOBES

158 Old South Lambeth Road, **London**
SW8 1XX
TEL   071 587 1593
FAX   071 587 1593
OPEN   9–6 Mon–Fri By Appointment Only.

Specialise in restoring globes.

PROVIDE Home Inspections. Chargeable Estimates.
SPEAK TO Sylvia Sumira.
Member of IPC, IIC, UKIC and SIS.

BATES AND BASKCOMB

191 St John's Hill, **London SW11 1TH**
TEL   071 223 1629
OPEN   9.30–5.30 Mon–Fri and By Appointment.

Specialise in restoring works of art on paper, including maps.

PROVIDE Local Home Inspections. Free/Chargeable Collection/Delivery Service.
SPEAK TO Debbie Bates or Camilla Baskcomb.
SEE Oil Paintings.

KEITH HOLMES

27 Dalebury Road, **London**
SW17 7HQ
TEL   081 672 4606
OPEN   8–8 Daily.

Specialise in restoring archival and any paper or related material e.g. vellum.

PROVIDE Home Inspections. Free Estimates. Chargeable Local Collection/Delivery Service.
SPEAK TO Keith Holmes.
Member of IIC. This workshop is included on the register of conservators maintained by the Conservation Unit of the Museums and Galleries Commission.
SEE Oil Paintings.

PH7 PAPER CONSERVATORS

Unit 210, The Business Village, 3–9 Broomhill Road, **London SW18 4JQ**
TEL   081 871 5075
FAX   081 877 1940
OPEN   9–5.30 Mon–Fri or By Appointment.

Specialise in restoring works of art on paper, including posters, letters, documents and ephemera.

PROVIDE Home Inspections. Free Estimates. Free Collection/Delivery Service.
SPEAK TO Victoria Pease.
Member of IPC, UKIC and IIC. This workshop is included on the register of conservators maintained by the Conservation Unit of the Museums and Galleries Commission.
SEE Oil Paintings.

DIANA WASHINGTON

17 Cicada Road, **London SW18 2NN**
TEL   081 874 6223
OPEN   9–5 Mon–Fri By Appointment Only.

Specialise in restoring maps and archives.

PROVIDE Home Inspections. Free

Estimates. Collection Delivery Service.
SPEAK TO Diana Washington.
Member of IPC, UKIC, IIC and AIC.
This workshop is included on the register
of conservators maintained by the
Conservation Unit of the Museums and
Galleries Commission.
SEE Oil Paintings, Picture Frames.

CLARE PRINCE BOOK CONSERVATOR
26 Abingdon Court, Abingdon Villas,
London W8 6BT
TEL   071 937 9198
OPEN   By Appointment.

Specialise in conserving rare books and
fine bindings. Can provide condition
surveys and emergency treatment.

PROVIDE Home Inspections.
Free/Chargeable Estimates. Chargeable
Collection/Delivery Service.
SPEAK TO Clare Prince.
Member of IPC, Designer Bookbinders,
Society of Bookbinders.

GERALD H. MORRIS
2 Beaconsfield Terrace Road, **London
W14 0PR**
TEL   071 603 7838
OPEN   9–6.30 Mon–Sat.

Specialise in restoring and conserving
most paper–based articles, including
maps and documents.

PROVIDE Home Inspections. Free
Estimates. Free/Chargeable
Collection/Delivery Service.
SPEAK TO Gerald Morris.
Member of IPC.
SEE Oil Paintings.

ABBOTT & HOLDER
30 Museum Street, **London WC1A
1LH**
TEL   071 637 3981
OPEN   9.30–6 Mon–Fri.

Specialise in restoring prints and

ephemara, including posters and theatre
bills.

PROVIDE Inspections. Free Estimates.
SPEAK TO Susan C. Smith
Member of IPC. This workshop is
included on the register of conservators
maintained by the Conservation Unit of
the Museums and Galleries Commission
SEE Oil Paintings.

PAPERSAFE
146 Chapel Road, Oldham, **Greater
Manchester OL8 4QJ**
TEL   061 682 9652
OPEN   By Appointment.

Specialise in restoring books and
bindings and printed documents.

PROVIDE Home Inspections. Free
Estimates. Chargeable
Collection/Delivery Service.
SPEAK TO Graham Moss.
Member of IPC and Society of
Bookbinders.
SEE Lighting.

LYVER & BOYDELL GALLERIES
15 Castle Street, Liverpool, **Merseyside
L2 4SX**
TEL   051 236 3256
OPEN   10–30–5.30 Mon–Fri; By
           Appointment Sat.

Specialise in restoring and framing
maps.

PROVIDE Home Inspections. Free
Estimates.
SPEAK TO Paul or Gill Breen.
SEE Oil Paintings, Picture Frames

ANN HORNE PAPER CONSERVATOR
36 Lebanon Park, Twickenham,
Middlesex TW1 3DG
TEL   081 892 0688
FAX   081 744 2177
OPEN   By Appointment Only.

Specialise in restoring documents.

PROVIDE Local Home Inspections. Free Estimates. Free Local Collection/Delivery Service.
SPEAK TO Ann Horne.
SEE Oil Paintings

R. & S. LANE BOOKBINDING
Heath House, 2 Smiths Lane, Fakenham, **Norfolk NR21 8LG**
TEL   0328 862151
OPEN   By Appointment.

Specialise in all types of bookbinding, journals and theses, presentation copies and full restoration.

PROVIDE Home Inspections. Free Estimates. Free Collection/Delivery Service.
SPEAK TO Richard or Susan Lane.

ARTHUR AND ANN RODGERS
7 Church Street, Ruddington, Nottingham, **Nottinghamshire NG11 6HA**
TEL   0602 216214
OPEN   9–5 Tues, Wed; 9–1 Thur, Fri; 9–5 Sat.

Specialise in hand–colouring, cleaning, restoring and repairing of maps.

PROVIDE Home Inspections. Chargeable Estimates. Free Collection/Delivery Service.
SPEAK TO Arthur Rodgers.
SEE Oil Paintings

CHRIS HICKS
64 Merewood Avenue, Sandhills, Oxford, **Oxfordshire OX13 8EF**
TEL   0865 69346
OPEN   By Appointment.

Specialise in restoring and conserving printed books and bindings of all periods.

PROVIDE Home Inspections. Free/Chargeable Estimates. Free/ Collection/Delivery Service by arrangement.
SPEAK TO Chris Hicks.
Member of IPC.

PETER HANKS
149 Manor Rise, Walton Stone, **Staffordshire ST15 0HY**
TEL   0785 815730
OPEN   By Appointment.

Specialise in restoring books, maps and archives.

PROVIDE Home Inspections. Free Estimates. Chargeable Collection/Delivery Service.
SPEAK TO Peter Hanks.
Member of IPC and Society of Bookbinders. This workshop is included on the register of conservators maintained by the Conservation Unit of the Museums and Galleries Commission.

PHILIPPA ELLISON
Fords Farm, Winston, Nr. Stowmarket, **Suffolk IP14 6BD**
TEL   0728 860572
OPEN   9–5 Mon–Fri.

Specialise in restoring works of art on paper, particularly plate books, repair work and facsimile. Advice on general care available.

PROVIDE Home Inspections. Free Estimates. Collection/Delivery Service.
SPEAK TO Philippa Ellison.
Member of IPC. This workshop is included on the register of conservators maintained by the Conservation Unit of the Museums and Galleries Commission.
SEE Oil Paintings, Picture Frames.

JUDITH GOWLAND MA PhD

6 Duke Street, Haughley, **Suffolk IP14 3QS**
TEL   0449 770181
OPEN   By Appointment.

Specialise in restoring maps.

PROVIDE Home Inspections. Chargeable Estimates. Chargeable Collection/Delivery Service.
SPEAK TO Judith Gowland.
Member of IPC.
SEE **North Yorkshire**
SEE Oil Paintings.

C. W. P. KEYES

36 High Street, Debenham, Stowmarket, **Suffolk IP14 6QN**
TEL   0728 860624
OPEN   10–3 Mon–Sat.

Specialise in restoring maps.

PROVIDE Home Inspections. Chargeable Estimates. Chargeable Collection/Delivery Service.
SPEAK TO Charles Keyes.
Member of IPC.
SEE Oil Paintings, Picture Frames

JOHN HILL

"Farthings", Trindles Road, South Nutfield, **Surrey RH1 4JG**
TEL   0737 823404
OPEN   9–5 Mon–Fri.

Specialise in restoring maps.

PROVIDE Home Inspections. Free Estimates. Chargeable Collection/Delivery Service.
SPEAK TO John Hill.
Member of IPC.
SEE Oil Paintings, Picture Frames.

KING'S COURT GALLERIES

54 West Street, Dorking, **Surrey RH4 1BS**
TEL   0306 881757
FAX   0306 875305
OPEN   9.30–5.30 Mon–Sat.

Specialise in paper conservation and restoration, including antique maps.

PROVIDE Home Inspections. Free Estimates.
SPEAK TO Mrs J. Joel.
SEE Oil Paintings.

MUCH BINDING

Lower Hammonds Farm, Ripley Lane, West Horsley, **Surrey KT24 6JP**
TEL   0483 283175
OPEN   By Appointment.

Specialise in hand bookbinding and the restoration and repair of all types of leather and cloth bindings, albums etc.

PROVIDE Home Inspections. Free Estimates.
SPEAK TO Gina Isaac.
Member of the Surrey Guild of Craftsmen. Mrs Isaac is Hon. Sec. of the Society of Bookbinders.

MARNY PARK

Loseberry, 30 Hare Lane, Claygate, **Surrey KT10 9BU**
TEL   0372 463628
FAX   0372 470140
OPEN   9–5 Mon–Fri.

Specialise in restoring maps.

PROVIDE Home Inspections. Free Estimates. Free Local Collection/Delivery Service.
SPEAK TO Marny Park (Mrs Ann Margaret Park).
Member of IPC.
SEE Oil Paintings.

ROBINSONS BOOKBINDERS

78 Mytchett Road, Mytchett, Nr. Camberley, **Surrey GU16 6ET**
TEL   0252 512281
OPEN   8.30–6 Mon–Fri; 8.30–1 Sat.

Specialise in restoring leather and cloth bindings, re–sewing on tapes/cords, re–

backing spines, strenghtening and rebuilding damaged boards.

PROVIDE Free Estimates.
SPEAK TO John Robinson.
Member of Society of Bookbinders.

THE CONSERVATION WORKSHOP
6 Green Man Yard, Boreham Street, Nr. Herstmonceux, **East Sussex BN27 4SF**
TEL   0323 833842
OPEN   9.30–6 Mon–Fri or By
       Appointment.

Specialise in conserving books and manuscripts.

PROVIDE Home Inspections. Free Estimates. Free Local Collection/Delivery Service.
SPEAK TO Ian Maver or Corinne Hillman.
Members of IPC, UKIC, Royal Photographic Society, Society of Archivists and Wallpaper History Society. This workshop is included on the register of conservators maintained by the Conservation Unit of the Museums and Galleries Commission.
SEE Oil Paintings.

ANNA HORNSTEIN
Flat 2, 57 Croft Road, Hastings, **East Sussex TN34 3HJ**
TEL   0424 433260
OPEN   By Appointment.

Specialise in conservation of books and archives, protective boxes and portfolios made to specification.

PROVIDE Home Inspections. Free Estimates. Free Local Collection/Delivery Service.
SPEAK TO Anna Hornstein.
Member of IPC. This workshop is included on the register of conservators maintained by the Conservation Unit of the Museums and Galleries Commission.

SUSSEX CONSERVATION STUDIO
'Hill Bank', Broad Street, Cuckfield, **West Sussex RH17 5DX**
TEL   0444 451964
OPEN   8.30–5.30 Mon–Fri or By
       Appointment.

Specialise in restoring maps and documents. Cleaning, repair work and retouching are all carried out to conservation standards using up-to-date techniques.

PROVIDE Free Estimates. Home Inspections by arrangement. Free Local Collection/Delivery Service.
SPEAK TO Reginald or Bernadette Selous.
Members of the IPC. This workshop is included on the register of conservators maintained by the Conservation Unit of the Museums and Galleries Commission.
SEE Oil Paintings.

NOLAN B. WATTS
4 Hayes Cottages, Five Oaks, Nr. Billingshurst, **West Sussex RH14 9AR**
TEL   0403 784073
FAX   0403 783918
OPEN   9–5 Mon–Sat By Appointment.

Specialise in restoring and repairing antiquarian and modern books. Binding of periodicals, journals, reports and documents for corporate and public libraries. Also make special albums boxes and cases for coins, medals, postage stamps and other collectable items.

PROVIDE Home Inspections. Free Estimates. Chargeable Collection/Delivery Service.
SPEAK TO Nolan B. Watts.
Member of the Society of Bookbinders.

WEST DEAN COLLEGE
West Dean, Chichester, **West Sussex PO18 0OZ**
TEL   0243 63 301
FAX   0243 63 342
OPEN   9–5 Mon–Fri.

Specialise in training conservators and restorers in the field of early manuscripts and rare books and will also undertake restoration.

PROVIDE Local Home Inspections. Free Estimates.
SPEAK TO Peter Sarginson.
SEE Clocks, Furniture, Porcelain, Silver

FOSTER RESTORERS
7 Rivermead Drive, Tiddington, Stratford–upon–Avon, **Warwickshire CV37 7AL**
TEL   0789 204899
FAX   0789 267974
OPEN   10.30–5 Tues, Thur, Fri.

Specialise in restoring antique maps.

PROVIDE Home Inspections. Chargeable Estimates. Free/Chargeable Collection/Delivery Service. Packing and Shipping Service.
SPEAK TO Jerrold E. F. Foster.
Member of UKIC and BAFRA. This workshop is included on the register of conservators maintained by the Conservation Unit of the Museums and Galleries Commission.
SEE Oil Paintings

D. M. BEACH
52 High Street, Salisbury, **Wiltshire SP1 2PG**
TEL   0722 333801
OPEN   9–5.30 Mon–Sat.

Specialise in restoring maps and repairing bookbindings.

PROVIDE Chargeable Home Inspections. Free Estimates. Free Local Collection Service.
SEE Oil Paintings.

ANDREW FANE
Thistle Cottage, Great Bedwyn, Nr. Marlborough, **Wiltshire SN8 3LH**
TEL   0672 870549
OPEN   8.30–5.30 Mon–Fri or By
       Appointment.

Specialise in restoring documents.

PROVIDE Home Inspections. Free Estimates. Free/Chargeable Collection/Delivery Service.
SPEAK TO Andrew Fane.
Member of IPC.
SEE Oil Paintings.

JOHN SMART BOOKBINDERS AND RESTORERS EST'D 1935
The Old Wagon and Horses, Brinkworth, Chippenham, **Wiltshire SN15 5AD**
TEL   0666 510517
OPEN   8–8 Mon–Sat.

Specialise in restoring books and documents, washing, paper restoration.

PROVIDE Home Inspections. Free Estimates. Chargeable Collection/Delivery Service.
SPEAK TO John or Richard Smart.
Member of IPC, Society of Bookbinders, Society of Designer Bookbinders. This workshop is included on the register of conservators maintained by the Conservation Unit of the Museums and Galleries Commission.

WINSTANLEY SALISBURY BOOKBINDERS
213 Devizes Road, Salisbury, **Wiltshire SP2 9LT**
TEL   0722 334998
OPEN   8.30–5.30 Mon–Fri.

Specialise in book restoration and paper conservation.

PROVIDE Free Estimates. Chargeable Collection/Delivery Service
SPEAK TO Alan Winstanley.
Mr Winstanley also makes fine new bindings to individual requirements.
SEE Oil Paintings.

STEPHEN AND PAMELA ALLEN

St Andrew's Cottage, Constable Burton, Leyburn,
North Yorkshire DL8 5RG
TEL   0677 50295
OPEN   By Appointment.

Specialise in restoring works on paper, including maps.

PROVIDE Home Inspections. Free Estimates. Chargeable Collection/Delivery Service.
SPEAK TO Stephen Allen or Pamela Allen. Member of IPC. This workshop is included on the register of conservators maintained by the Conservation Unit of the Museums and Galleries Commission.
SEE Oil Paintings.

ARTHUR HENRY FAIRHURST

23A Raincliffe Avenue, Scarborough,
North Yorkshire YO12 5BU
TEL   0723 372780
OPEN   10–5 Mon–Fri.

Specialise in bookbinding and restoring and repairing books.

PROVIDE Home Inspections. Free Estimates. Local Collection/Delivery Service.
SPEAK TO Arthur Fairhurst.
Mr Fairhurst runs weekend courses for beginners, improved and advanced.

JUDITH GOWLAND MA PhD

East Ayrlow Banks, East Hauxwell, Leyburn, **North Yorkshire DL8 5NJ**
TEL   0677 50364
OPEN   By Appointment.

Specialise in restoring maps.

PROVIDE Home Inspections. Chargeable Estimates. Chargeable Collection/Delivery Service.
SPEAK TO Judith Gowland.
Member of IPC.
SEE **Suffolk**
SEE Oil Paintings.

AMELIA RAMPTON

29 Portland Street, York, **North Yorkshire YO3 7EH**
TEL   0904 628048
OPEN   9–5 Mon–Fri By Appointment Only.

Specialise in conserving and restoring archives.

PROVIDE Home Inspections. Free/Chargeable Estimates. Free Collection/Delivery Service.
SPEAK TO Amelia Rampton.
SEE Oil Paintings.

CHARTERHOUSE BOOKBINDING

62 Granville Road, Shipley, **West Yorkshire BD18 2DN**
TEL   0274 480693
OPEN   10–6 Mon–Fri.

Specialise in the restoration and conservation of 19th century cloth–bound books as well as all types of printed and manuscript items on paper i.e. books, pamphlets, posters and handbills. They can restore or rebind almost any style of bookbinding.

PROVIDE Home Inspections. Free Estimates. Free Collection/Delivery Service.
SPEAK TO Eamonn Fitzmaurice.
This workshop is included on the register of conservators maintained by the Conservation Unit of the Museums and Galleries Commission.

REBINDING & RESTORATION SERVICE

31 Greenhead Lane, Dalton, Huddersfield, **West Yorkshire HD5 8PP**
TEL   0484 425670
OPEN   9–5 Mon–Fri.

Specialise in restoring cloth, leather and antiquarian books.

PROVIDE Local Home Inspections. Free

Estimates. Local Free
Collection/Delivery Service.
SPEAK TO Barry M. Knell.
Member of the Society of Bookbinders.

RILEY, DUNN & WILSON LTD

Red Doles Lane, Leeds Road,
Huddersfield, **West Yorkshire**
HD2 1YE
TEL   0484 534323
FAX   0484 435048
OPEN   8.15–3.45 Mon–Fri.

Specialise in the restoring, repairing and
rebinding of antiquarian books,
including paper conservation. Also
supply book boxes.

PROVIDE Home Inspections. Free
Estimates. Free Collection/Delivery
Service.
SPEAK TO Geoff Crosland.
Member of the Society of Bookbinders
and the Institute of Paper Conservation.
SEE **London EC1, Stirling**.

SUSAN CORR

Paper Conservation Studio, 48 Woodley
Park, Dundrum, Dublin 14. **Co. Dublin**
TEL   01 2987661
OPEN   By Appointment.

Specialise in conservation of archive
documents.

PROVIDE Home Inspections. Free
Estimates. Collection/Delivery Service
by arrangement.
SPEAK TO Susan Corr.
Member of IPCRA and IPC.
SEE Oil Paintings.

PATRICK McBRIDE

Paper Conservation Studio, IDA Tower
Complex, Pearse Street, Dublin 2, **Co.**
Dublin
TEL   01 775656
FAX   01 775487
OPEN   By Appointment.

Specialise in the conservation of archival
material.

PROVIDE Home Inspections. Chargeable
Estimates. Free Collection/Delivery
Service.
SPEAK TO Patrick McBride.
Member of IPCRA, IPC and ICOM.
SEE Oil Paintings.

KAREN REIHILL

30 Hollybank Avenue, Lower Ranelagh,
Dublin 6, **Co. Dublin**
TEL   01 962462
OPEN   By Appointment.

Specialise in restoring and conserving
works of art on paper, including maps
and letters.

PROVIDE Free/Chargeable Estimates.
SPEAK TO Karen Reihill.
Member of IPCRA.
SEE Oil Paintings.

CELBRIDGE PAPER CONSERVATION STUDIO

The Mill, Celbridge, **Co. Kildare**
TEL   01 6272913
OPEN   By Appointment.

Specialise in conserving works of art on
paper – large maps, posters, screens,
wallpaper, archival material.

PROVIDE Home Inspections. Chargeable
Estimates. Free Collection/Delivery
Service.
SPEAK TO David Skinner or Rosalind
Smith.
Member of IPCRA.

JAMES FLAVELL BOOKBINDER AND RESTORER

26 Foreland Road, Bembridge, **Isle of**
Wight PO35 5XW
TEL   0983 872856
OPEN   9–5.30 Mon–Fri; 9–12.30 Sat.

Specialise in restoring antiquarian books, documents and manuscripts, maps. Gold tooling, designer and presentation binding, paper de–acidification, general binding.

PROVIDE Home Inspections. Free Estimates. Free Collection/Delivery Service.
SPEAK TO James Flavell.
Mr Flavell is City and Guilds qualified, Member of the Society of Bookbinders, Associate Member of Designer Bookbinders. This workshop is included on the register of conservators maintained by the Conservation Unit of the Museums and Galleries Commission.
SEE Oil Paintings, Furniture

MRS ELIZABETH LUMSDEN
Craft Bookbinder and Restorer, The Glack, Dunkeld, Perthshire, **Borders PH8 0ER**
TEL   035072 8849
OPEN   8–8 Daily.

Specialise in restoring all leather and cloth bindings, paper and archive restoration.

PROVIDE Home Inspections. Free Estimates. Chargeable Collection/Delivery Service.
SPEAK TO Mrs E. Lumsden.
This workshop is in the Scottish Conservation Directory.

RILEY, DUNN & WILSON LTD
Bellevue Bindery, Glasgow Road, Camelon, Falkirk, **Central FK1 4HP**
TEL   0324 21591
FAX   0324 611508
OPEN   8.30–5 Mon–Fri.

Specialise in restoring antiquarian books, repairing bindings and rebinding. Paper conservation including manuscripts and maps.

PROVIDE Home Inspections. Free

Estimates. Free Collection/Delivery Service.
SPEAK TO John Penman.
SEE **London EC1, West Yorkshire**.
SEE Oil Paintings.

TOM VALENTINE
Caronvale Bindery, 18 The Main Street, Larbert, Falkirk, **Central FK5 3AN**
TEL   0324 552247
OPEN   By Appointment.

Specialise in archival work, restoring books and manuscripts, bookbinding, paper conservation.

PROVIDE Home Inspections. Free Collection/Delivery Service.
SPEAK TO Tom Valentine.
Mr Valentine is a member of the Society of Bookbinders.

A. W. LUMSDEN CRAFT BOOKBINDING
Edgefield Road Industrial Estate, Loanhead, **Lothian EH20 9TB**
TEL   031 440 0726
FAX   031 440 2628
OPEN   8–4.45 Mon–Fri; 8–1.30 Sat.

Specialise in restoring books, spray de–acidification, tissue and silk repairs, all styles of bookbinding.

PROVIDE Local Home Inspections. Free Estimates. Free Collection/Delivery Service.
SPEAK TO Fraser Lumsden.
Member of IPC, SSCR. This workshop is in the Scottish Conservation Directory.

FIONA ANDERSON

Rhugarbh Church, Barcaldine, Oban,
Argyll, **Strathclyde PA37 1SE**
TEL   0631 72504
OPEN   9–5 By Appointment.

Specialise in restoring antiquarian books
and good second–hand books. If
necessary paper can be de–acidified and
re–sized, leather bindings restored and
re–backed. Cloth bindings also repaired.
PROVIDE Home Inspections. Free
Estimates. Free Local
Collection/Delivery Service.
SPEAK TO Fiona Anderson.
This workshop is in the Scottish
Conservation Directory.

CARL UTTERIDGE

Capel Bethel, Dinas Mawddwy,
Machynlleth, **Powys SY20 9JA**
TEL   0650 531432
OPEN   9–6 Mon–Sat.

Specialise in restoring maps.

PROVIDE Home Inspections. Free
Estimates. Free Local
Collection/Delivery Service.
SPEAK TO Carl Utteridge or Jennifer
A'Brook.
Member of UKIC. This workshop is
included on the register of conservators
maintained by the Conservation Unit of
the Museums and Galleries Commission.
SEE Oil Paintings.

COLLECTORS' ITEMS

CAMERAS

LES FRANKHAM FRPS
166 Westcote Drive, Leicester,
Leicestershire LE3 0SP
TEL   0533 550825
OPEN   9–4 Mon–Fri.

Specialise in restoring classic cameras,
Zeiss–Ikon, Voigtlander, Rollei and all
cameras post–1890.
SPEAK TO Les Frankham.

DOLLS AND DOLLS' HOUSES

THE TEXTILE RESTORATION STUDIO
20 Hargreaves Road, Timperley,
Altrincham, **Cheshire WA15 7BB**
TEL   061 904 9944
FAX   061 903 9144
OPEN   9.30–5 Mon–Fri.

Specialise in cleaning, conserving and
repairing antique dolls.

PROVIDE Home Inspections. Free
Estimates. Collection/Delivery Service
by arrangement.
SPEAK TO Jacqueline Hyman.
Established 1982. This workshop is
included on the register of conservators
maintained by the Conservation Unit of
the Museums and Galleries Commission.
SEE Carpets, Lighting, Silver.

LILIAN MIDDLETON'S ANTIQUE DOLL SHOP
Talbot House, The Square, Stow–on–
the–Wold, **Gloucestershire
GL54 1AB**
TEL   0451 830381
OPEN   9–5 Mon–Sat; 11–5 Sun.

Specialise in providing a comprehensive
dolls' hospital service. Make bisque
dolls' heads on the premises (180
different types).

PROVIDE Home Inspections. Free
Estimates. Free Collection/Delivery
Service.
SPEAK TO Lilian Middleton.

HERTFORDSHIRE CONSERVATION SERVICE

Seed Warehouse, Maidenhead Yard, The Wash, Hertford, **Hertfordshire SG14 1PX**
TEL   0992 588966 or 0992 504662
FAX   0992 503184
OPEN   9–6 Mon–Fri By Appointment.

Specialise in restoring china dolls.

PROVIDE Home Inspections. Free/Chargeable Estimates. Chargeable Collection/Delivery Service.
SPEAK TO J. M. Macqueen.
This workshop is included on the register of conservators maintained by the Conservation Unit of the Museums and Galleries Commission.
SEE Carpets, Porcelain, Lighting, Furniture, Oil Paintings, Picture Frames.

THE LILLIPUT MUSEUM OF ANTIQUE DOLLS AND TOYS

High Street, Brading, **Isle of Wight PO36 0DJ**
TEL   0983 407231
OPEN   Daily 1–5 winter, 9.30–9.30 summer; closed mid–Jan to mid–March

Specialise in restoring all types of dolls and teddy bears.

PROVIDE Free Estimates.
SPEAK TO G. K. Munday.
Member of the Guild of Master Craftsmen.

MARCELLA FLETCHER

24–26 Leyland Road, Penwortham, Preston, **Lancashire PR1 9XS**
TEL   0772 744970
OPEN   By Appointment.

Specialise in dolls' hospital service for Victorian and Edwardian dolls.

PROVIDE Home Inspections. Free Estimates. Chargeable Collection/Delivery Service.
SPEAK TO Marcella Fletcher.

CHELSEA LION

Chenil Galleries, 181–183 Kings Road, **London SW3 5EB**
TEL   071 351 9338
OPEN   11–5 Mon–Sat.

Specialise in restoring antique dolls.

PROVIDE Free Estimates.
SPEAK TO Steve Clark.
SEE Collectors (Toys).

THE DOLLS' HOSPITAL

16 Dawes Road, **London SW6 7EN**
TEL   071 385 2081
OPEN   9.30–5 Mon, Tues, Fri; 10–4 Sat.

Specialise in repairing and restoring antique dolls.

PROVIDE Free Estimates.
SPEAK TO Mr J. Smith

FAITH S. EATON

16 Clifton Gardens, **London W9 1DT**
TEL   071 289 2359
OPEN   By Appointment.

Specialise in wax restoration and conservation of dolls and dolls' houses. Ms Eaton also advises on security and display.

PROVIDE Home Inspections if expenses paid. Refundable Estimates. Chargeable Collection/Delivery Service.
SPEAK TO Faith Eaton.
Author of Care and Repair of Antique and Modern Dolls, Founder Member of Doll Club of Great Britain, Dollmakers Circle.
This workshop is included on the register of conservators maintained by the Conservation Unit of the Museums and Galleries Commission.

MARGARET GLOVER
42 Hartham Road, Isleworth,
Middlesex TW7 5ES
TEL   081 568 4662
OPEN   By Appointment.

Specialise in restoring wax dolls of every kind.

PROVIDE Free Estimates.
SPEAK TO Margaret Glover.
SEE Collectors (Mechanical Music, Wax)

A. F. DUDLEY trading as 'THE FURNITURE CLINIC'
Wykeham Hall, Saham Toney, Thetford,
Norfolk IP25 7ES
TEL   0953 883200
FAX   0953 885800
OPEN   By Appointment.

Specialise in restoring dolls.

PROVIDE Home Inspections. Free
Estimates. Free Collection/Delivery
Service.
SPEAK TO Mr A. Dudley.
Member of the Guild of Master
Craftsmen and the Association of Master
Upholsterers.
SEE Clocks, Furniture, Collectors
(Mechanical Music, Toys).

SARAH BROMILOW
Juniper, Harpsden, Henley–on–Thames,
Oxfordshire RG9 4HL
TEL   0491 577001
FAX   0491 410735
OPEN   9–5 Mon–Fri.

Specialise in repairing and restoring
dolls' houses.

PROVIDE Verbal Estimates over the
telephone. Chargeable
Collection/Delivery Service
SPEAK TO Sarah Bromilow.
SEE Collectors (Toys).

PETER STRANGE
'The Willows', Sutton, Nr. Witney,
Oxford, **Oxfordshire OX8 1RU**
TEL   0865 882020
OPEN   By Appointment Only.

Specialise in china doll restoration,
especially the invisible repairing of
broken and damaged bisque dolls' heads
and bisque figurines, as well as sleeping
eyes and lashes.

PROVIDE Home inspections. Free
Estimates. Chargeable
Collection/Delivery Service.
SPEAK TO Peter Strange.

RECOLLECT STUDIOS (C. JACKMAN)
The Old School, London Road, Sayers
Common, **West Sussex BN6 9HX**
TEL   0273 833314
OPEN   10–5 Tues–Sat.

Specialise in restoring antique and
modern collectors' dolls, wax doll
making, porcelain heads, composition
parts, bodies. (Antique dolls not
accepted by post.)

PROVIDE Free Estimates.
Speak to Mrs Carol Jackman or Mr Paul
Jago.
Member of UKIC for doll repair. Also
teach doll restoration.

CAROLINE J. BOOTH TEXTILE CONSERVATOR
Popples Barn House, Widdop Road,
Heptonstall, Hebden Bridge, **West
Yorkshire HX7 7HD**
TEL   0422 842051
OPEN   10–5 Mon–Fri.

Specialise in a full range of services for
small embroidered, woven and printed
historic textiles, including materials for
dolls' houses and costumes for dolls and
automata. Condition and conservation
reports provided and advice given on
handling, storage and display. Ms Booth

uses traditional conservation techniques so that any work done is reversible.

PROVIDE Home Inspections. Chargeable Estimates. Chargeable Collection/Delivery Service.
SPEAK TO Caroline Booth.
SEE Carpets.

SECOND CHILDHOOD

20 Byram Arcade, Westgate, Huddersfield, **West Yorkshire HD1 1ND**
TEL   0484 530117 or 603854
OPEN   10.30–3.30 Tues–Sat

Specialise in restoring antique dolls and related items, dolls' hospital.

PROVIDE Free Estimates. Free Local Collection/Delivery Service.
SPEAK TO Michael or Elizabeth Hoy.
SEE Collectors (Toys).

DAPHNE FRASER

Glenbarry, 58 Victoria Road, Lenzie, Glasgow, **Strathclyde G66 5AP**
TEL   041 776 1281
OPEN   By Appointment.

Specialise in restoring dolls and dolls' houses.

PROVIDE Free Estimates.
SPEAK TO Daphne Fraser.
This workshop is in the Scottish Conservation Directory.
SEE Collectors (Toys), Oil Paintings, Furniture, Picture Frames.

HAIR

CHARLES CLEMENTS

4–5 Burlington Arcade, Piccadilly, **London W1V 9A13**
TEL   071 493 3923
OPEN   9–5.30 Mon–Sat.

Specialise in rebristling hairbrushes, replacing mirrors and combs.

PROVIDE Free Estimates.
SPEAK TO Charles Clements.

MECHANICAL MUSIC

D. N. CARD

1A Chester Street, Caversham, Reading, **Berkshire RG4 8JH**
TEL   0734 470777
OPEN   9–12.30, 2–5 Mon–Fri or By Appointment.

Specialise in restoring music boxes.

PROVIDE Home Inspections. Free Estimates. Chargeable Collection/Delivery Service.
SPEAK TO David Card.
Mr Card is CMBHI. This workshop is included on the register of conservators maintained by the Conservation Unit of the Museums and Galleries Commission.
SEE Clocks.

S. J. BIRT & SON

21 Windmill Street, Brill, Aylesbury, **Buckinghamshire HP18 9TG**
TEL   0844 237440
OPEN   By Appointment.

Specialise in restoring musical boxes.

PROVIDE Home Inspections. Free Estimates. Free Collection/Delivery Service.
SPEAK TO Mr S. J. Birt.
SEE Clocks.

J. V. PIANOS & CAMBRIDGE PIANOLA CO.

The Limes, Landbeach, Cambridge, **Cambridgeshire CB4 4DR**
TEL   0223 861408 or 861348 or 861507
FAX   0223 441276
OPEN   By Appointment.

Specialise in complete rebuilding of player–pianos, pianolas and nickelodeons.

PROVIDE Home Inspections. Chargeable Estimates. Chargeable Collection/Delivery Service.
SPEAK TO F. T. Poole
SEE Musical Instruments.

MILL FARM ANTIQUES
50 Market Street, Disley, Stockport, **Cheshire SK12 2DT**
TEL   0663 764045
OPEN   9–6 Mon–Sat.

Specialise in restoring cylinder– and disc–playing musical boxes.

PROVIDE Home Inspections. Free Estimates. Free Collection/Delivery Service.
SPEAK TO F. E. Berry.
SEE Clocks.

KEITH HARDING'S WORLD OF MECHANICAL MUSIC
Oak House, High Street, Northleach, **Gloucestershire GL54 3EU**
TEL   0451 860181
FAX   0451 861133
OPEN   10–6 Daily.

Specialise in restoring musical boxes and automata.

PROVIDE Home Inspections. Free Estimates. Free Local Collection/Delivery Service.
SPEAK TO Keith Harding.
SEE Clocks.

GEORGE WORSWICK
108–110 Station Road, Bardney, Lincoln, **Lincolnshire LN3 5UF**
TEL   0526 398352
OPEN   By Appointment.

Specialise in restoring and repairing mechanisms of antique musical boxes of the cylinder type and music combs of disc-playing music boxes.

PROVIDE Free Estimates.
SPEAK TO George Worswick.
Mr Worswick is FBHI.

DAVID NEWELL
55 Shelton Street, **London WC2H 9HE**
TEL   071 836 1000
FAX   071 240 9764
OPEN   10–6 Mon–Fri By Appointment.

Specialise in restoring musical boxes and automata.

PROVIDE Free Estimates in shop.
SPEAK TO David Newell.
Mr Newell is FBHI.
SEE Clocks.

MARGARET GLOVER
42 Hartham Road, Isleworth, **Middlesex TW7 5ES**
TEL   081 568 4662
OPEN   By Appointment.

Specialise in re–dressing automata in exact reproduction of original dress using antique materials.

PROVIDE Free Estimates.
SPEAK TO Margaret Glover.
SEE Collectors (Dolls, Wax).

A. F. DUDLEY trading as 'THE FURNITURE CLINIC'
Wykeham Hall, Saham Toney, Thetford, **Norfolk IP25 7ES**
TEL   0953 883200
FAX   0953 885800
OPEN   By Appointment.

Specialise in restoring automata.

PROVIDE Home Inspections. Free Estimates. Free Collection/Delivery Service.
SPEAK TO Mr A. Dudley.
Members of the Guild of Master

Craftsmen and the Association of Master Upholsterers.
SEE Clocks, Furniture, Dolls, Toys.

WICKENDEN CLOCKS
53 Gorse Road, Thorpe St Andrew, Norwich, **Norfolk NR7 OAY**
TEL   0603 32179
OPEN   9–5 Sun–Sat.

Specialise in restoring music boxes.

PROVIDE Home Inspections. Free Estimates. Free Local Collection/Delivery Service.
SPEAK TO Eric Wickenden.
SEE Clocks.

RICHARD HIGGINS
The Old School, Longnor, Nr. Shrewsbury, **Shropshire SY5 7PP**
TEL   0743 718162
OPEN   8–6 Mon–Fri.

Specialise in restoring music boxes.

PROVIDE Home Inspections. Free/Chargeable Estimates. Collection/Delivery Service by arrangement.
SPEAK TO Richard Higgins.
Member of BAFRA and UKIC. This workshop is included on the register of conservators maintained by the Conservation Unit of the Museums and Galleries Commission.
SEE Furniture, Clocks.

JOHN COWDEROY ANTIQUES
42 South Street, Eastbourne, **East Sussex BN21 4XB**
TEL   0323 720058
FAX   0323 410163
OPEN   9.30–1, 2.30–5 Mon–Fri; 9.30–1 Wed, Sat.

Specialise in restoring musical boxes.

PROVIDE Home Inspections. Free Estimates. Chargeable

Collection/Delivery Service.
SPEAK TO David or Richard Cowderoy.
Member of LAPADA.
SEE Clocks, Furniture.

T. P. BROOKS
Sycamores, School Lane, Lodsworth, Petworth, **West Sussex GU28 9DH**
TEL   07985 248

Specialise in restoring musical boxes and automata.

PROVIDE Home Inspections. Free Estimates. Free Collection/Delivery Service.
SPEAK TO Mr T. P. Brooks.
Member of UKIC. This workshop is included on the register of conservators maintained by the Conservation Unit of the Museums and Galleries Commission.
SEE Clocks.

TIME RESTORED & CO.
18–20 High Street, Pewsey, **Wiltshire SN9 5AQ**
TEL   0672 63544
FAX   0672 63544
OPEN   By Appointment.

Specialise in restoring musical boxes and automata.

PROVIDE Home Inspections. Free Estimates. Free Collection/Delivery Service.
SPEAK TO J. H. Bowler–Reed.
SEE Clocks.

DAVID BARKER
Antique Clock Restoration, Inglenook, Ferncliffe Drive, Utley, Keighley, **West Yorkshire BD20 6HN**
TEL   0535 606306
OPEN   Mon–Sat By Appointment.

Specialise in restoring automata and small antique mechanisms.

PROVIDE Home Inspections. Free Estimates. Free/Chargeable

Collection/Delivery Service.
SPEAK TO David Barker.
This workshop is included on the register of conservators maintained by the Conservation Unit of the Museums and Galleries Commission.
SEE Clocks.

GRANT LEES
98 Gala Park, Galashiels, Selkirkshire, **Borders TD1 1EZ**
TEL   0896 3721
OPEN   9–6 Mon–Sat, closed Wed and Sat a.m.

Specialise in musical boxes.

PROVIDE Home Inspections. Free Estimates. Chargeable Collection/Delivery Service.
SPEAK TO Grant Lees.
This workshop is in the Scottish Conservation Directory.
SEE Clocks, Furniture.

J. TUBBECKE
Antique Clocks, 11 Island Street, Galashiels, **Borders TD1 1NZ**
TEL   0896 58958
OPEN   10–5 Mon, Tues, Thur, Fri; 10–1.30 Sat.

Specialise in restoring music boxes.

PROVIDE Home Inspections. Free Estimates. Free Collection/Delivery Service.
SPEAK TO J. Tubbecke or T. Treeby.
This workshop is in the Scottish Conservation Directory.
SEE Clocks.

JIM WEIR
Woodbank, Charleston, Glamis, by Forfar, Angus, **Highland DD8 1UF**
TEL   0307 840473
FAX   0307 840473
OPEN   By Appointment.

Specialise in restoring antique musical boxes.

PROVIDE Home Inspections. Free Estimates. Chargeable Collection/Delivery Service.
SPEAK TO Jim Weir.
This workshop is in the Scottish Conservation Directory.

PAPER

JANE McNAMARA CONSERVATOR
14 Chelsfield Gardens, **London SE26 4DJ**
TEL   081 699 7173
OPEN   9–5 Mon–Fri By Appointment.

Specialise in conservation of three–dimensional paper artefacts, fans, paper–covered boxes and parchment.

PROVIDE Home Inspections. Free Estimates. Free Local Collection/Delivery Service.
SPEAK TO Jane McNamara.
Member of IPC. This workshop is included on the register of conservators maintained by the Conservation Unit of the Museums and Galleries Commission.
SEE Oil Paintings.

COLLERAN AND CIANTAR LTD
Hillingdon Studio, 80 Denecroft Crescent, Hillingdon, **Middlesex UB10 9HY**
TEL   0895 256410
FAX   0895 256410
OPEN   9–5.30 Mon–Fri.

Specialise in conservation and restoration of paper and related materials, including three–dimensional paper objects and flat paper objects. Reports and on–site visits available.

PROVIDE Home Inspections. Free/Chargeable Estimates.

Free/Chargeable Collection/Delivery
Service.
SPEAK TO Marcel Ciantar.
Member of UKIC, IPC, AIC and IIC.
SEE Oil Paintings.

PENS AND PENCILS

CLASSIC PENS LIMITED
Bassett Business Units, Hurricane Way,
North Weald, Epping, **Essex
CM16 6AA**
TEL   0992 524444
OPEN   8.30–5 Mon–Fri.

Specialise in repairing vintage and
modern pens by major pen
manufacturers.

PROVIDE Free Estimates.
SPEAK TO Andy Lambrou.

JASMIN CAMERON
Antiquarius J6, 131–141 Kings Road,
London SW3 5ST
TEL   071 351 4154
FAX   071 351 5350
OPEN   10.15–5.30 Tues–Sat.

Specialise in restoring vintage and
collectors' fountain pens.

PROVIDE Free Estimates.
SPEAK TO Jasmin Cameron.

PENFRIEND
(BURLINGTON) LTD
34 Burlington Arcade, Piccadilly,
London W1V 9AD
TEL   071 499 6337
OPEN   9.30–5.30 Mon–Sat.

Specialise in restoring fountain pens and
pencils.

PROVIDE Free Estimates.

VINTAGE FOUNTAIN
PENS
Gray's Antique Market, 58 Davies Street,
London W1
Showcases 215 &216 (Nr. Coffee Shop–
downstairs)
TEL   071 493 0208 Day. 081 504
       1969 Evening.
FAX   071 493 9344
OPEN   10–6 Mon–Fri.

Specialise in restoring vintage fountain
pens.

PROVIDE Home Inspections. Chargeable
Estimates. Chargeable
Collection/Delivery Service.
SPEAK TO Chris Robinson.
Member of the Writing Equipment
Society.

PENFRIEND (LONDON)
LTD
Bush House Arcade, Bush House,
Strand, **London WC2B 4PH**
TEL   071 836 9809
OPEN   9.30–5.30 Mon–Fri.

Specialise in restoring fountain pens and
pencils.

PROVIDE Free Estimates.
SPEAK TO Mr P. Woolf.

'VINTAGE PENCILS'
11–13 High Street, Harefield,
Middlesex UB9 6BX
TEL   0895 824920
OPEN   10–5.30 Mon, Tues, Thur, Fri.

Specialise in repair service for
mechanical pencils from antique to
modern. Other forms of writing material
also undertaken which require patience,
skill and re–building rather than the mere
replacement of broken parts.

PROVIDE Free/Chargeable Estimates.
SPEAK TO N. W. J. Davis.

VINTAGE FOUNTAIN PENS

Trevor Russell, 5 Stoneyford Terrace, Uttoxeter, **Staffordshire ST14 8BW**
TEL   0889 562009 Workshop
OPEN   Postal Service Only.
       Exhibits at antique fairs.
       Ring for details.

Specialise in restoring/repairing/servicing fountain pens/propelling pencils.
SPEAK TO Trevor Russell.

SCIENTIFIC INSTRUMENTS

PETER D. BOSSON

10B Swan Street, Wilmslow, **Cheshire SK9 1HE**
TEL   0625 525250 and 527857
OPEN   10–12.45, 2.15–5 Tues–Sat.

Specialise in restoring scientific instruments.

PROVIDE Home Inspections. Free Estimates. Free Collection/Delivery Service within fifty miles.
SPEAK TO Peter Bosson.
SEE Clocks.

THE CHETTLE GUILD

The Stables, Chettle House, Chettle, Blandford, **Dorset DT11 8DB**
TEL   0258 89576
OPEN   9–6 Mon–Sat.

Specialise in restoring scientific instruments.

PROVIDE Home Inspections. Free Estimates. Free Local Collection/Delivery Service.
SPEAK TO Alastair or Andrew Arnold.
SEE Arms, Clocks, Furniture.

THE BAROMETER SHOP

4 New Street, Leominster, **Hereford & Worcester HR6 8BT**
TEL   0568 613652
OPEN   9–5.30 Mon–Sat.

Specialise in restoring scientific instruments.

PROVIDE Home Inspections. Free Estimates. Free Collection/Delivery Service.
SPEAK TO Richard Cookson.
Mr Cookson is CMBHI.
SEE Furniture, Clocks.

ELLIOTT NIXON

5 Alexandra Road, Stoneygate, Leicester, **Leicestershire LE2 2BB**
TEL   0533 703227
OPEN   9–6 Mon–Sat.

Specialise in a full restoration and conservation service for scientific instruments.

PROVIDE Home Inspections. Free Estimates. Free Local Collection/Delivery Service.
SPEAK TO Elliott Nixon.
Mr Nixon is FBHI. This workshop is included on the register of conservators maintained by the Conservation Unit of the Museums and Galleries Commission.
SEE Clocks.

RELCY ANTIQUES

9 Nelson Road, **London SE10 9JB**
TEL   081 858 2812
FAX   081 293 4135
OPEN   10–6 Mon–Sat.

Specialise in restoring scientific and nautical instruments.

PROVIDE Home Inspections. Free/Chargeable Estimates. Collection/Delivery Service by arrangement.
SPEAK TO Robin Challis.
SEE Furniture, Oil Paintings, Silver.

NIDD HOUSE ANTIQUES
Nidd House, Bogs Lane, Harrogate, **North Yorkshire HG1 4DY**
TEL   0423 884739
OPEN   9–5 Mon–Fri or By
       Appointment.

Specialise in restoring scientific instruments.

PROVIDE Home Inspections. Free Local Estimates. Chargeable Collection/Delivery Service.
SPEAK TO Mr D. Preston.
Member of the Guild of Master Craftsmen, UKIC. This workshop is included on the register of conservators maintained by the Conservation Unit of the Museums and Galleries Commission.
SEE Furniture, Porcelain, Silver.

NOLF & MANN
29 Breadalbane Terrace, Wick, **Highland KW1 5AT**
TEL   0955 4284
FAX   0955 4284
OPEN   By Appointment.

Specialise in restoring scientific instruments.

PROVIDE Home Inspections. Free/Chargeable Estimates. Chargeable Collection/Delivery Service.
SPEAK TO T. Nolf.
SEE Arms.

SHIP MODELS

CHARLES PERRY RESTORATIONS LTD
Praewood Farm, Hemel Hempstead Road, St Albans, **Hertfordshire AL3 6AA**
TEL   0727 853487
FAX   0727 846668
OPEN   Mon–Fri 8.30–6; Sat By
       Appointment.

Specialise in restoring ship models.

PROVIDE Home Inspections. Free Estimates. Chargeable Collection/Delivery Service.
SPEAK TO John Carr.
Mr Carr is a member of BAFRA and the Guild of Master Craftsmen.
By Appointment to HM Queen Elizabeth II, Antique Furniture Restorers. This workshop is included on the register of conservators maintained by the Conservation Unit of the Museums and Galleries Commission.
SEE Furniture, Clocks, Books, Collectors (Toys).

SCALE MODELS INTERNATIONAL
Museum Building, Church Road, Waterloo, Liverpool, **Merseyside L22 5NB**
TEL   051 924 4998
OPEN   9–5.30 Mon–Fri or By
       Appointment.

Specialise in restoring ship models and ship model display cases and maritime artefacts.

PROVIDE Home Inspections. Free Estimates. Chargeable Collection/Delivery Service.
SPEAK TO T. L. Nelson–Ewen
Member of UKIC. This workshop is included on the register of conservators maintained by the Conservation Unit of the Museums and Galleries Commission.

KELVIN THATCHER
22 Croxton Hamlet, Nr. Fulmodeston, Fakenham, **Norfolk NR21 0NP**
TEL   0328 878051
OPEN   10–7 Mon–Sat.

Specialise in cleaning and restoring ship models, providing new showcases and movement and transportation of fragile models.

PROVIDE Home Inspections. Free Local Estimates. Chargeable Collection/Delivery Service.

SPEAK TO Kelvin Thatcher.
Member of UKIC. This workshop is included on the register of conservators maintained by the Conservation Unit of the Museums and Galleries Commission.

DONALD SMITH MODELMAKERS

Bridge Road, Kintore, Aberdeenshire, **Grampian AB51 0UL**
TEL   0467 32493 or 0836 365021
FAX   0467 32493
OPEN   8.30–5.30 Mon–Fri.

Specialise in restoring ship models of all types ranging from Board of Admiralty models to builders' full and half–models.

PROVIDE Free Estimates. Chargeable Collection/Delivery Service.
SPEAK TO Donald Smith.
Member of the Guild of Master Craftsmen. This workshop is in the Scottish Conservation Directory.

TAXIDERMY

MR S. MASSAM

27 St Mark's Road, Hadleigh Benfleet, **Essex SS7 2PY**
TEL   0702 555398
OPEN   9–5 Mon–Fri.

Specialise in restoring items of taxidermy, cased or uncased.

PROVIDE Local Home Inspections. Free Estimates. Chargeable Collection/Delivery Service.
SPEAK TO Mr S. Massam.
Member of AMS
SEE and the Guild of Taxidermists. This workshop is included on the register of conservators maintained by the Conservation Unit of the Museums and Galleries Commission.

ANN & JOHN BURTON

Natural Craft Taxidermy, 21 Main Street, Ebrington, Nr. Chipping Camden, **Gloucestershire GL55 6NL**
TEL   038678 231
OPEN   By Appointment.

Specialise in taxidermy commissions and restoration work.

PROVIDE Home Inspections. Free Estimates. Chargeable Collection/Delivery Service.
SPEAK TO Ann or John Burton.

MALCOLM PAUL HARMAN

North Lodge, Quex Park, Birchington, **Kent CT7 0BG**
TEL   0843 42042
FAX   0843 42042
OPEN   By Appointment.

Specialise in all types of taxidermy mounts and casework, including rugs, fish, birds, African and Asian big game and large–scale dioramas for museums. They also mount fresh material and will provide a maintenance service. They do not sell or buy material.

PROVIDE Home Inspections. Free Estimates. Chargeable Collection/Delivery Service.
SPEAK TO Mr Malcolm Harman.
This workshop is included on the register of conservators maintained by the Conservation Unit of the Museums and Galleries Commission.

GET STUFFED

105 Essex Road, **London N1 2SL**
TEL   071 226 1364
OPEN   10.30–4 Mon–Wed, Fri; 10.30–
        1 Thur; 11–4 Sat.

Specialise in all aspects of taxidermy and also supply glass domes.

PROVIDE Free Estimates. Chargeable Collection/Delivery Service.
SPEAK TO Robert Sinclair.

HEADS 'N' TAILS
Bourne House, Church Street,
Wiveliscombe, **Somerset TA4 2LT**
TEL   0984 23097
OPEN   By Appointment.

Specialise in fine taxidermy, including
restoration, particularly cased fish.

PROVIDE Home Inspections. Free
Estimates. Chargeable
Collection/Delivery Service.
SPEAK TO D. McKinley.

MARK WINSTON–SMITH
5 Pigeon Green, Snitterfield, Stratford–
Upon–Avon, **Warwickshire CV37 0LP**
TEL   0789 731485
OPEN   10–10 Daily By Appointment.

Specialise in all taxidermy, producing
mounted natural history specimens of
anatomical accuracy and lifelike, artistic
appearance.

PROVIDE Home Inspections. Free
Estimates. Chargeable
Collection/Delivery Service.
SPEAK TO Sally Winston–Smith. Member
of the Guild of Taxidermists.

BORDER TAXIDERMY STUDIOS
2 Raeson Park, Hawick, Roxburgh,
Borders TD9 7HG
TEL   0450 76092
OPEN   8.30–5 Mon–Fri or By
        Appointment.

Specialise in providing taxidermy
services for birds, fish, mammals and
groundwork. Will do surveys of
collections.

PROVIDE Local Home Inspections. Free
Estimates. Local Collection/Delivery
Service.
SPEAK TO Colin Scott.
Member of the Guild of Taxidermists.
This workshop is in the Scottish
Conservation Directory.

GEORGE C. JAMIESON
'Cramond Tower', Kirk Cramond,
Edinburgh, **Lothian EH4 6NS**
TEL   031 336 1916
FAX   031 336 1916
OPEN   8.30–5.30 Mon–Fri or By
        Appointment.

Specialise in all aspects of taxidermy, fish
casts repaired, game head restorations,
museum work and case work.

PROVIDE Chargeable Home Inspections.
Free Local Estimates. Chargeable
Collection/Delivery Service.
SPEAK TO George Jamieson.
Professional Member of the Guild of
Taxidermists in birds, mammals and fish.
This workshop is in the Scottish
Conservation Directory.

CHRIS CAMPBELL
Unit 4, Foundry Road, Bonnybridge,
Stirlingshire FK4 2BD
TEL   0324 813410
FAX   0324 813410
OPEN   9–5.30 Mon–Fri or By
        Appointment.

Specialise in restoring damaged
taxidermy items, including cleaning,
fumigation, repairs to casework,
renovation.

PROVIDE Home Inspections. Free
Estimates. Chargeable
Collection/Delivery Service.
SPEAK TO Chris Campbell.
This workshop is in the Scottish
Conservation Directory.

TOYS AND ROCKING HORSES

JOHN MARRIOTT ROCKING HORSES
86 Village Road, Bromham,
Bedfordshire MK43 8HU
TEL   02302 3173
OPEN   8–8 Daily.

Specialise in manufacturing and

restoring traditionally styled rocking and carousel horses.

PROVIDE Home Inspections. Free Estimates. Collection/Delivery Service by arrangement.
SPEAK TO John Marriott.

MICHAEL BARRINGTON
The Old Rectory, Warmwell, Dorchester, **Dorset DT2 8HQ**
TEL   0305 852104
OPEN   8.30–5.30 or By Appointment.

Specialise in restoring model steam engines.

PROVIDE Free Local Estimates. Free/Chargeable Collection/Delivery Service.
SPEAK TO Michael Barrington.
SEE Clocks, Furniture.

HADDON ROCKING HORSES LTD
5 Telford Road, Clacton–On–Sea, **Essex CO15 4LP**
TEL   0255 424745
OPEN   8–5 Mon–Thur; 8–1 Fri.

Specialise in restoring rocking horses.

PROVIDE Free Estimates. Chargeable Collection/Delivery Service.
SPEAK TO Graham Warren or Paul Stollery.

CHARLES PERRY RESTORATIONS LTD
Praewood Farm, Hemel Hempstead Road, St Albans, **Hertfordshire AL3 6AA**
TEL   0727 853487
FAX   0727 846668
OPEN   Mon–Fri 8.30–6; Sat By Appointment.

Specialise in restoring rocking horses.

PROVIDE Home Inspections. Free Estimates. Chargeable Collection/Delivery Service.

SPEAK TO John Carr.
Mr Carr is a member of BAFRA and the Guild of Master Craftsmen.
By Appointment to HM Queen Elizabeth II, Antique Furniture Restorers.
This workshop is included on the register of conservators maintained by the Conservation Unit of the Museums and Galleries Commission.
SEE Clocks, Furniture, Books, Collectors (Ship Models).

J. & D. WOODS
180 Chorley Road, Westhoughton, Bolton, **Lancashire BL5 3PN**
TEL   0942 816246
OPEN   By Appointment.

Specialise in constructing and restoring all types of rocking horses. They also supply accessories and are one of the few companies able to restore and make skin–covered horses.

PROVIDE Home Inspections. Free Estimates. Chargeable Collection/Delivery Service.
SPEAK TO John Woods.

ANTHONY JACKSON
20 Westry Corner, Barrowby, Grantham, **Lincolnshire NG32 1DF**
TEL   0476 67477
OPEN   8–5 Mon–Fri or By Appointment.

Specialise in restoring rocking horses.

PROVIDE Home Inspections. Free Estimates. Free Local Collection/Delivery Service.
SPEAK TO Anthony or Amanda Jackson.

CHELSEA LION
Chenil Galleries, 181–183 Kings Road, **London SW3 5EB**
TEL   071 351 9338
OPEN   11–5 Mon–Sat.

Specialise in restoring teddy bears.

PROVIDE Free Estimates.
SPEAK TO Steve Clark.
SEE Collectors (Dolls).

PHIL HILL (ROCKING HORSES)
188 Alcester Road South, Kings Heath, Birmingham, **West Midlands B14 6DE**
TEL   021 444 0102
OPEN   9.30–6 Mon–Fri or By Appointment.

Specialise in restoring wooden rocking horses and carousel animals.

PROVIDE Home Inspections. Free Estimates. Free Collection/Delivery Service.
SPEAK TO Phil Hill.
SEE Furniture.

PETER WATTS ROCKING HORSES
10 Cremorne Road, Four Oaks, Sutton Coldfield, **West Midlands B75 5AH**
TEL   021 308 1477
OPEN   Mon–Sat By Appointment.

Specialise in restoring any wooden rocking horses, also metal and plastic horses where possible. No stuffed horses considered.

PROVIDE Home Inspections. Free Estimates. Chargeable Collection/Delivery Service.
SPEAK TO Peter Watts.
Member of the Guild of West Midlands Artists and Craftsmen Ltd. This workshop is included on the register of conservators maintained by the Conservation Unit of the Museums and Galleries Commission.

A. F. DUDLEY trading as 'THE FURNITURE CLINIC'
Wykeham Hall, Saham Toney, Thetford, **Norfolk IP25 7ES**
TEL   0953 883200
FAX   0953 885800
OPEN   By Appointment.

Specialise in restoring rocking horses.

PROVIDE Home Inspections. Free Estimates. Free Collection/Delivery Service.
SPEAK TO Mr A. Dudley.
Members of the Guild of Master Craftsmen and the Association of Master Upholsterers.
SEE Clocks, Furniture, Collectors (Dolls, Mechanical Music).

SARAH BROMILOW
Juniper, Harpsden, Henley–on–Thames, **Oxfordshire RG9 4HL**
TEL   0491 577001
FAX   0491 410735
OPEN   9–5 Mon–Fri.

Specialise in repairing and restoring rocking horses and other wooden toys.

PROVIDE Verbal Estimates over the telephone. Chargeable Collection/Delivery Service
SPEAK TO Sarah Bromilow.
SEE Collectors (Dolls).

THE ROCKING HORSE WORKSHOP
Ashfield House, The Foxholes, Wem, **Shropshire SY4 5UJ**
TEL   0939 232335
OPEN   9–6 Daily.

Specialise in restoring all types of rocking horses 17th century to present day. Also manufacture new horses and supply parts for do–it–yourself rocking horses.

PROVIDE Home Inspections. Free Estimates. Chargeable Collection/Delivery Service.
SPEAK TO Mr David James Kiss or Mrs Noreen Kiss.

CLIVE GREEN
The Lychgate, 20 Broadmark Lane, Rustington, **West Sussex BN16 2HJ**
TEL   0903 786639
OPEN   By Appointment.

Specialise in restoring carved wooden rocking horses.

PROVIDE Local Home Inspections.
SPEAK TO Clive Green.
Mr Green is co–author with Anthony Dew of Restoring Rocking Horses, a Member of UKIC and Chairman of the British Toymakers Guild 1991, 1992. This workshop is included on the register of conservators maintained by the Conservation Unit of the Museums and Galleries Commission.

ROBERT MULLIS ROCKING HORSE MAKER
55 Berkley Road, Wroughton, Nr. Swindon, **Wiltshire SN4 9BN**
TEL   0793 813583
OPEN   By Appointment Only.

Specialise in restoring rocking horses on bow rockers or safety stands using traditional methods. New horses made to order according to individual requirements.

PROVIDE Home Inspections. Free Estimates. Chargeable Collection/Delivery Service.
SPEAK TO Robert Mullis.

ANTHONY DEW
The Rocking Horse Shop, Old Road, Holme upon Spalding Moor, York, **North Yorkshire YO4 4AB**
TEL   0430 860563
FAX   0430 860563
OPEN   By Appointment.

Specialise in restoring and making rocking horses and will supply all parts and accessories and makes tailor–made–to–measure kits for restorers.

PROVIDE Free Estimates. Collection/Delivery Service by arrangement.
SPEAK TO Pat Dew.
Mr Dew will also take commissions for other carving work.

SECOND CHILDHOOD
20 Byram Arcade, Westgate, Huddersfield, **West Yorkshire HD1 1ND**
TEL   0484 530117 or 603854
OPEN   10.30–3.30 Tues–Sat.

Specialise in teddy bear repairs.

PROVIDE Free Estimates. Local Free Collection/Delivery Service.
SPEAK TO Michael or Elizabeth Hoy.
SEE Collectors (Dolls).

DAPHNE FRASER
Glenbarry, 58 Victoria Road, Lenzie, Glasgow, **Strathclyde G66 5AP**
TEL   041 776 1281
OPEN   By Appointment.

Specialise in restoring rocking horses.

PROVIDE Free Estimates.
SPEAK TO Daphne Fraser.
This workshop is in the Scottish Conservation Directory.
SEE Collectors (Dolls), Oil Paintings, Picture Frames, Furniture.

ALAN LEES
38 Patna Road, Kirkmichael, Maybole, Ayrshire, **Strathclyde KA19 7PJ**
TEL   06555 386
OPEN   By Appointment.

Specialise in restoring and conserving rocking horses and equestrian toys of any age and condition using traditional methods and materials. They can also make replica horses to commission using traditional methods and materials.

PROVIDE Local Home Inspections. Free Estimates. Free Local Collection/Delivery Service.
SPEAK TO Mr Alan Lees.
This workshop is in the Scottish Conservation Directory.

A. P. E. S. ROCKING HORSES

Ty Isaf, Pont Y Gwyddel, Llanfair T.H., Abergele, **Clwyd LL22 9RA**
TEL   0745 79365
OPEN   By Appointment.

Specialise in restoring rocking horses, tricycles (horses), horses and carts, pull–along horses etc. All horses are sympathetically restored and photographs of previous work are available on request. Also designers and makers of full–size and miniature rocking horses.

PROVIDE Home Inspections. Free Estimates. Chargeable Collection/Delivery Service.
SPEAK TO Mr J. Stuart MacPherson or Mrs P. MacPherson.
Member of UKIC. This workshop is listed on the register of conservators maintained by the Conservation Unit of the Museums and Galleries Commission.

WAX

MARGARET GLOVER

42 Hartham Road, Isleworth, **Middlesex TW7 5ES**
TEL   081 568 4662
OPEN   By Appointment.

Specialise in restoring all types of wax artefacts, including wax portraits and small sculptures.

PROVIDE Free Estimates.
SPEAK TO Margaret Glover.
SEE Collectors (Dolls, Mechanical Music).

JENNY SLEVIN

9 Innisboffin, Bailey View, Harbour Road, Dalkey, **Co. Dublin**
TEL   01 280 3429
OPEN   By Appointment.

Specialise in restoring wax figures.

PROVIDE Home Inspections. Free/Chargeable Estimates. Collection/Delivery Service by arrangement.
SPEAK TO Jenny Slevin.
Member of IPCRA.
SEE Carpets, Furniture, Picture Frames, Porcelain.

MUSICAL INSTRUMENTS

ROBERT SHAFTOE

58 High Street, Pavenham, Bedford, **Bedfordshire MK43 7PE**
Workshop; The Chapel, Park Road, Stevington, Bedford, **Bedfordshire MK43 7QG**
TEL   0234 823609 (evenings).
OPEN   8–6.30 Mon–Sat or By Appointment.

Specialise in restoring pipe organs and early keyboard instruments.

PROVIDE Home Inspections. Free/Chargeable Estimates. Collection/Delivery Service.
SPEAK TO Robert Shaftoe.
Established 1964. This workshop is included on the register of conservators maintained by the Conservation Unit of the Museums and Galleries Commission.

DAVID P. HUNT

26 Station Road, Willingham, Cambridge, **Cambridgeshire CB4 5HF**
TEL   0954 260962
OPEN   By Appointment.

Specialise in restoring pianos built pre–1837.

PROVIDE Home Inspections. Free Estimates. Chargeable Collection/Delivery Service.
SPEAK TO David P. Hunt.
Member of UKIC. This workshop is

included on the register of conservators maintained by the Conservation Unit of the Museums and Galleries Commission.

J.V. PIANOS & CAMBRIDGE PIANOLA CO.

The Limes, Landbeach, Cambridge, **Cambridgeshire CB4 4DR**

TEL   0223 861408 or 861348 or 861507
FAX   0223 441276
OPEN   By Appointment.

Specialise in complete rebuilding of pianos.

PROVIDE Home Inspections. Chargeable Estimates. Chargeable Collection/Delivery Service. Tuning Service.
SPEAK TO F. T. Poole.
SEE Collectors (Mechanical Music).

MICHAEL JOHNSON

Upper Sunnyside, Lowther Street, Penrith, **Cumbria CA11 7UW**

TEL   0768 64424
OPEN   By Appointment.

Specialise in all aspects of restoration to violins, violas, cellos, basses and bows. New instruments are finely made in the Italian tradition, specialising in copies of fine instruments.

PROVIDE Home Inspections. Free Estimates. Chargeable Collection/Delivery Service.
SPEAK TO Michael Johnson.

JOHN DIKE

The Manse, Gold Street, Stalbridge, **Dorset DT10 2LX**

TEL   0963 62285
OPEN   9–5 Mon–Fri; 9–12.30 Sat.

Specialise in restoring instruments and bows of the violin family.

PROVIDE Home Inspections. Free

Estimates. Collection/Delivery Service by arrangement.
SPEAK TO John Dike.

PAXMAN (CASES) LTD

3 Tudor Court, Harold Court Road, Romford, **Essex RM3 OAE**

TEL   04023 45415
OPEN   10–6 Mon–Fri.

Specialise in restoring musical instrument cases and brass, string and woodwind instruments.

PROVIDE Free Estimates.
SPEAK TO Peter Robinson.
SEE **London WC2**

MICHAEL COLE

Little Tatchley, 334 Prestbury Road, Cheltenham, **Gloucestershire GL52 3DD**

TEL   0242 517192
OPEN   8.30–5.30 Mon–Sat By Appointment.

Specialise in restoring early pianos, pre–1820, and harpsichords. All aspects of musical instrument restoration, including furniture work and musical function, tuning and concert hire. Parts and materials supplied, including new strings.

PROVIDE Home Inspections. Free Estimates. Chargeable Collection/Delivery Service.
SPEAK TO Michael Cole.
Member of UKIC and FOMRHI. This workshop is included on the register of conservators maintained by the Conservation Unit of the Museums and Galleries Commission.

SAXON ALDRED ORGAN BUILDER

28 Crouch Hall Lane, Redbourn, **Hertfordshire AL3 7EU**

TEL   0582 793408 or 792871
FAX   0582 793402
OPEN   8.30–6 Mon–Fri.

Specialise in restoration and maintenance of pipe organs. Will also build new organs.

PROVIDE Free Local Home Inspections. Free Local Estimates. Free Local Collection/Delivery Service.
SPEAK TO J. S. Aldred.
Associate of the Incorporated Society of Organ Builders and Member of the Federation of Organ Builders. This workshop is included on the register of conservators maintained by the Conservation Unit of the Museums and Galleries Commission.

BRUCE LUCKHURST
Little Surrenden WSorkshops, Bethersden, **Kent TN26 3BG**
TEL   0233 829589
OPEN   9–5 Mon–Fri.

Specialise in instrument cases of all kinds.

PROVIDE Home Inspections. Chargeable Estimates. Chargeable Collection/Delivery Service.
SPEAK TO Bruce Luckhurst.
Member of BAFRA and UKIC. This workshop is included on the register maintained by the Conservation Unit of the Museums and Galleries Commission.
SEE Furniture, Clocks.

PERIOD PIANO COMPANY
Park Farm Oast, Hareplain Road, Biddenden, Nr. Ashford, **Kent TN27 8LJ**
TEL   0580 291393
FAX   0580 712588
OPEN   By Appointment.

Specialise in restoring early pianos from 1780 to 1900, also harpsichords and spinets. Recently restored Beethoven's 1817 grand piano in the Hungarian National Museum and the 1848 grand piano used by Chopin for his last English tour. They will do commissioned

reproductions and also sell restored instruments.

PROVIDE Home Inspections. Free/Chargeable Estimates. Chargeable Collection/Delivery Service.
SPEAK TO David Winston.
Member of UKIC. This workshop is included on the register of conservators maintained by the Conservation Unit of the Museums and Galleries Commission.

JEFFREY CLAMP
Lime Cottage, Oasby, Nr. Grantham, **Lincolnshire NG32 3NB**
TEL   05295 466
OPEN   8.30–6 Daily or By Appointment.

Specialise in restoring keyboard musical instruments, Viennese and English forte pianos, square pianos, harpsichords etc. They also have a nationwide tuning and maintenance service.

PROVIDE Home Inspections. Free Estimates. Free Collection/Delivery Service.
SPEAK TO Jeffrey Clamp.
Member of UKIC. This workshop is included on the register of conservators maintained by the Conservation Unit of the Museums and Galleries Commission.

N. P. MANDER LTD
St Peter's Close, Warner Place, Hackney Road, **London E2 7AF**
TEL   071 739 4747
FAX   071 729 4718
OPEN   By Appointment.

Specialise in construction and repair of pipe organs.

PROVIDE Home Inspections. Refundable Estimates (normally £100), Free Collection/Delivery Service.
SPEAK TO Mr J. P. Mander.

JOSEPH MALACHI O'KELLY

Luthier, 2 Middleton Road, **London E8 4BL**

TEL   071 254 7074
OPEN   By Appointment

Specialise in restoring plucked–string musical instruments, lutes, guitars and 'ouds. Mr O'Kelly works with wood, ivory and tortoisehell on both Western and Islamic instruments.

PROVIDE Free Verbal Estimates. Chargeable Home Inspections. Chargeable Collection/Delivery Service.
SPEAK TO Joseph O'Kelly.
Also give estimates on restoration for instruments in auction.
This workshop is included on the register of conservators maintained by the Conservation Unit of the Museums and Galleries Commission.

JOHN PAGE

Unit B66, Clerkenwell Workshops, 29–31 Clerkenwell Close, **London EC1R 0AT**

TEL   071 2223298
OPEN   By Appointment.

Specialise in restoring harps, including gilding.

PROVIDE Home Inspections. Free Estimates.
SPEAK TO John Page.

MICHAEL PARFETT

Unit 407, Clerkenwell Workshops, 31 Clerkenwell Close, **London EC1R 0AT**

TEL   071 490 8768
OPEN   By Appointment.

Specialise in all aspects of restoration to harpsichords, harps, square pianos and other keyboard instruments. Decoration of harpsichord cases undertaken.

PROVIDE Home Inspections. Free Estimates. Local Free Collection/Delivery Service.
SPEAK TO Michael Parfett.

Licenciate of the City and Guilds of London, Member of UKIC. This workshop is included on the register of conservators maintained by the Conservation Unit of the Museums and Galleries Commission.
SEE Furniture, Picture Frames.

BRIDGEWOOD & NEITZERT

Ilex Works, 10 Northwold Road, **London N16 7HR**

TEL   071 249 9398
FAX   071 249 9398
OPEN   9–6 Mon–Sat.

Specialise in repairing and restoring violins, violas, cellos, double basses and bows, particularly of the baroque and classical periods, lutes and viols.

PROVIDE Home Inspections. Free Estimates. Chargeable Collection/Delivery Service.
SPEAK TO Gary Bridgewood or Tom Neitzert.
This workshop is included on the register of conservators maintained by the Conservation Unit of the Museums and Galleries Commission.

ROBERT MORLEY & CO. LTD

34 Engate Street, **London SE13 7HA**

TEL   081 318 5838
OPEN   9–5 Mon–Sat.

Specialise in repairing and restoring pianos, harpsichords, celestes, spinets, virginals and clavichords, both antique and modern.

PROVIDE Home Inspections. Free Local Estimates. Free Local Collection/Delivery Service.
SPEAK TO John Morley.

J. & A. BEARE LTD

7 Broadwick Street, **London W1V 1FJ**

TEL   071 437 1449
FAX   071 439 4520
OPEN   9–12.15, 1.30–5 Mon–Fri.

Specialise in restoring violins, violas, cellos and bows.

PROVIDE Free Estimates.

J. P. GUIVIER & CO. LTD
99 Mortimer Street, **London W1N 7TA**
TEL   071 580 2560
FAX   071 436 1461
OPEN 9–5 Mon–Fri.

Specialise in restoring and repairing violins, violas, cellos.

PROVIDE Free Estimates.
SPEAK TO Mr White or Mr Hamilton.

PHIL PARKER LTD
106A Crawford Street, **London W1H 1AL**
TEL   071 486 8206
OPEN 10–5.30 Mon–Fri, 10–3 Sat.

Specialise in restoring brass instruments.

PROVIDE Free Estimates.
SPEAK TO Dave Woodhead.

THE HARPSICHORD WORKSHOP
130 Westbourne Terrace Mews, **London W2 6QG**
TEL   071 723 9650
OPEN By Appointment.

Specialise in repairing and restoring harpsichords, spinets and virginals.
SPEAK TO Mark Ransom.

JON RANGER
5 Summerfield Road, **London W5 1ND**
TEL   081 997 1793
ANS   081 997 1793
OPEN By Appointment.

Specialise in restoring pianos and the harpsichord family, especially Early and 19th century forte pianos and squares. Authentic materials and conservation principles always discussed and incorporated in working instruments. Tuning, voicing and concert preparation,

condition reports and specialist piano moving.

PROVIDE Home Inspections.
Free/Chargeable Estimates.
Free/Chargeable Collection/Delivery Service.
SPEAK TO Jonathan Ranger.
Member of UKIC, IMIT, MPTA, Guild of Master Craftsmen, executive of NEMA. This workshop is included on the register of conservators maintained by the Conservation Unit of the Museums and Galleries Commission.

PAXMAN (CASES) LTD
116 Long Acre, **London WC2**
TEL   071 240 3642
OPEN 9–5 Mon–Fri; 10–5 Sat.

Specialise in restoring musical instrument cases and brass, string and woodwind instruments.

PROVIDE Free Estimates.
SPEAK TO Bob Paxman.
SEE **Essex.**

J. G. TREVOR–OWEN
181–193 Oldham Rd, Rochdale, **Greater Manchester OL16 5QZ**
TEL   0706 48138
OPEN 1.30–7 Mon–Fri or By Appointment.

Specialise in restoring violins.

PROVIDE Home Inspections. Refundable Estimates.
SPEAK TO J. G. Trevor–Owen.
SEE Clocks, Oil Paintings.

MARTIN BLOCK INSTRUMENT REPAIRS
12 Elm Park, Stanmore, **Middlesex HA7 4BJ**
TEL   081 954 4347
      ANS 081 954 4347
OPEN 9–6 Mon–Fri, evenings and weekends by arrangement.

Specialise in repairing and restoring saxophones and clarinets.

PROVIDE Free Estimates.
SPEAK TO Martin Block.
Mr Block is a Member of the Institute of Musical Instrument Technology.

COLLINGHAM PIANOS
11 High Street, Collingham, Newark, **Nottingham NG23 7LA**
TEL   0636 892553
OPEN   By Appointment.

Specialise in restoring pianos, player–pianos (pianolas) and reed organs (harmoniums).

PROVIDE Home Inspections. Free Estimates. Chargeable Collection/Delivery Service.
SPEAK TO Nicholas Wynne.
Member of the Guild of Master Craftsmen.

GOETZE AND GWYNN
The Tan Gallop, Welbeck, Worksop, **Nottinghamshire S80 3LW**
TEL   0909 485635
OPEN   8–6 Mon–Fri.

Specialise in restoring organs, mainly pre–Victorian.

PROVIDE Home Inspections. Free Estimates. Collection/Delivery Service.
SPEAK TO Martin Goetze or Dominic Gwynn.
Member of IIC, UKIC, International Society of Organbuilders, British Institute of Organ Studies. This workshop is included on the register of conservators maintained by the Conservation Unit of the Museums and Galleries Commission.

EARLY KEYBOARD AGENCY
Heyford Galleries, High Street, Upper Heyford, Oxford, **Oxfordshire OX5 3LE**
TEL   0865 65989
OPEN   8–6 Mon–Fri.

Specialise in restoring second–hand or new harpsichords, clavichords, spinets and virginals etc. Also supply parts and accessories and make wound strings.

PROVIDE Home Inspections. Free Estimates. Chargeable Collection/Delivery Service.
SPEAK TO Martin J. Robertson.

ALISTAIR FRAYLING–CORK
2 Mill Lane, Wallingford, **Oxfordshire OX10 0DH**
TEL   0491 26221
OPEN   10–6 Mon–Fri; By Appointment Sat.

Specialise in restoring stringed instruments.

PROVIDE Home Inspections. Free Estimates. Chargeable Collection/Delivery Service.
SPEAK TO Alistair Frayling–Cork.
Member of BAFRA.
SEE Furniture, Clocks.

DAVID LEIGH C/O LAURIE LEIGH ANTIQUES
36 High Street, Oxford, **Oxfordshire OX1 4AN**
TEL   0865 244197 or 0608 810607
OPEN   11–5 Mon–Fri, closed Thur, Sun.

Specialise in restoring early keyboard instruments, including spinets, harpsichords, pre–1820 square pianos and pre–1825 grand pianos.

SPEAK TO David Leigh.
Mr Leigh is a professional classical soloist.

PAUL NEVILLE, HARPSICHORDS AND FORTEPIANOS
C.K.S. Workshop, 74 The Street, Blundeston, Lowestoft, **Suffolk NR32 5AB**
TEL   0502 730356
OPEN   By Appointment after 6 p.m.

Specialise in structural, musical and decorative restoration of harpsichords and fortepianos. Also supply specialist materials.

PROVIDE Home Inspections. Refundable Estimates. Chargeable Collection/Delivery Service.
SPEAK TO Paul Neville.
This workshop is included on the register of conservators maintained by the Conservation Unit of the Museums and Galleries Commission.

JOHN ROBINSON PIANOS
Red Lion Cottage, Barnardiston, Haverhill, **Suffolk CB9 7TT**
TEL   044086 613
OPEN   By Appointment.

Specialise in restoring grand and upright pianos. Action re-conditioning, re-stringing, regulating and tuning, soundboard repairs, casework repairs and French polishing.

PROVIDE Home Inspections. Free Estimates. Chargeable Collection/Delivery Service.
SPEAK TO John Robinson.
Established 1978. Member of the Guild of Master Craftsmen and affiliate of the Piano Tuners Association.

SHARON McCALLUM
Workshop, 27 Lesbourne Road, Reigate, **Surrey RH2 7BU**
TEL   0737 223481
OPEN   By Appointment.

Specialise in repairing and restoring brass instruments, especially trombones.

PROVIDE Free Estimates.
SPEAK TO Sharon McCallum.

DAVID J. LAW
Ash House, East Street, Long Compton, Shipston–On–Stour, **Warwickshire CV36 5JJ**
TEL   0608 84493
OPEN   By Appointment.

Specialise in restoring harpsichords, virginals, spinets, clavichords and square and fortepianos to 1830. Full documentation, photographic report and drawing service available.

PROVIDE Home Inspections. Free Estimates. Chargeable Collection/Delivery Service.
SPEAK TO David Law.
Mr Law is co-author of A Handbook of Historical Stringing Practice for Keyboard Instruments 1671–1856. This workshop is included on the register of conservators maintained by the Conservation Unit of the Museums and Galleries Commission.

PETER CONACHER AND COMPANY LTD
Springwood Organ Works, Water Street, Huddersfield, **West Yorkshire HD1 4BB**
TEL   0484 530053
FAX   0484 530053
OPEN   9–5 Mon–Fri.

Specialise in restoring pipe organs of all types, including barrel organs, fairground organs, harmoniums and reed organs. They also carry out tuning and small repairs.

PROVIDE Home Inspections. Chargeable Estimates. Chargeable Collection/Delivery Service.
SPEAK TO John Sinclair Willis.
Established 1854. Fellow of the Institute of Musical Instrument Technology, Fellow of the Incorporated Society of Organ Builders and Fellow of the RSA. This workshop is included on the register of conservators maintained by the Conservation Unit of the Museums and Galleries Commission.

WILLIAM D. PATTERSON
Mellifontstown, Bartlemy, Fermoy, **Co. Cork**
TEL 025 36549
OPEN By Appointment.

Specialise in restoring stringed instruments and bows.

PROVIDE Home Inspections. Free Estimates. Collection/Delivery Service by arrangement.
SPEAK TO William Patterson.
Member of IPCRA.

WILLIAM HOFMANN
Unit 1A, Greystones Shopping Centre, Mill Road, Greystones, **Co. Wicklow**
TEL 01 287 3299
FAX 01 287 7555
OPEN 10.30–1.30 Tues–Sat.

Specialise in restoring violins, violas, cellos and their bows.

PROVIDE Free/Chargeable Estimates.
SPEAK TO William Hoffman.
Member of IPCRA and ILA.

GRANT O'BRIEN
St Cecilia's Hall, Niddry Street, Edinburgh, **Lothian EH1 1LJ**
TEL 031 556 8075 and 650 2805
OPEN By Appointment.

Specialise in restoring early keyboard instruments.

PROVIDE Home Inspections. Free/Chargeable Estimates. Collection/Delivery Service by arrangement.
SPEAK TO Grant O'Brien.

BRIAN RATTRAY
34 Spylaw Street, Colinton, Edinburgh, **Lothian EH13 0JT**
TEL 031 441 1098
OPEN 9–5.30 Mon–Fri.

Specialise in restoring stringed instruments of the violin family.

PROVIDE Free Estimates.
SPEAK TO Brian Rattray.
This workshop is in the Scottish Conservation Directory.

SAN DOMENICO STRINGED INSTRUMENTS
175 Kings Road, Cardiff, **South Glamorgan CF1 9DF**
TEL 0222 235881
FAX 0222 344510
OPEN 10–4.30 Mon–Fri; 10–1 Sat.

Specialise in restoring violins, violas, cellos and bows.

PROVIDE Home Inspections. Free Estimates. Free Collection/Delivery Service.
SPEAK TO Howard Morgan.

ARMS AND ARMOUR AND SPORTING EQUIPMENT

DO

As little restoration as possible – originality is important to antiques
Always store in a dry environment at room temperature
Keep metal parts lightly oiled or greased
Clean barrels after use
Always ensure that fine quality guns are overhauled and repaired by gun specialists –
more guns are ruined by bad workmanship than anything else
Avoid denting the barrels as the process of raising the dents causes overall wear

DON'T

Polish, as this produces wear
Operate the firing mechanism when you are not intending to fire the weapon, as this
can cause damage
Attempt to take your gun to pieces
Store in a baize-lined case for long periods – any dampness in the baize can cause serious
corrosion
Re-blue barrels unless absolutely necessary, as this will cause wear

ARMS AND ARMOUR

JASON ABBOT GUNMAKERS LTD
1–3 Bell Street, Princes Risborough,
Buckinghamshire P17 OAD
TEL 08444 6677
FAX 0844 274155
OPEN By Appointment.

Specialise in restoring fine quality
English guns.

PROVIDE Free Estimates.
Collection/Delivery Service.
SPEAK TO Jason Abbot.

JOCK HOPSON CONSERVATION SERVICE
Holes Lane, Olney, **Buckinghamshire MK46 4BX**
TEL 0234 712306
FAX 0234 241634
OPEN By Appointment.

Specialise in restoring Japanese armour.

PROVIDE Home Inspections.
Free/Chargeable Estimates. Chargeable
Collection/Delivery Service.
SPEAK TO Jock Hopson.
Member of UKIC. This workshop is
included on the register of conservators
maintained by the Conservation Unit of
the Museums and Galleries Commission.
SEE Furniture, Picture Frames.

TERENCE PORTER ANTIQUE ARMS
The Beeches, 116 Chalmers Hill, Steeple
Claydon, **Buckinghamshire MK18 2PE**
TEL 0296 738255
FAX 0296 730810
OPEN 10–5 Mon–Fri.

Specialise in restoration work on all
American and European arms and
armour.

PROVIDE Home Inspections. Free
Estimates. Chargeable
Collection/Delivery Service.
SPEAK TO Sarah Porter or Terry Porter.

THE CHETTLE GUILD
The Stables, Chettle House, Chettle,
Blandford, **Dorset DT11 8DB**
TEL 0258 89576
OPEN 9–6 Mon–Sat.

Specialise in restoring arms and armour.

PROVIDE Home Inspections. Free
Estimates. Free Local
Collection/Delivery Service.
SPEAK TO Alastair or Andrew Arnold.
SEE Clocks, Furniture, Collectors
(Scientific Instruments).

H. S. GREENFIELD AND SON
4–5 Upper Bridge Street, Canterbury,
Kent CT1 2NB
TEL 0227 456959
FAX 0227 765030
OPEN 8.30–5.30 Mon–Sat.

Specialise in repairing and valving
vintage shotguns and fishing tackle.

PROVIDE Home Inspections. Free
Estimates. Chargeable
Collection/Delivery Service.
SPEAK TO T. S. Greenfield.

LINCOLNSHIRE CONSERVATION STUDIO
c/o Museum of Lincolnshire Life,
Burton Road, Lincoln, **Lincolnshire LN1 3LY**
TEL 0522 533207
OPEN 9 5 Mon–Fri.

Specialise in restoring arms and armour
to museum conservation standards.

PROVIDE Home Inspections.

Free/Chargeable Estimates. Chargeable Collection/Delivery Service.
SPEAK TO Stephanie Margrett or David Fisher.
Member of UKIC. This workshop is included on the register of conservators maintained by the Conservation Unit of the Museums and Galleries Commission.
SEE Porcelain, Furniture, Lighting.

ARTISTRY AND METAL
Oakset Drive, Welbeck, Nr. Worksop, **Nottinghamshire S80 3LW**
TEL   0909 486029
OPEN   8–5 Mon–Fri.

Specialise in restoring edged weapons and armour.

PROVIDE Home Inspections.
Free/Chargeable Estimates. Chargeable Collection/Delivery Service.
SPEAK TO F. J. M. Craddock.
Member of UKIC, BABA and GBS.

WARDLE'S COTTAGE
Holbeck Woodhouse, Welbeck, Nr. Worksop, **Nottinghamshire S80 3NQ**
TEL   0909 720448
OPEN   805 Mon–Fri.

Specialise in restoring edged weapons and armour.

PROVIDE Home Inspections.
Free/Chargeable Estimates. Chargeable Collection/Delivery Service.
SPEAK TO S. Clarke.
Member of UKIC, BABA and GBS.

PHOEBE CLEMENTS
19 Middlethorpe Drive, York, **North Yorkshire YO2 2NG**
TEL   0904 708279
OPEN   By Appointment.

Specialise in restoring iron and steel work, including armour.

PROVIDE Home Inspections.
Free/Chargeable Estimates. Free Collection/Delivery Service.

SPEAK TO Phoebe Clements.
This workshop is included on the register of conservators maintained by the Conservation Unit of the Museums and Galleries Commission.
SEE Furniture, Silver.

D. W. DYSON (ANTIQUE WEAPONS)
Wood Lea, Shepley, Huddersfield, **West Yorkshire HD8 8ES**
TEL   0484 607331
FAX   0484 604114
OPEN   By Appointment.

Specialise in restoration of all types of arms including pistols, guns and swords and all items made of wood, metal and similar materials.

PROVIDE Home Inspections. Free Estimates. Collection/Delivery Service by arrangement.
SPEAK TO David Dyson.
Also manufacture miniature arms and presentation pieces to customers' specifications. Experienced in working with precious metals using archaic techniques such as mercury gilding, inlaying in bone, ivory etc.

NOLF & MANN
29 Breadalbane Terrace, Wick, **Highland KW1 5AT**
TEL   0955 4284
OPEN   By Appointment.

Specialise in restoring firearms.

PROVIDE Home Inspections.
Free/Chargeable Estimates. Chargeable Collection/Delivery Service.
SPEAK TO T. Nolf.
SEE Collectors (Scientific Instruments).

THE HIGHLAND SHOP
Blair Atholl, **Tayside PH18 5SG**
TEL   0796 481303
OPEN   9–5 Daily (Summer); 9–5 Tue–Sat (Winter).

Specialise in restoring antique weapons, individual and collections, edged and firearm.

PROVIDE Home Inspections. Free Estimates. Chargeable Collection/Delivery Service.
SPEAK TO Edward H. Slaytor.
Mr Slaytor is an indentured gunsmith (London).

WESTPORT GALLERY
3 Old Hawkhill, Dundee, **Tayside DD1 5EU**
TEL   0382 21751
OPEN   9–5 Mon–Fri.

Specialise in restoring firearms.

PROVIDE Free Estimates. Chargeable Collection/Delivery Service.

SPEAK TO Neil Livingstone.
SEE Furniture, Oil Paintings, Picture Frames, Silver.

HERMITAGE ANTIQUITIES
10 West Street, Fishguard, **Dyfed SA65 9AE**
TEL   0348 873037 and 872322
OPEN   9.30–5.30 Mon–Sat; 9.30–1 Wed and Sat.

Specialise in antique arms restoration, especially 16th and 17th century.

PROVIDE Home Inspections. Free Estimates. Chargeable Collection/Delivery Service.
SPEAK TO J. B. Thomas.

SPORTING EQUIPMENT

BILLIARDS

WILLIAM BENTLEY BILLIARDS
(Antique Billiards Specialist), Standen Manor Farm, Hungerford, **Berkshire RG17 0RB**
TEL   0488 681711
FAX   0488 685197
OPEN   9–5 Mon–Fri or By Appointment.

Specialise in restoring billiard tables, cabinets and billiard dining tables including French polishing.

PROVIDE Home Inspections. Free/Chargeable Estimates. Free/Chargeable Collection/Delivery Service.
SPEAK TO Travers Nettleton.

HAMILTON AND TUCKER BILLIARD CO. LTD
Park Lane, Knebworth, **Hertfordshire SG3 6PJ**
TEL   0438 811995
FAX   0438 814939
OPEN   9–5 Mon–Fri.

Specialise in restoring period billiard tables and associated accessories.

PROVIDE Home Inspections. Free Estimates. Chargeable Collection/Delivery Service.
SPEAK TO Hugh Hamilton.

GOLF

HICKORY STICKS GOLF CO. (ST ANDREWS) LTD

6 Abbey Street, St Andrews, **Fife**
KY16 9LA
TEL   0334 77099 FAX
OPEN   8.30–5.30 Mon–Fri.

Specialise in restoring golf clubs and associated equipment of any age, especially pre–1900 clubs.

PROVIDE Home Inspections. Free Estimates. Chargeable Collection/Delivery Service.
SPEAK TO Barry Kerr.
Mr Kerr has had thirty–two years' experience as a clubmaker and a golf professional. He is a member of British Golf Collectors Society, American Golf Collectors Society and Professional Clubmakers Society. This workshop is in the Scottish Conservation Directory.

OLD ST ANDREWS GALLERY

9 Albany Place, St Andrews, **Fife**
KY16 9HH
and 10 Golf Place, St Andrews, **Fife**
KY16 9JA
TEL   0334 7840 and 78712
OPEN   10–5 Mon–Sat.

Specialise in advice on care of antique golf clubs.

PROVIDE Home Inspections. Free Estimates. Free Collection/Delivery Service.
SPEAK TO Mr or Mrs Brown.
SEE Silver.

RIDING

TRENT SADDLERS WORKSHOP

Unit 10, Chaucer Court Workshops,
Chaucer Street, Nottingham,
Nottinghamshire NG1 5LP
TEL   0602 473832
OPEN   9.30–6 Mon, Tues, Thur; 10–4
          first Saturday of each month.

Specialise in repairs to leather goods such as hand and shoulder bags, executive cases and luggage. This includes the renovation and repair of reptile leather. Also servicing, repair and refurbishment of saddlery and bridlework and associated equine equipment.

PROVIDE Chargeable Home Inspections. Free Verbal Estimates. Chargeable Collection/Delivery Service.
SPEAK TO Christopher or Clare Beswick

ART RESEARCHERS AND HERALDRY

ART RESEARCHERS

TIMOTHY P. SAXON
229 New Bedford Road, Luton,
Bedfordshire LU3 1LN
TEL   0582 27790
OPEN   By Appointment.

Specialise in freelance fine art and picture research, especially biographical information on lesser known Modern British documented artists and searching for their paintings using genealogical methods. History, literary and family history research also undertaken.

SPEAK TO Timothy P. Saxon.
Member of Association of Genealogists and Record Agents (AGRA).

MICHAEL NAXTON
'Whistlers', 6 The Mount, Caverham,
Reading, **Berkshire RG4 7RU**
TEL   0734 475535
FAX   0734 476693

Specialise in research and compilation of histories for ships of the Royal Navy and mercantile marine, all periods, sail or steam. Also identification of ship portraits and naval battle scenes.

SPEAK TO Michael Naxton.

ALLYSON McDERMOTT (INTERNATIONAL CONSERVATION CONSULTANTS)
Lintz Green Conservation Centre, Lintz Green House, Lintz Green, Rowlands Gill, **Durham NE39 1NL**
TEL   0207 71547 or 0831 104145 or
          0831 257584
FAX   0207 71547
OPEN   9–5.30 Mon–Fri.

Specialise in historical research and authentication.

PROVIDE Home Inspections. Free Estimates. Chargeable Collection/Delivery Service.

SPEAK TO Allyson McDermott or Gillian Lee.

They have a Southern Regional Office at 45 London Road, Cheltenham, **Gloucestershire**.

SEE Carpets, Lighting, Oil Paintings, Picture Frames, Specialist Photographers.

ANN HILDER
7 The Shrubbery, Upminster, **Essex RM14 3AH**

TEL　0708 221453

OPEN　By Appointment.

Specialise in research into Medieval Art 18th and 19th century English.

SPEAK TO Ann Hilder.

Member of the Association of Art Historians.

JUNE MACFARLANE–COHEN
Tilbury–juxta–Clare, Halstead, **Essex CO9 4JJ**

TEL　0787 237526

OPEN　By Appointment.

Specialise in research into the Norwich School, East Anglian School, Omega Workshops, post–revolutionary Russian Art, Bauhaus, Victorian studies, Classicism and Romanticism; British painting and sculpture 1900–1945.

SPEAK TO June Macfarlane–Cohen.

Member of the Association of Art Historians.

VERONICA WILLIAMS
Head of Religious Studies & Philosophy, King Alfred's College, Sparkford Road, Winchester, **Hampshire SO22 6EZ**

TEL　0962 841515

OPEN　By Appointment.

Specialise in research into religion and art from 1100–1500 A.D. including some Oriental traditions.

SPEAK TO Veronica Williams.

Member of the Association of Art Historians.

WARREN HEARNDEN
Flat 4, 98 Greencroft Gardens, **London NW6 3PH**

TEL　071 624 8075

OPEN　By Appointment.

Specialise in research into Renaissance Art, 18th century French paintings, Rembrandt and 19th century European Art.

PROVIDE Home Inspections.

SPEAK TO Warren Hearnden. Member of the Association of Art Historians.

DR BRIGITTE CORLEY
51 Middleway, **London NW11 6SH**

TEL　081 455 4783

OPEN　By Appointment.

Specialise in research into Northern European Art 1350–1500, particularly German paintings.

SPEAK TO Dr Brigitte Corley.

Member of the Association of Art Historians, FRSA, Turner Society, Renaissance Society.

JAMES NALL–CAIN
Flat 2, 14 Gloucester Square, **London W2 2TB**

TEL　071 402 4989

FAX　081 943 2228

OPEN　By Appointment.

Specialise in research into fine and decorative arts.

SPEAK TO James Nall-Cain.

MARINA WALLACE
29 Chepstow Road, **London W2 5BP**

TEL　071 727 0323

OPEN　By Appointment.

Specialise in research into 15th and 16th century Venetian, Renaissance, Italian and Ottoman Art. Also researches Modern Italian Art.

PROVIDE Home Inspections.
SPEAK TO Marina Wallace. Member of the Association of Art Historians and of the Accordia Research Centre.

CAROLINE KNIGHT
49 Benbow Road, **London W6 0AU**
TEL   081 748 0981
OPEN   By Appointment.

Specialise in research into British interior decoration of the 16th to 18th centuries.
SPEAK TO Caroline Knight.
Member of the Association of Art Historians.

MADELEINE MARSH
3 Iffley Road, **London W6 0PB**
TEL   081 741 0410
FAX   081 741 4947

Specialise in research into fine and decorative arts, provenance investigation, catalogue compilation.
SPEAK TO Madeleine Marsh.
Author of 'How To Research Your Paintings, Antiques and Collectables'.

DR NICHOLAS EASTAUGH
1–2 Park Street, Teddington, **Middlesex TW11 0LT**
TEL   081 943 4448
FAX   081 943 2228
OPEN   By Appointment Only.

Specialise in research into methods and materials of paintings, including infra–red reflectography and x–radiography to study artists' techniqes, underdrawing, alterations and condition, macro–photography, ultra–violet and surface examination, pigment, layer structure and media analysis for dating purposes, comparative studies of paintings in their historical context with critical literature reviews.

PROVIDE Free Estimates.
SPEAK TO Dr Nicholas Eastaugh Ph.D; Dip. Cons.; B.Sc. This workshop is included on the register of conservators maintained by the Conservation Unit of the Museums and Galleries Commission.

THE FINE ART & ANTIQUE RESEARCH CONSULTANCY
34 Crane Road, Twickenham, **Middlesex TW2 6RY**
TEL   081 894 2513
OPEN   By Appointment.

Specialise in researching paintings, sculpture and decorative arts of all periods.

PROVIDE Home Inspections.
SPEAK TO Sara Peterson.

MICHAEL ORR PATERSON
24 Adamsrill Close, Enfield, **Middlesex EN1 2BP**
TEL   081 360 8898
OPEN   By Appointment.

Specialise in research into 18th century English and Victorian paintings, modern figurative art and Wedgwood pottery.

PROVIDE Home Inspections.
SPEAK TO Michael Orr Paterson.
Member of the Association of Art Historians.

BRIAN DAVIS
Little Drift, Necton, Swaffham, **Norfolk PE37 8HZ**
TEL   0760 440 420
OPEN   By Appointment.

Specialise in research into British Art 1750–1850, British Romanticism, 19th century British architecture and 19th century French Art.

PROVIDE Home Inspections.
SPEAK TO Brian Davis.

Member of the Association of Art Historians.

DR JOHN M. MITCHELL CBE

The Cottage, Pains Hill Corner, Limpsfield, **Surrey RH8 ORB**
TEL　0883 723354
OPEN　By Appointment.

Specialise in translations from French and German on 19th and 20th century European Art.
SPEAK TO Dr John Mitchell.
Member of the Association of Art Historians.

IAN PICKFORD

Tolverne, Station Road, Chobham, Nr. Woking, **Surrey GU24 8AL**
TEL　0276 858494
OPEN　By Appointment.

Specialise in research into English silver and Old Sheffield Plate.

PROVIDE Home Inspections.
SPEAK TO Ian Pickford. Member of the Association of Art Historians and Freeman of the Goldsmiths' Company.

DR ANTHONY F. HOBSON

Pear Tree Cottage, Ilmington, Shipston–on–Stour, **Warwickshire CV36 4LG**
TEL　0608 682423
OPEN　By Appointment.

Specialise in research into 19th and early 20th century English, Italian and American Art. Also research into heraldry.

PROVIDE Home Inspections.
SPEAK TO Dr Anthony Hobson. Member of the Association of Art Historians and Hon. FHS.
Dr Hobson is also a portrait painter and has exhibited at the RA, RP, ROI, RBA etc.

DR CHRISTA GARDNER VON TEUFFEL

108 Kenilworth Road, Coventry, **Warwickshire CV4 7AH**
TEL　0203 418261
OPEN　By Appointment.

Specialise in research into 14th and 15th century Italian Art, the Renaissance, 14th, 15th and 16th century German painting.

PROVIDE Home Inspections.
SPEAK TO Dr Christa Gardner von Teuffel.
Member of the Association of Art Historians.

LESLIE KNIGHTSBRIDGE– KNIGHT

Broadwell Leigh, White Street, Market Lavington, **Wiltshire SN10 4DP**
TEL　0380 812750
OPEN　By Appointment.

Specialise in research into Franco–Flemish manuscripts of the 15th century and Renaissance Art in Northern Europe.

PROVIDE Home Inspections.
SPEAK TO Leslie Knightsbridge–Knight.
Member of the Association of Art Historians.

NICOLA GORDON BOWE

Parsley Cottage, 11 Ashfield Avenue, Ranelagh, Dublin 6, **Co. Dublin**
TEL　01 97 5822
OPEN　By Appointment.

Specialise in researching 19th and 20th century art design, especially the Arts and Crafts Movement.

PROVIDE Chargeable Home Inspections.
SPEAK TO Nicola Gordon Bowe.
Member of the Association of Art Historians, the Design History Society, the Decorative Arts Society and the American Decorative Arts Society.

DR SYLVIA AULD

Fine Art Department, University of Edinburgh, 19 George Street, Edinburgh, **Lothian EH8 9LD**
TEL   031 650 3975
OPEN   By Appointment.

Specialise in research into 15th and early 16th century Islamic Art.

PROVIDE Home Inspections.
SPEAK TO Dr Sylvia Auld. Member of the Association of Art Historians, Fellow of the Society of Scottish Antiquaries.

CERI THOMAS

Villa Seren, 23 Park Road, Barry, **South Glamorgan CF62 6NW**
TEL   0446 735616
OPEN   By Appointment.

Specialise in researching Renaissance art and architecture and post–war British and Italian painting and sculpture. Also a practising figurative artist.

PROVIDE Home Inspections. Free/Chargeable Estimates. Chargeable Collection/Delivery Service.
SPEAK TO Ceri Thomas. Member of the Association of Art Historians and founder member of the Euro–Wales 92 Group.

HERALDRY

COLLEGE OF ARMS

Queen Victoria Street, **London EC4V 4BT**
TEL   071 248 2762
OPEN   10–4 Mon–Fri.

Specialise in searches in the Official Heraldic and Genealogical Records of the College of Arms, undertaken on a professional basis.
SPEAK TO the Officer–in–Waiting.
SEE Books.

PETER BEAUCLERK DEWAR RD, FSA Scot, FHG (Hon)

45 Airedale Avenue, **London W4 2NW**
TEL   081 995 6770
FAX   081 747 8459
OPEN   By Correspondence or Arrangement.

Specialise in heraldic, genealogical and historical research. Also provide an armorial identification service. Several times Falkland Pursuivant Extraordinary.

PROVIDE Home Inspections by arrangement. Free Estimates.
SPEAK TO Peter Beauclerk Dewar.

JOHN ALLEN

Applecroft, Binfield Heath, Henley–on–Thames, **Oxfordshire RG9 4LT**
TEL   0734 478712
OPEN   By Appointment.

Specialise in researching armorials found on paintings, antiques etc., providing an armorial identification service. Documentary support of all identifications is provided as a matter of routine.

PROVIDE Home Inspections by arrangement. Free Estimates. Postal service on photocopies, polaroids or sketches.
SPEAK TO John Allen.

OFFICE OF THE CHIEF HERALD OF IRELAND

2 Kildare Street, Dublin 2, **Co. Dublin**
TEL   01 611626
OPEN   10–12, 2–4.30 Mon–Fri.

Specialise in granting coats–of–arms and will do arms searches if given relevant information, consultancy service on ancestry tracing provided; State Heraldic Museum with circa 500 artefacts.
SPEAK TO Fergus Gillespie.

COURT OF THE LORD LYON

HM New Register House, Edinburgh,
Lothian EH1 3YT
TEL   031 556 7255
FAX   031 557 2148

OPEN   10–12.30, 2–4 Mon–Fri.
Specialise in researching heraldry.
SPEAK TO Mrs C. V. G. Roads, MVO,
Lyon Clerk and Keeper of the Records.

INSURANCE AND
SECURITY

TOWRY LAW (GENERAL INSURANCE) LIMITED

Godolphin Court, Stoke Poges Lane, Slough, **Berkshire SL1 3PB**

TEL 0753 821241
FAX 0753 570881
OPEN 9–5 Mon–Fri.

Specialise in household insurance for collectors of fine art and antiques.

PROVIDE Home Inspections. Free Estimates.
SPEAK TO Roger Parkinson.

FRIZZELL COUNTRYSIDE INSURANCE

Bolton House, 56–58 Parkstone Road, Poole, **Dorset BH15 2PH**

TEL 0202 765050
FAX 0202 502363
OPEN 9–5 Mon–Fri.

Specialise in providing insurance tailored for the needs of clients in respect of their homes, fine art and valuables.

PROVIDE Home Inspections. Free Quotations and Advice.
SPEAK TO Eric Parry.

ROGER LARK AND SEDGWICK

Wickham House, Wakering Road, Barking, **Essex IG11 6PB**

TEL 081 594 9711
FAX 081 594 7083 or 591 5339.
OPEN 9–5 Mon–Fri.

Specialise in advice for high value personal insurance, household buildings and contents, fine art, antiques, jewellery and other valuables.

PROVIDE Home Inspections.
SPEAK TO Paul Scott or Stuart Chauncy. Member of IBRC and BIIBA, Lloyds broker.

ARTSCOPE INTERNATIONAL INSURANCE SERVICES LIMITED

2 Victoria Road, Farnborough, **Hampshire GU14 7NS**

TEL 0252 544000
FAX 0252 543152
OPEN 9–5 Mon–Fri.

Specialise in providing specialist insurance and advice for private collectors and galleries.
SPEAK TO Richard King or Richard Evans.
SEE **London E1**

ID–LINK LTD
Rowberry House, Copse Cross Street, Ross–on–Wye, **Hereford & Worcester HR9 5PD**
TEL   0989 769399
FAX   0989 769499
OPEN   9–5 Mon–Fri.

Specialise in supplying electronic ID tags for high value items at risk of loss or theft. They have a fully integrated service and database facility.
SPEAK TO Mrs M. Lloyd or Mr Ian Jebbett.

ARTSCOPE INTERNATIONAL INSURANCE SERVICES LIMITED
6 Braham Street, **London E1 8ED**
TEL   071 709 7444
FAX   071 480 7450
OPEN   8.30–6.30 Mon–Fri.

Specialise in providing specialist insurance and advice for private collectors and galleries.
SPEAK TO Richard King or Richard Evans.
SEE **Hampshire**

MINET LIMITED
Fine Arts and Jewellery Division, Minet House, 66 Prescot Street, **London E1 8BU**
TEL   071 481 0707
FAX   071 488 9786
OPEN   9–5.30 Mon–Fri.

Specialise in arranging insurance in the field of jewellery and fine arts.
SPEAK TO James M. A. Mark, Managing Director.

HOMEGUARD LIMITED
80–84 St Mary Road, **London E17 9RE**
TEL   081 520 4464
FAX   081 520 8335
OPEN   9–12.15, 1.30–5 Mon–Fri.

Specialise in security installations and door maintenance, safes opened and serviced.
PROVIDE Free/Chargeable Home Inspections . Chargeable Estimates.
SPEAK TO A. J. Camfield or P. M. Camfield.
Established 1948. This workshop is included on the register of conservators maintained by the Conservation Unit of the Museums and Galleries Commission.
SEE Furniture.

SNEATH KENT & STUART LTD
Stuart House, 53–55 Scrutton Street, **London EC2A 4QQ**
TEL   071 739 5646
FAX   071 739 6467 or 739 2656
OPEN   9–5.30 Mon–Fri.

Specialise in insurance for dealers, auctioneers and collectors.
SPEAK TO David Ezzard, Clive Massey or Geoffrey Sneath.
They are official brokers to LAPADA and the FATG.

CAMERON RICHARD AND SMITH INSURANCE SERVICES LTD
Boundary House, 7–17 Jewry Street, **London EC3N 2HP**
TEL   071 488 4554
FAX   071 481 1406
OPEN   9.30–5.30 Mon–Fri.

Specialise in fine art insurance, including furniture, jewellery, objets d'art and classic cars.
PROVIDE Home Inspections by arrangement.
SPEAK TO Charles Williams.

CROWLEY COLOSSO LTD
European Division, Lowndes Lambert House, 53 Eastcheap, **London EC3P 3HL**
TEL　　071 283 2000
FAX　　071 626 4245
OPEN　9–6.30 Mon–Fri.

Specialise in fine arts and antiques insurance for private collectors, museums, galleries, shippers/packers, auction houses and restorers/conservators.

PROVIDE Free Estimates.
SPEAK TO Dominic Hepworth.

R. K. HARRISON INSURANCE BROKERS LTD
3–4 Royal Exchange Buildings, London EC3V 3NL
TEL　　071 626 0184
FAX　　071 626 0115
OPEN　9–5.30 Mon–Fri.

Specialise in the placing of insurance for fine art collections and historic homes, also insurances for the farmer and landowner and commercial and industrial insurances.

PROVIDE Home Consultations. Free Quotations.
SPEAK TO Derek J. Woodward.

THE ART LOSS REGISTER
13 Grosvenor Place, **London SW1X 7HH**
TEL　　071 235 3393
FAX　　071 235 1652
OPEN　9–5.30 Mon–Fri.

Specialise in registering, identifying and recovering stolen works of art. Also provide security identification tags.
SPEAK TO Caroline Wakeford.

HANOVER INSURANCE BROKERS
13 Relton Mews, Knightsbridge, **London SW7 1ET**
TEL　　071 581 1477
FAX　　071 225 1411
OPEN　9–5 Mon–Fri.

Specialise in insurance, particularly for collectors of fine art, jewellery and antiques. They can tailor–make policies for individual clients.

PROVIDE Home Inspections. Free Estimates.
SPEAK TO Barbara Hollis.

TELESHIELD LIMITED
152 New Cavendish Street, **London W1M 7FJ**
TEL　　071 631 3605
FAX　　071 580 5787

Specialise in security installations and door maintenance, safes opened and serviced.

PROVIDE Free/Chargeable Home Inspections.
SPEAK TO B. D. Camfield.

STERLING SECURITY SYSTEMS
Sterling House, 305–307 Chiswick High Road, **London W4 4HH**
TEL　　081 747 0072
FAX　　081 994 4394
OPEN　8.30–6 Mon–Fri.

Specialise in intruder alarms, access control systems and c.c.t.v. systems.

PROVIDE Home Inspections. Free Estimates to BS 5750 standards.
SPEAK TO M. A. Hill.

TOLSON MESSENGER LTD

Insurance Brokers, 148 King Street,
London W6 OQU

TEL   081 741 8361
FAX   081 741 9395
OPEN   9–6 Mon–Fri.

Specialise in insurance for house contents – antiques, pictures, silver, objets d'art, providing a personal service for security–conscious householders seeking more realistic premiums but who also value tailor–made arrangements with professional service and advice.

BELLEVUE INSURANCE (HOME DIVISION)

66 Silver Street, Enfield, **Middlesex EN1 3EP**

TEL   081 836 7447, 363 4966 and
        367 0878
FAX   081 367 5780
OPEN   9.30–5.30 Mon–Fri.

Specialise in offering a specialised service for insurance of home contents and buildings, only placed with leading insurance companies.

PROVIDE Home Inspections by arrangement. Free Estimates.
SPEAK TO Jeremy Pringle – 081 367 2252/0878.

PENROSE FORBES LTD

29–30 Horsefair, Banbury, **Oxfordshire OX16 OAE**

TEL   0295 259892
FAX   0295 269968
OPEN   9–5.30 Mon–Fri.

Specialise in fine art insurance.
SPEAK TO Michael Forbes.

BAIN CLARKSON LTD

Garrod House, Chaldon Road,
Caterham, **Surrey CR3 5YW**

TEL   0883 340001
FAX   0883 341331
OPEN   9–5 Mon–Fri.

Specialise in insurance scheme for historic houses, fine arts and antiques. Discounts available for members of the Historic Houses Association and the National Art Collections Fund.
SPEAK TO Mr. Ian D. Houghton–Brown.

LIGHTING, DISPLAY
AND SUPPLIERS

ALL WRAPPED UP PACKAGING SUPPLIES
45 St John's Road, Moggerhanger,
Bedfordshire MK44 3RJ
TEL   0767 40777
OPEN   By Appointment.

Specialise in wrapping and labels of all kinds in 'small user' quantities.

PROVIDE Postal Service.
SPEAK TO Mr J. Harvey.

CONSERVATION BY DESIGN LIMITED
6 Pembroke Street, Bedford,
Bedfordshire MK40 3RH
TEL   0234 217 258
FAX   0234 328 164
OPEN   9–6 Mon–Fri.

Specialise in supplying conservation design consultancy products for storage and display of cultural objects, textiles and paper based materials, including photographs and ephemera.

PROVIDE Home Inspections. Estimates.
Collection/Delivery Service.

SPEAK TO Stuart M. Welch or Emma Nichamin.
Member of UKIC and IPC.

DURABLE SOLAR CONTROL LTD
9–11 Southview Park, Marsack Street,
Caversham, Reading, **Berkshire
RG4 0AF**
TEL   0734 483500
FAX   0734 462114
OPEN   9–5 Mon–Fri.

Specialise in supplying 3M solar control and security films for glazing. Benefits include reduction in solar heat gain and prevention of accelerated fading of fabrics and furnishings associated with the sun's harmful rays.

PROVIDE Home Inspections. Complete Supply and Installation Service.
SPEAK TO Mr J. Neale.
Address enquiries to Mrs G. Gilbert, Marketing Co–ordinator.

309

THE TEXTILE RESTORATION STUDIO
20 Hargreaves Road, Timperley,
Altrincham, **Cheshire WA15 7BB**
TEL   061 904 9944
FAX   061 903 9144
OPEN   9.30–5 Mon–Fri.

Specialise in supply of completely acid–
free storage boxes and acid-free tissue
paper for the safe storage of treasured
textiles, along with moth-killing crystals,
UV absorbing film for windows (for DIY
application) and acid-free mounting
card.

PROVIDE Free Mail Order Catalogue.
SPEAK TO Michael Hyman.
SEE Carpets, Silver, Collectors (Dolls).

ALLYSON McDERMOTT (INTERNATIONAL CONSERVATION CONSULTANTS)
Lintz Green Conservation Centre, Lintz
Green House, Lintz Green, Rowlands
Gill, **Durham NE39 1NL**
TEL   0207 71547 or 0831 104145 or
       0831 257584
FAX   0207 71547
OPEN   9–5.30 Mon–Fri.

Specialise in providing chemical and
microscopic analysis, environmental
control and collection management,
storage and exhibition.

PROVIDE Home Inspections. Free
Estimates. Chargeable
Collection/Delivery Service.
SPEAK TO Allyson McDermott or Gillian
Lee.
SEE Art Researchers, Carpets, Oil
Paintings, Picture Frames, Specialist
Photographers.

HERTFORDSHIRE CONSERVATION SERVICE
Seed Warehouse, Maidenhead Yard, The
Wash, Hertford, **Hertfordshire
SG14 1PX**
TEL   0992 588966 or 0992 504662
ANS   0992 588966
FAX   0992 503184
OPEN   9–6 Mon–Fri By Appointment.

Specialise in carrying out collection
surveys and offer advice on storage,
aftercare and environmental monitoring.

PROVIDE Home Inspections.
Free/Chargeable Estimates. Chargeable
Collection/Delivery Service.
SPEAK TO J. M. Macqueen.
This workshop is included on the register
of conservators maintained by the
Conservation Unit of the Museums and
Galleries Commission.
SEE Collectors (Dolls), Furniture,
Carpets, Porcelain, Oil Paintings,
Picture Frames.

UTILITARIAN FOLDING BOOKCASES
4 Wrenwood, Welwyn Garden City,
Hertfordshire AL7 1QG
TEL   0707 332965
OPEN   By Appointment.

Specialise in supplying folding
bookcases.

PROVIDE Home Inspections. Free
Estimates. Chargeable Delivery Service.
SPEAK TO Nicky Tutt.

ANTIQUE RESTORATIONS
The Old Wheelwright's Shop, Brasted
Forge, Brasted, Westerham, **Kent
TN16 1JL**
TEL   0959 563863
FAX   0959 561262
OPEN   9–5 Mon–Fri; 10–1 Sat.

Specialise in brass castings, including

handles and mounts. Anything not in their catalogue can be cast by special order.

PROVIDE Refundable Estimates. 28–Day Postal Service.
SPEAK TO Raymond Konyn.
Member of BAFRA and the Antique and Fine Art Disasters Ememrgency Mobile Unit.
SEE Clocks, Furniture.

C. & A. J. BARMBY
140 Lavender Hill, Tonbridge, **Kent TN9 2NJ**
TEL   0732 771590
OPEN   9.30–5 Mon–Sat or Mail Order.

Specialise in supplying display stands, ultra-violet lamps, magnifiers, metal-testers, digital scales, swing balances, Chelsea filters.

PROVIDE Home Inspections. Chargeable Collection/Delivery Service.
SPEAK TO Chris Barmby.
SEE Specialist Booksellers.

J. L. BOLLOM & CO. LTD
P. O. Box 78, Croydon Road, Beckenham, **Kent BR3 4BL.**
TEL   081 658 2299
FAX   081 658 8671
OPEN   9–5.30 Mon–Fri.

Specialise in providing a complete range of wood finishes and restoration products.

PROVIDE Delivery Service.
SPEAK TO Tony Wickenden.

LIBERON WAXES LTD
Mountfield Industrial Estate, Learoyd Road, New Romney, **Kent TN28 8XU**
TEL   0679 67535 FAX
OPEN   9–5.30 Mon–Fri.

Specialise in antique restoration and care products.
SPEAK TO Roland Morris.

HIRST CONSERVATION MATERIALS LTD
Laughton, Sleaford, **Lincolnshire NG34 0HE**
TEL   05297 517
FAX   05297 518
OPEN   9–5 Mon–Fri.

Specialise in supplying historic materials, including lime putty, mortars and plasters, coatings and paints.

PROVIDE Home Inspections. Free Estimates. Chargeable Collection/Delivery Service.
SPEAK TO Isabel Welby Everard.

LINCOLNSHIRE CONSERVATION STUDIO
c/o Museum of Lincolnshire Life, Burton Road, Lincoln, **Lincolnshire LN1 3LY**
TEL   0522 533207
OPEN   9–5 Mon–Fri.

Specialise in advising on display, storage, packaging, security and environmental control.

PROVIDE Home Inspections. Free/Chargeable Estimates. Chargeable Collection/Delivery Service.
SPEAK TO Stephanie Margrett or David Fisher.
Member of UKIC. This workshop is included on the register of conservators maintained by the Conservation Unit of the Museums and Galleries Commission.
SEE Arms, Furniture, Porcelain.

RANKINS (GLASS) COMPANY LIMITED
The London Glass Centre, 24–34 Pearson Street, **London E2 8JD**
TEL   071 729 4200
FAX   071 729 7135
OPEN   8–5.50 Mon–Fri.

Specialise in non–reflective safety glass for paintings, custom-made display cabinets and anti-bandit and bullet resistant glass.

PROVIDE Chargeable Estimates. Free/Chargeable Collection/Delivery Service.
SPEAK TO Mrs S. Graham or Mr C. Clifford.

CHATSWORTH COMMERCIAL LIGHTING
6 Highbury Corner, **London N5 1RD**
TEL   071 609 9829
FAX   071 700 4804
OPEN   9–6 Mon–Fri (24–hour answering service).

Specialise in picture and gallery lighting from domestic and professional gallery sector to museums.

PROVIDE Home Inspections. Free Estimates.
SPEAK TO John Khan.

W. S. JENKINS & CO. LTD
Jeco Works, Tariff Road, **London N17 0EN**
TEL   081 808 2336
FAX   081 365 1534
OPEN   9–5 Mon–Fri.

Specialise in providing a complete range of wood finishings and restoration material for antique furniture and listed buildings.

PROVIDE Free Catalogue and Price List. Free Delivery Service.
SPEAK TO Paul Humphrey.
Their technical department will be pleased to help anyone with any problems on restoration of antiques.

PICREATOR ENTERPRISES LTD
44 Park View Gardens, **London NW4 2PN**
TEL   081 202 8972
OPEN   By Appointment.

Specialise in supply of materials for

professional restoration and conservation of fine art objects. Manufacture 'Renaissance' wax polish and other own–brand restoration products. Mail order.
SPEAK TO John Lawson.

ACRYLIC DESIGN
697 Harrow Road, **London NW10 5NY**
TEL   081 969 0478 and 960 7215
FAX   081 960 8149
OPEN   8–4.30 Mon–Thur, 8–4 Fri.

Specialise in supplying display stands for all types of antiques, point–of–sale display aids, notice holders, made–to–measure stands.

PROVIDE Home Inspections. Free Estimates. Chargeable Collection/Delivery Service.
SPEAK TO Mr R. Jennings.
Catalogue available if you send two first class stamps.

LIGHT PROJECTS LTD
23 Jacob Street, **London SE1 2BG**
TEL   071 231 8282
FAX   071 237 4342
OPEN   9.30–5.30 Mon–Fri.

Specialise in supplying fine art lighting for galleries, historic houses and private residences including lighting design, project management, installation.

PROVIDE Home Inspections. Free Estimates. Chargeable Collection/Delivery Service.
SPEAK TO Richard Aldridge.

AIR IMPROVEMENT CENTRE
23 Denbigh Street, **London SW1V 2HF**
TEL   071 834 2834
FAX   071 630 8485
OPEN   9.30–5.30 Mon–Fri; 10–1 Sat

Specialise in humidity control. Advise on and supply humidifiers, dehumidifiers, hygrometers and mobile air conditioners.

PROVIDE Local Home Inspections. Free Estimates. Free Delivery Service.
SPEAK TO Valerie Taplin.

GREEN AND STONE
259 Kings Road, **London SW3 5EL**
TEL   071 352 6521
FAX   071 351 1098
OPEN   9–5.30 Mon–Fri; 9.30–6 Sat.

Specialise in supplying all fine art materials for painting, restoration and decorative trades.

PROVIDE Local Home Inspections. Free Estimates. Free Local Collection/Delivery Service.
SPEAK TO Mrs Hiscott or Miss Moore.
SEE Oil Paintings, Picture Frames.

ABSOLUTE ACTION LIMITED
Mantle House, Broomhill Road, **London SW18 4JQ**
TEL   081 871 5005
FAX   081 877 9498
OPEN   8.30–6 Mon–Fri.

Specialise in fibre optic lighting systems for display and conservation.

PROVIDE Home Inspections. Free Estimates. Chargeable Collection/Delivery Service.
SPEAK TO Emma Dawson–Tarr.

PLOWDEN AND SMITH LTD
190 St Ann's Hill, **London SW18 2RT**
TEL   081 874 4005
FAX   081 874 7248
OPEN   9–5.30 Mon–Fri.

Specialise in exhibition mounting and display and environmental control.

PROVIDE Home Inspections. Free Estimates. Free/Chargeable Collection/Delivery Service.

SPEAK TO Bob Butler.
SEE Oil Paintings, Furniture, Porcelain, Silver.

CONNOLLY LEATHER LTD
Wandle Bank, **London SW19 1DW**
TEL   081 542 5251 and 543 4611
FAX   081 543 7455
OPEN   9–12.45, 1.30–4 Mon–Fri.

Specialise in supplying leather table tops, wall panels and screens.

PROVIDE Home Inspections. Free Estimates. Free Collection/Delivery Service.
SPEAK TO Mr C. Carron.
SEE Furniture.

PICTURE PLAQUES
142 Lambton Road, **London SW20 0TJ**
TEL   081 879 7841
        By Appointment.

Specialise in hand–finished wooden picture plaques in gold leaf or white gold leaf.

PROVIDE Free Estimates.
SPEAK TO Kate Sim.

COSTERWISE LIMITED
16 Rabbit Row, **London W8 4DX**
TEL   071 221 0666
FAX   071 229 7000
OPEN   9–5 Mon–Fri.

Specialise in supplying protective packaging materials, bubble pack etc.

PROVIDE Free Estimates. Collection/Delivery Service.
SPEAK TO Helen Clegg.

JUSTIN F. SKREBOWSKI
82E Portobello Road, **London W11 2QD**
TEL   071 792 9742
OPEN   1–6.30 Tues–Fri; 7 a.m.–6 p.m. Sat.

Specialise in supplying stands, easels, browsers, folio stands.

PROVIDE Chargeable Estimates. Chargeable Collection/Delivery Service.
SPEAK TO Justin Skrebowski.

DRYSDALE AND HALAHAN

57 Boscombe Road, **London W12 9HU**
TEL   081 743 9708
FAX   081 743 9708
OPEN   9–5 Mon–Fri.

Specialise in conservation consultancy, including preventive conservation, collection surveys, environmental monitoring, project management, assessment of conservation services, seminars and training, conservation trouble–shooting, disaster planning.

PROVIDE Home Inspections. Free Estimates.
SPEAK TO Laura Drysdale or Frances Halahan.
Member of IIC, UKIC, Museums Association. This workshop is included on the register of conservators maintained by the Conservation Unit of the Museums and Galleries Commission.
SEE **Norfolk.**

PAPERSAFE

146 Chapel Road, Oldham, **Greater Manchester OL8 4QJ**
TEL   061 682 9652
OPEN   By Appointment.

Specialise in supplying book and paper repair materials.

PROVIDE Home Inspections. Free Estimates. Chargeable Collection/Delivery Service. Free Catalogue.
SPEAK TO Graham Moss.
Member of IPC and Society of Bookbinders.
SEE Books.

PROTEC

62 Windermere Avenue, Wembley, **Middlesex HA9 8RY**
TEL   081 908 4601
OPEN   By Appointment or Mail Order.

Specialise in supplying bubble wrap, tissue, film–fronted bags, adhesive tapes plus Protec clearview dustwrapper film.

PROVIDE packaging supplies list on request.
SPEAK TO Lawrence Tierney.

TURNROSS & CO.

130 Pinner Road, Harrow, **Middlesex HA1 4JE**
TEL   081 863 5036
OPEN   9–5 Thur–Sat.

Specialise in upholstery supplies, brass castors and fittings.

PROVIDE Free Estimates.
SPEAK TO A. R. Rosman.

DRYSDALE AND HALAHAN

The Cardinal's Hat, Back Street, Reepham, **Norfolk NR10 4SJ**
TEL   0603 871832 FAX
OPEN   9–5 Mon–Fri.

Specialise in conservation consultancy, including preventive conservation, collection surveys, environmental monitoring, project management, assessment of conservation services, seminars and training, conservation trouble–shooting, disaster planning.

PROVIDE Home Inspections. Free Estimates.
SPEAK TO Laura Drysdale or Frances Halahan.
Member of IIC, UKIC, Museums Association. This workshop is included on the register of conservators maintained by the Conservation Unit of the Museums and Galleries Commission.
SEE **London W12**

VICTORIA MARBLING
The Studios, St Mary Works, Duke Street, Norwich, **Norfolk NR3 1QA**
TEL 0603 764411
OPEN By Appointment.

Specialise in supplying hand–marbled and other decorative papers for use by bookbinders etc. Particularly strong in antiquarian styles, papers are suitable for box linings etc. and recreate period designs from mid-18th century onwards. More than twenty standard designs available.
SPEAK TO Victoria Hall.
Member of Society of Bookbinders and Associate of Designer Bookbinders.

THE LEATHER CONSERVATION CENTRE
34 Guildhall Road, Northampton, **Northamptonshire NN1 1EW**
TEL 0604 232723
FAX 0604 602070
OPEN 9–6 Mon–Fri.

Specialise in giving advice on sources of appropriate specialist leather and conservation materials.
PROVIDE Home Inspections. Chargeable Estimates. Chargeable Collection/Delivery Service.
SPEAK TO Roy Thomson.
SEE Carpets, Furniture.

MIDLAND SCHOOL OF FRENCH POLISHING
18A Mansfield Road, Eastwood, **Nottinghamshire NG16 3AQ**
TEL 0773 531157 or 715911
OPEN 9–4.30 Mon–Thur.

Specialise in courses throughout the year (maximum of three students per course) in French polishing, wax and ornamental finishes.
SPEAK TO Alfred Fry.

BERKELEY STUDIO
The Old Vicarage, Castle Cary, **Somerset BA7 7EJ**
TEL 0963 50748
FAX 0963 51107
OPEN 9–5 Mon–Fri By Appointment Only.

Specialise in making picture plaques and display cabinets.

PROVIDE Home Inspections. Free Estimates. Free Collection/Delivery Service.
SPEAK TO John Harries.

SUFFOLK BRASS
Thurston, Bury St Edmunds, **Suffolk IP31 3SN**
TEL 0359 30888 and 0379 898670
OPEN 9–6 Mon–Fri; 9–12 Sat.

Specialise in casting brass by the hot wax or sand process from original brassware for furniture fittings. Also make hand–forged iron fittings.

PROVIDE Free Estimates. Free Collection/Delivery Service (same day).
SPEAK TO Mark Peters or Thane Meldrum.
SEE Silver.

DRYMASTER INTERNATIONAL LTD
Navigation House, 5 High Street, Hampton Wick, Kingston–upon–Thames, **Surrey KT1 4DA**
TEL 081 977 2350
FAX 081 977 2350
OPEN 9.30–5.30 Mon–Fri.

Specialise in supplying dehumidifiers, humidifiers, air cleaning units and air conditioners.

PROVIDE Free Estimates.
SPEAK TO Mr J. Oades.

COLEBROOKE CONSULTING LTD – BOB HAYES

Diamonds, Bells Yew Green, **East Sussex TN3 9AX**

TEL   0892 750307
FAX   0892 750222
OPEN   9–5.30 Mon–Fri.

Specialise in environmental control and the care, maintenance and management of historic buildings with their contents.
SPEAK TO Bob Hayes.
Mr Hayes is Technical Advisor to the National Trust's Historic Buildings Department.

ALBERT PLUMB

31 Whyke Lane, Chichester, **West Sussex PO19 2JS**

TEL   0243 788468
OPEN   9.30–5 Mon–Sat.

Specialise in supplying waxes and other items for restoration. Brass fittings, handles, upholstery fittings.

PROVIDE Home Inspections. Free Estimates. Collection/Delivery Service.
SPEAK TO Albert Plumb.
SEE Furniture.

SUGG LIGHTING LIMITED

Sussex Manor Business Park, Gatwick Road, Crawley, **West Sussex RH10 2GD**

TEL   0293 540111
FAX   0293 540114
OPEN   By Appointment.

Specialise in supplying traditional gas and electric pendant lights.

PROVIDE Free Estimates.
SPEAK TO Sales Office.
SEE Silver.

SUN-X (U.K.) LIMITED

2 Madeira Parade, Madeira Avenue, Bognor Regis, **West Sussex PO22 8DX**

TEL   0243 826441
FAX   0243 829691
OPEN   8.30–12.30, 1.30–5 Mon–Fri.

Specialise in supplying and fitting ultra-violet filters, solar control and bomb blast protection films to all types of glass and artificial lighting. Manufacturers of traditional and modern blinds.

PROVIDE Home Inspections. Free Estimates. Chargeable Collection/Delivery Service.
SPEAK TO David French.

WILLARD DEVELOPMENTS LIMITED

Leigh Road, Terminus Road Industrial Estate, Chichester, **West Sussex PO19 2TS**

TEL   0243 784711
FAX   0243 533845
OPEN   9–5 Mon–Fri.

Specialise in supplying art conservation equipment; electrically heated spatulas and tacking/lining irons, associated control units and temperature monitors, hot air pens, electrically heated vacuum lining tables, glueing jugs (designed primarily to assist in work on wood panels), textile washing tables and conservation treatment tables, multi-purpose low pressure humidifying conservation tables, small portable low pressure suction tables, lighting panels, motorised and manually–operated scanning easels. Also have a design and manufacturing service where equipment is required for a particular application.

PROVIDE Free Estimates. Chargeable Collection/Delivery Service.
SPEAK TO Roger Strood or Angela Johnson.

ALAN MORRIS (WHOLESALE)

10 Coughton Lane, Alcester,
Warwickshire B49 5HN
TEL   0789 762800
OPEN   By Appointment or Mail Order.

Specialise in supplying display stands for ceramics, dolls and pictures as well as wire and disc plate-hangers. Also provide peelable price labels and strung tickets, jewellery boxes and polishing and cleaning cloths.
SPEAK TO Alan Leadbeater.

ROD NAYLOR

208 Devizes Road, Hilperton,
Trowbridge, **Wiltshire BA14 7QP**
TEL   0225 754497
OPEN   By Appointment.

Specialise in supplying hard–to–find items for restorers such as three-dimensional copying machines, embossed lining paper.

PROVIDE Home Inspections. Free Local Estimates. Free Local Collection/Delivery Service.
SPEAK TO Rod Naylor.
SEE Furniture, Porcelain.

SPECIALIST
PHOTOGRAPHERS
AND BOOKSELLERS

SPECIALIST PHOTOGRAPHERS

ALLYSON McDERMOTT (INTERNATIONAL CONSERVATION CONSULTANTS)

Lintz Green Conservation Centre, Lintz Green House, Lintz Green, Rowlands Gill, **Durham NE39 1NL**

TEL   0207 71547 or 0831 104145 or 0831 257584
FAX   0207 71547
OPEN   9–5.30 Mon–Fri.

Specialise in photography for insurance and catalogues.

PROVIDE Home Inspections. Free Estimates. Chargeable Collection/Delivery Service.
They have a Southern Regional Office at 45 London Road, Cheltenham, **Gloucestershire**.
SPEAK TO Allyson McDermott or Gillian Lee.
SEE Art Researchers, Carpets, Lighting, Oil Paintings, Picture Frames.

SHELAGH COLLINGWOOD

18 Clarence Road, Harpenden, **Hertfordshire AL5 4AH**

TEL   0582 761191
OPEN   8.30–7 Mon–Sat or By Appointment.

Specialise in high quality photographs of furniture, pictures, jewellery, silver, porcelain etc. as an insurance record against loss, theft or damage. Objects are photographed in situ with studio lights. Special assignments undertaken.

PROVIDE Free Estimates.
SPEAK TO Shelagh Collingwood.
Ms Collingwood is registered with Hertfordshire Crime Prevention and the Art Loss Register.

318

JOHN JONES FRAMES LTD
4 Morris Place, off Stroud Green Road, **London N4 3JG**
TEL   071 281 5439
FAX   071 281 5956
OPEN   8–6 Mon–Fri, 9–2 Sat, 12–4 Sun.

Specialise in providing a fully equipped fine art photographic service.

PROVIDE Free Estimates. Chargeable Collection/Delivery Service.
SPEAK TO John Jones, John Dawson or Nick Hawker.
SEE Oil Paintings, Picture Frames.

ALEX SAUNDERSON PHOTOGRAPHY
103 Riversdale Road, **London N5 2SU**
TEL   071 359 1605
OPEN   9–6 Mon–Sat.

Specialise in photographing furniture and fine art. They provide quality transparencies and black and white prints of furniture, sculpture, paintings, interiors, exteriors and portraits.

PROVIDE Home Inspections. Free Estimates. Chargeable Colection/Delivery Service.
SPEAK TO Alex Saunderson.

IMAGETREND
12 Chesterford Gardens, **London NW3 7DE**
TEL   071 435 7383
FAX   071 431 0960
OPEN   By Appointment.

Specialise in photographing paintings and sculpture and any two– or three–dimensional art work. They provide a comprehensive service for artists and galleries both in their studio or on location.

PROVIDE Home Inspections. Free Estimates. Free Local Collection/Delivery Service.
SPEAK TO Ken Grundy.

JANE AND PAUL ZAGEL
31 Pandora Road, **London NW6 1TS**
TEL   071 794 1663
OPEN   9–6 Mon–Fri.

Specialise in fine art photography as part of restoration record and for publication.
SPEAK TO Jane Zagel.
SEE Books, Oil Paintings.

CUBITT AND FANE LTD SECURITY PHOTOGRAPHERS
7 Tedworth Gardens, **London SW3 4DN**
TEL   071 376 8197
OPEN   By Appointment.

Specialise in photographing art and antiques for security and insurance purposes. The photographs are taken on site on colour transparency film (no negatives) all of which are returned to the client. They keep only minimal records of past and present communications with clients and these are in code and at a separate address. All enquiries are dealt with in complete confidence and references are available on request. They are recognised by the Art and Antique Squad at Scotland Yard.

PROVIDE Home Inspections. Free Estimates.
SPEAK TO Amanda Cubitt or Caroline Fane.

JOHN R. SIMMONS
21 Park Mansions, Prince of Wales Drive, **London SW11 4HQ**
TEL   071 622 0048
OPEN   By Appointment.

Specialise in photographing paintings, sculpture, furniture, jewellery, miniatrures to murals. Transparencies, negatives, prints and duplicates supplied.

PROVIDE Chargeable Collection/Delivery Service.
SPEAK TO John R. Simmons.

A. C. COOPER LTD
10 Pollen Street, **London W1R 9PH**
TEL   071 629 7585
FAX   071 409 3449
OPEN   8.30–5.30 Mon–Fri.

Specialise in fine art colour or black and white photography either in studio or on location. In-house printing and processing.

PROVIDE Home Inspections. Free Estimates.
SPEAK TO Trevor Chriss.
Established seventy–five years.

PRUDENCE CUMING ASSOCIATES LTD
28–29 Dover Street, **London W1X 3PA**
TEL   071 629 6430
FAX   071 495 2458
OPEN   8.30–5.30 Mon–Fri.

Specialise in photographing works of art including paintings, drawings, sculptures, jewellery, furniture, silver, ceramics.

PROVIDE Studio and location shooting.
SPEAK TO Prudence Cuming.
Established 1967.

P. J. GATES (PHOTOGRAPHY) LTD
94 New Bond Street, **London W1Y 9LA**
TEL   071 629 4962
OPEN   9.15–5.30 Mon–Fri.

Specialise in photographing works of art worldwide with a particular aim for top quality results at all times. Large-format colour transparencies as well as life–size reproductions available.

PROVIDE Home Inspections. Free Estimates.
SPEAK TO P. J. Gates.

RODNEY TODD–WHITE AND SON
3 Clifford Street, **London W1X 1RA**
TEL   071 734 9070
FAX   071 287 9727
OPEN   9–5.30 Mon–Fri.

Specialise in photographing fine art objects and paintings.

PROVIDE Home Inspections. Free Estimates. Chargeable Collection/Delivery Service.
SPEAK TO Michael Todd–White.

KEN SMITH PHOTOGRAPHY
6 Lussielaw Road, Edinburgh, **Lothian EH9 3BX**
TEL   031 667 6159 or 657 4327
OPEN   By Appointment.

Specialise in photography of fine and decorative arts and architecture including jewellery, silverware, ceramics, glass, paintings, furniture, militaria.

PROVIDE Home Inspections. Free Estimates. Chargeable Collection/Delivery Service.
SPEAK TO Leslie Paul–Florence.
Member of the Association of Historical and Fine Art Photographers.

SPECIALIST BOOKSELLERS

REFERENCE WORKS
12 Commercial Road, Swanage, **Dorset BH19 1DF**
TEL   0929 424423
FAX   0929 422597
OPEN   By Appointment; Telephone Orders 9–5.30 Mon–Sat.

Specialise in books on ceramics of all countries.

PROVIDE Mail Order Service.
SPEAK TO Barry Lamb.

PHILLIPS OF HITCHIN
The Manor House, Hitchin,
Hertfordshire SG5 1JW
TEL 0462 432067
FAX 0462 441368
OPEN 9–5.30 Mon–Sat.

Specialise in reference books on antiques, particularly furniture.
SPEAK TO Jerome Phillips.
SEE Furniture.

C. & A. J. BARMBY
140 Lavender Hill, Tonbridge, **Kent TN9 2AY**
TEL 0732 771590
OPEN 9.30–5 Mon–Sat or Mail Order.

Specialise in antique reference books.

PROVIDE Chargeable Collection/Delivery Service.
SPEAK TO Chris Barmby.
SEE Lighting.

THOMAS HENEAGE ART BOOKS
42 Duke Street, **London SW1Y 6DJ**
TEL 071 930 9223
FAX 071 839 9223
OPEN 10–6 Mon–Fri.

Specialise in books on the fine and decorative arts.

ST GEORGE'S GALLERY BOOKS LTD
8 Duke Street, **London SW1Y 6BN**
TEL 071 930 0935
FAX 071 930 3534
OPEN 10–6 Mon–Fri.

Specialise in new and out-of-print books on the fine and decorative arts.

SIMS REED LTD
43A Duke Stret, **London SW1Y 6DD**
TEL 071 493 5660
FAX 071 493 8468
OPEN 10–6 Mon–Fri.

Specialise in monographs, art reference and modern illustrated books.

PROVIDE Home Inspections. Free/Chargeable Estimates. Chargeable Collection/Delivery Service.
SPEAK TO Nina Neve.

DON KELLY
Antiquarius MB, 135 Kings Road, **London SW3 4PW**
TEL 071 352 4690
FAX 071 351 5350
OPEN 10–5.30 Mon–Sat.

Specialise in selling new and out-of-print reference books on the fine and applied arts. Searches undertaken. Mail order available.
SPEAK TO Don Kelly.

THE ART BOOK REVIEW
1 Stewarts Court, 220 Stewarts Road, **London SW8 4UD**
TEL 071 720 1503
FAX 071 720 3158
OPEN By Appointment or Mail Order.

Specialise in selling in–print reference works on all aspects of the fine and applied arts, architecture, design and photography.

PROVIDE Chargeable Collection/Delivery Service.
SPEAK TO Kate Sayner or Cathy Dean, Editors.
Four issues published per year featuring over 200 new titles from publishers worldwide.

THE ATRIUM BOOKSHOP LTD
5 Cork Street, **London W1X 1PB**
TEL 071 495 0073
FAX 071 409 7417
OPEN 10–6 Mon–Fri; 11–4 Sat.

Specialise in selling in–print books and exhibition catalogues on all aspects of the fine and decorative arts and archirtecture.
SPEAK TO Jo Walton.

MARLBOROUGH RARE BOOKS LTD

144 New Bond Street, **London W1Y 9FD**
TEL   071 493 6993
FAX   071 499 2479
OPEN   9.30–6 Mon–Fri.

Specialise in selling all fields of antiquarian books

PROVIDE Home Inspections. Chargeable Estimates. Chargeable Collection/Delivery Service.
SPEAK TO Alex Fotheringham.

CAROL MANHEIM

31 Ennismore Avenue, **London W4 1SE**
TEL   081 994 9740
FAX   081 995 5396
OPEN   Mail Order Service.

Specialise in 19th and 20th century British and Continental out-of-print art reference books and catalogues, including sculpture, fashion and photography.

PROVIDE Free Book Search Service.
SPEAK TO Carol Manheim.

NOTTING HILL BOOKS

132 Palace Gardens Terrace, **London W8 4RT**
TEL   071 727 5988
OPEN   10.30–6 Mon–Sat; 10.30–1 Thur.

Specialise in buying and selling books on fine art and antiques.
SPEAK TO Sheila Ramage.

BALLANTYNE AND DATE

38 Museum Street, **London WC1A 1LP**
TEL   071 242 4249
FAX   071 430 0684
OPEN   10.30–6 Mon–Sat; 12–6 Sun.

Specialise in buying and selling books and prints relating to 20th century fine and applied art, photography, architecture, illustrated design etc.
SPEAK TO Roger Ballantyne–Way or Robert Date.
Member of PBFA.

ANN CREED BOOKS LTD

22 Cecil Court, **London WC2N 4HE**
TEL   071 836 7757
FAX   071 240 1439
OPEN   10.30–6.30 Mon–Sat.

Specialise in books and catalogues on all aspects of fine and applied arts, graphic design, art theory etc. from 1500 to the present with an emphasis on the 20th century. They produce frequent catalogues on all areas of stock as well as specific colections, when available. They are happy to receive want lists and operate an active search service.

PROVIDE Home Inspections. Free/Chargeable Estimates. Free Collection/Delivery Service.
SPEAK TO Ann Creed.

ZWEMMER ART BOOKS

24 Litchfield Street, **London WC2H 9NJ**
TEL   071 379 7886
FAX   071 497 3290
OPEN   9.30–6 Mon–Wed, Fri; 10–6 Thur & Sat.

Specialise in books on the fine and decorative arts including out-of-print and foreign language books.
SPEAK TO Clare Howell.
Established in 1921.

JOHN IVES BOOKSELLER

5 Normanhurst Drive, Twickenham,
Middlesex TW1 1NA
TEL   081 892 6265
OPEN   By Appointment.

Specialise in scarce and out-of-print
books on antiques and collecting,
costume and needlework and
architecture.

PROVIDE Mail Order Service.
SPEAK TO John Ives.

RITA SHENTON MBHI

148 Percy Road, Twickenham,
Middlesex TW2 6JG
TEL   081 894 6888
FAX   081 893 8766
OPEN   By Appointment.

Specialise in horological bookselling,
antiquarian out-of-print and new books.

PROVIDE Home Inspections. Chargeable
Collection/Delivery Service. Free
Catalogue.
SPEAK TO Rita Shenton.

NICHOLAS MERCHANT

Parkside House, 17 East Parade,
Harrogate, **North Yorkshire HG1 5LF**
TEL   0423 505370
FAX   0423 506183
OPEN   By Appointment.

Specialise in reference books on all
aspects of the decorative arts, including
antiques, fine art, architecture and
interior design.

PROVIDE Mail Order Service.
SPEAK TO Nicholas Merchant.

POTTERTON BOOKS

The Old Rectory, Sessay, Thirsk, **North
Yorkshire YO7 3LZ**
TEL   0845 401218
FAX   0845 401439
OPEN   9.30–4.30 Mon–Fri or By
       Appointment.

Specialise in books on architecture, fine
and decorative arts and all branches of
antiques and collecting.
SPEAK TO Clare Jameson.

TRANSPORT AND
SHIPPING

ALAN FRANKLIN TRANSPORT

Unit 8, 27 Blackmoor Road, Ebblake
Industrial Estate, Verwood, **Dorset
BH31 6BE**

TEL   0202 826539
FAX   0202 827337
OPEN   8.30–6 Mon–Fri; 8–2 Sat.

Specialise in the transportation of
antiques and works of art throughout
Europe, air freight and containerised
shipments worldwide. Storage facilities
in United Kingdom and France.

SPEAK TO Alan Franklin or James Scollen.

GEO. COPSEY & CO. LTD

Danes Road, Romford, **Essex
RM7 0HL**

TEL   081 592 1003
FAX   0708 727305
OPEN   8–5 Mon–Fri.

Specialise in packing and removal of fine
art and antiques.

PROVIDE Home Inspections. Free
Estimates.
SPEAK TO Barry Tebbutt.

SPANPAK EXPORT SERVICES LTD

Unit 3, Pacific Wharf, Hertford Road,
Barking, **Essex IG11 8BL**

TEL   081 594 4474
MOB   0831 396369
FAX   081 594 4475
OPEN   8–5.30 Mon–Fri.

Specialise in a fully comprehensive
service for antique and fine art packing
and shipping worldwide, all
documentation and administration, all
risk door–to–door insurance. Specialist
Spanish service, door–to–door
groupage, full load service to Europe,
container services to USA and all major
destinations, worldwide airfreight.
Competitive prices, fast, reliable and
personal service.

PROVIDE Home Inspections. Free
Estimates. Chargeable
Collection/Delivery Service.
SPEAK TO Miss Amanda Reuben.

ALBAN SHIPPING LTD
43 Hatfield Road, St Albans,
Hertfordshire AL1 4JE
TEL   0727 41402
FAX   0727 46370
OPEN   8–5.30 Mon–Fri.

Specialise in the collection, packaging and export or delivery of antiques and collectors' items.

PROVIDE Home Inspections. Free Estimates.
SPEAK TO Andrew Jackman.

01 FINE ART SERVICES LTD
London Fields, 282 Richmond Road,
London E8 3QS
TEL   081 533 6124
FAX   081 533 2718
OPEN   9–6 Mon–Fri.

Specialise in the transportation of paintings and sculpture within the South East of England from one painting to entire exhibitions. They can also offer an installation and storage service.

PROVIDE Home Inspections. Free Estimates. Chargeable Collection/Delivery Service.
SPEAK TO Elizabeth Cooper.

MOMART PLC.
199–205 Richmond Road, **London E8 3NJ**
TEL   081 986 3624
FAX   081 533 0122
OPEN   Daily By Appointment.

Specialise in fine art handling, including 'state of the art' storage, transportation both national and international, case making/packing and exhibition installation.

SPEAK TO Richard Chapman, Transport Director
Kevin Richardson, Shipping Director.

LOCKSON SERVICES LTD
29 Broomfield Street, **London E14 6BX**
TEL   071 515 8600 or 0831 621428
       Sat and Sun.
FAX   071 515 4043
OPEN   9–6 Mon–Fri.

Specialise in fine art, antique and general packing and shipping and transportation within the UK.

PROVIDE Free Estimates.
SPEAK TO David Armitage Snr.

L. J. ROBERTON LTD
Marlborough House, Cooks Road,
London E15 2PW
TEL   081 519 2020
FAX   081 519 8571
OPEN   9–5 Mon–Fri.

Specialise in export packing and shipping of antiques and fine art, including a countrywide collection service.

SPEAK TO Mr J. Tebbutt.
Member of LAPADA.

STEPHEN MORRIS SHIPPING LTD
Barpart House, Kings Cross Freight Depot, York Way, **London N1 0UZ**
TEL   071 713 0080
FAX   071 713 0151
OPEN   8–6 Mon–Fri for goods; 8–6
       Daily for quotations.

Specialise in packing and shipping fine art and antiques.

PROVIDE Home Inspections. Free Estimates.
SPEAK TO Stephen Morris or John Holser.

PITT & SCOTT LTD
20–24 Edengrove, **London N7 8ED**
TEL   071 607 7321
FAX   071 607 0566
OPEN   8–5 Mon–Fri.

Specialise in international packing and

shipping of fine art, domestic moving and storing.

PROVIDE Home Inspections. Free Estimates.
SPEAK TO Anthony Roberts.

KUWAHARA LIMITED

Unit 5, Bittacy Business Centre, Bittacy Hill, **London NW7 1BA**
TEL　　081 346 7744
FAX　　081 349 2916
OPEN　　9–5.30 Mon–Fri.

Specialise in packing and shipping and are international removers.

PROVIDE Home Inspections.
SPEAK TO S. Kuwahara or K. Blair.

ANGLO–PACIFIC (FINE ART) LIMITED

Bush Industrial Estate, Standard Road, North Acton,
London NW10 6DF
TEL　　081 965 0667 or 081 965 1234
FAX　　081 965 4954 or 081 965 4954
OPEN　　8–6 Mon–Fri.

Specialise in packing and worldwide shipping of antiques and fine art, plus international removals.

PROVIDE Free Estimates. Insurance Cover.
SPEAK TO Gerry Ward or Mary McDermot.

HEDLEYS HUMPERS LTD

Units 3 & 4, 97 Victoria Road, North Acton, **London NW10 6ND**
TEL　　081 965 8733
FAX　　081 965 0249
OPEN　　7–7 Mon–Fri.

Specialise in worldwide packing and shipping.

PROVIDE Home Inspections. Free Estimates.
SPEAK TO Bob Archer.

TRANS EURO WORLDWIDE MOVERS

Fine Art Division
Drury Way, **London NW10 0JN**
TEL　　081 784 0100
FAX　　081 451 0061
OPEN　　9–5.30 Mon–Fri.

Specialise in worldwide shipping of antiques and fine art.

PROVIDE Free Estimates and advice.
SPEAK TO Richard Edwards or Eileen Lewis–Smith.
Member of LAPADA.

C. R. FENTON & COMPANY

Unit 2, 129–131 Coldharbour Lane, **London SE5 9NY**
OPEN　　9–5.30 Mon–Fri.

Specialise in fine art packing, shipping and storage.

PROVIDE Home Inspections. Free Estimates.
SPEAK TO Brian Bath.
Member of the British International Freight Association.

TRANSNIC LTD

Arch 434, Gordon Grove, **London SE5 9DU**
TEL　　071 738 7555
FAX　　071 738 5190
OPEN　　9–6 Mon–Fri or By Appointment Sat.

Specialise in fine art transportation and storage. Also picture hanging.

PROVIDE Chargeable Collection/Delivery and Storage Service.
SPEAK TO Nicholas Tetley.

WINGATE AND JOHNSTON LTD

134 Queens Road, **London SE15 2HR**
TEL   071 732 8123
FAX   071 732 2631
OPEN   9–5.30 Mon–Fri.

Specialise in packing and shipping of antiques and fine art.

PROVIDE Home Inspections. Free Estimates.
SPEAK TO Paul Brecht.

EUROPE EXPRESS

125 Sydenham Road, **London SE26 5HB**
TEL   081 776 7556 MOB 0860 239660
FAX   081 776 7606
OPEN   9–6 Mon–Fri.

Specialise in road transport removals to Europe, including Sardinia and Sicily.
SPEAK TO Tony Morgan.

FEATHERSTON SHIPPING LTD

24 Hampton House, 15/17 Ingate Place, **London SW8 3NS**
TEL   071 720 0422
FAX   071 720 6330
OPEN   8–6 Mon–Fri.

Specialise in packing and shipping fine art and antiques.

PROVIDE Home Inspections. Free Estimates.
SPEAK TO Caedmon Featherston.

THE PACKING SHOP LTD

Units K & L, London Stone Business Estate, Broughton Street, **London SW8 3QR**
TEL   071 627 5605
FAX   071 622 7740
OPEN   9–6 Mon–Fri.

Specialise in same–day shipment of small consignments, as well as air freight, sea freight and packing.

PROVIDE Home Inspections. Free Estimates.
SPEAK TO Karen Bagot.
SEE **London SW10**

T. ROGERS & CO. (PACKERS) LTD

PO Box 8, 1A Broughton Street, London SW8 3QL
TEL   071 622 9151
FAX   071 627 3318
OPEN   8–5 Mon–Fri.

Specialise in transporting, packing, warehousing and shipping of fine art and antiques as well as security storage and picture hanging.

PROVIDE Home Inspections. Free Estimates.
SPEAK TO Michael Evans.

THE PACKING SHOP LTD

535 Kings Road, **London SW10 0SZ**
TEL   071 352 2021
FAX   071 351 7576
OPEN   9–6 Mon–Fri; 10–1 Sat.

Specialise in fine art and antique packing and shipping with emphasis on same–day collection and two to three day delivery worldwide.

PROVIDE Home Inspections. Free Estimates.
SPEAK TO Eileen Abbas.
SEE **London SW8**.

ROBINSON AND FOSTER LTD

75–81 Burnaby Street, **London SW10 0NS**
TEL   071 351 4404
FAX   071 352 6582
OPEN   9–5 Mon–Fri.

Specialise in removals and deliveries within the United Kingdom, storage facilities.

PROVIDE Free Estimates.
SPEAK TO Jonathan Moore.

PANTECHNICON GROUP LTD
Unit 3, The Gate Centre, Syon Gate Way, Great West Road, Brentford, **Middlesex TW8 9DD**
TEL   081 568 6195
FAX   081 847 3126
OPEN   8.30–5 Mon–Fri.

Specialise in UK, European and international removals of furniture, effects and antiques. They have regular services to France, Belgium and Spain. Storage facilities are available.

PROVIDE Home Inspections. Free Estimates.
SPEAK TO Gordon Williams.

VULCAN INTERNATIONAL SERVICES
Unit 14, Ascot Road, Clockhouse Lane, Feltham, **Middlesex TW14 8QF**
TEL   0784 244152
FAX   0784 248183
OPEN   8.30–6 Mon–Fri.

Specialise in transporting fine art and antiques. They also provide specialised export and import packing and international shipping services as well as a domestic removal service. Full insurance cover available.

PROVIDE Home Inspections. Free Estimates. Chargeable Collection/Delivery Service.
SPEAK TO Mr Dennis Jarvis, General Manager.

GANDER & WHITE SHIPPING LTD
New Pound, Wisborough Green, Nr. Billingshurst, **West Sussex RH14 0AY**
TEL   0403 700044
FAX   0403 700814
OPEN   9–6 Mon–Fri.

Specialise in packing, moving and shipping fine art, antiques and household removals.

PROVIDE Home Inspections. Free Estimates.
SPEAK TO Maureen De'Ath.

A SELECTION OF FULL-TIME COURSES FOR TRAINING IN CONSERVATION

Basford Hall College
Department of Construction
Stockhill Lane
Nottingham
NG6 0NB
TEL 0602 704541
Course Furniture Reproduction
Restoration and Design Craft.

Buckinghamshire College
Queen Alexandra Road
High Wycombe
Buckinghamshire HP11 2JZ
TEL 0494 522141
FAX 0494 524392
Course [a] Furniture Design and
Craftsmanship.
[b] Furniture Restoration and
Craftsmanship.

Camberwell College of Arts
School of Art History and Conservation
Wilson's Annexe
Wilson Road
London SE5 8LU
TEL 071 703 0987 ext 139
Course Paper Conservation.

**Carmarthenshire College of
Technology and Art**
Faculty of Art and Design
Job's Well Road
Carmarthen
Dyfed SA31 3HY
TEL 0554 759165
Course [a] Sculpture/Restoration
Sculpture.

[b] Design Crafts
(Sculpture/Restoration
Sculpture).

Central Manchester College
The John Unsworth Building
Lower Hardman Street
Manchester M3 3ER
TEL 061 953 5995
Course Advanced Furniture Crafts
(Restoration).

City & Guilds of London Art School
124 Kennington Park Road
London SE11 4DJ
TEL 071 582 7049
Course Restoration and Conservation
Studies.

Courtauld Institute of Art
Somerset House
Strand
London WC2R 0RN
TEL [a] 071 873 2191
[b] 071 873 2848
Course [a] Conservation of Paintings.
[b] Conservation of Wall
Paintings.

**Department of Conservation of Fine
Art**
Faculty of Arts and Design
University of Northumbria at Newcastle
Squires Building
Newcastle-upon-Tyne NE1 8ST
TEL 091 232 6002 ext 4414
Course [a]Conservation of Fine Art
(Easel Paintings).

[b] Conservation of Fine Art
(Works of Art on Paper).

Guildford College of Technology
Stoke Park
Guildford
Surrey GU1 1EZ
TEL 0483 31251
Course Fine Bookbinding and
Conservation.

Hamilton Kerr Institute
University of Cambridge
Mill Lane
Whittlesford
Cambridgeshire CB2 4NE
TEL 0223 832040
Course Conservation of Easel Paintings.

Herefordshire Technical College
Engineering Department
Folly Lane
Hereford
HR1 1LS
TEL 0432 352235
Course Restoration (Metalwork).

**Lincolnshire College of Art and
Design**
Lindum Road
Lincoln
LN2 1NP
TEL 0522 512912
Course Conservation and Restoration
Studies.

London College of Printing
Department of Print Finishing Processes
Elephant and Castle
London SE1 6SB
TEL 071 735 8484
Course Design (Bookbinding).

London Guildhall University
41 Commercial Road
London E1 1LA
TEL 071 320 1000
Course Furniture (Restoration).

Bruce Luckhurst
The Little Surrenden Workshops
Ashford Road
Bethersden
Kent TN26 3BG

TEL 023382 0589
Course Conservation and Restoration of
Antique Furniture.

Royal College of Art
Kensington Gore
London SW7 2EU
TEL 071 584 5020
Course Conservation.

Rycotewood College
Department of Fine Craftsmanship and
Design
Priest End
Thame
Oxfordshire OX9 2AF
TEL 084421 2501
Course Design (Crafts) Furniture
Restoration.

Textile Conservation Centre
Apartment 22
Hampton Court Palace
East Molesey
Surrey KT8 9AU
TEL 081 977 4943
Course Textile Conservation.

West Dean College
West Dean
Chichester
West Sussex PO18 0QZ
TEL 024 363 301
Course   [a] Antique Furniture
Restoration.
[b] Porcelain and Ceramic
Conservation.
[c] Bookbinding and the Care
of Books.
[d] Antique Clock Restoration.
[e] Metal Restoration.
[f] Tapestry Weaving.
[g] Musical Instrument
Making.

York College of Art and Technology
School of Construction
Carpentry and Joinery Section
Dringhouses
York
YO2 1UA
TEL 0904 704141
Course Antique Furniture Restoration.

GLOSSARY AND USEFUL
ADDRESSES

ABA
Antiquarian Booksellers Association
Suite 2
26 Charing Cross Road
London WC2H 0DG
TEL 071 379 3041

Association of Art Historians
Register of Freelance Art and Design
Historians
10 Davisville Road
London W12 9SJ
TEL 081 743 4697

ABPR
Association of British Picture Restorers
Station Avenue
Kew
Surrey TW9 3QA
TEL 081 948 5644

Association of Master Upholsterers
Francis Vaughan House
102 Commercial Street
Newport
Gwent NP9 1LU
TEL 0633 215454
FAX 0633 244488

BADA
British Antique Dealers' Association
20 Rutland Gate
London SW7 1BD
TEL 071 589 4128

BAFRA
British Antique Furniture Restorers
Association
c/o Richard Higgins
The Old School
Longnor
Nr Shrewsbury
Shropshire SY5 7PP
TEL 0743 718162

BHI
CMBHI
MBHI
British Horological Institute
Upton Hall
Upton, Newark
Nottinghamshire NG23 5TE
TEL 0636 813795

BWCMG
British Watch and Clockmakers Guild
West Wick
Marsh Road
Burnham-on-Crouch
Essex CM0 8NE
TEL 0621 783104

City and Guilds of London Institute
46 Britannia Street
London WC1Y 9RG
TEL 071 278 2468
FAX 071 278 9460

The Conservation Unit of the Museums
and Galleries Commission
16 Queen Anne's Gate
London W1H 9AA
TEL 071 233 3683
FAX 071 233 3686

Designer Bookbinders
6 Queen Square
London WC1N 3AR

FATG
The Fine Art Trade Guild
16–18 Empress Place
London SW6 1TT
TEL 071 381 6616
FAX 071 381 2596

GA
Gemmological Association of Great
Britain
27 Greville Street
London EC1N 8SU
TEL 071 404 3334

GADR
Guild of Antique Dealers and Restorers
23 Belle Vue Road
Shrewsbury
Shropshire SY3 7LN
TEL 0743 271 852

Historic Houses Association
2 Chester Street
London SW1X 7BB
TEL 071 259 5688
FAX 071 259 5590

IPC
The Institute of Paper Conservation
Leigh Lodge
Leigh
Worcester
WR6 5LB
TEL 0886 832323
FAX 0886 833688

IIC
International Institute for Conservation
of Historic and Artistic Works
6 Buckingham Street
London WC2N 6BA
TEL 071 839 5975
FAX 071 976 1564

IGS
42 Merrion Square
Dublin 2
TEL 01 6767053
FAX 01 6620290

IPCRA
Irish Professional Conservators' and
Restorers' Association
Mr Grellan D. Rourke (Chairman)
c/o The Office of Public Works
51 St Stephens Green
Dublin 2
TEL 01 6613111 ext. 2375

or Ms Anne Hyland (Hon. Secretary)
Beechmount

Roscrea
Co. Tipperary
TEL 0505 22310

LAPADA
London and Provincial Antique Dealers'
Association
535 Kings Road
London SW10 0SZ
TEL 071 823 3511
FAX 071 823 3522

National Piano Information Service
National Piano Centre Administration
Office
5 Summerfield Road
London W5 1ND
TEL 081 997 1793

RSA
Royal Society of Arts
8 John Adam Street
London WC2N 6EZ
TEL 071 930 5115

Rug Restorers' Association
c/o Dennis Woodman
Oriental Carpets
105 North Road
Kew
Surrey TW9 4HJ
TEL 081 878 8182

Scottish Conservation Bureau
Historic Scotland
3 Stenhouse Mill Lane
Edinburgh EH11 3LR
TEL 031 443 1666

SSCR
Sue Wilthew
The Glasite Meeting House
33 Barony Street
Edinburgh EH3 6NX
TEL 031 556 8417

Society of Bookbinders
c/o Mrs J A Isaac
Lower Hammonds Farm
Ripley Lane
West Horsley
Surrey KT24 6JP
TEL 0483 283175

UKIC
United Kingdom Institute for
Conservation
(In process of moving within the London
area)

INDEX